revise

GCSE

Matthew Boulton College Library

D Classification no. 5OO **'d**

This book must be returned by the latest date stamped
below. To renew, telephone 0121 446 4545 ext 3169.
Fines will be charged on books returned late.

Eilee **and**

Key to symbols

As you read through this book you will notice the following symbols. They will help you find your way around the book more quickly.

 shows a handy hint to help you remember something

 shows you a short list of key facts

 means remember!!!

 says Did you know this? – interesting points to note

 gives worked examples to help you with calculations and equations

 points you to other parts of the book where related topics are explained

 shows a sequence of linked processes

 refers you from a diagram to a checklist of related points

Acknowledgements

Copyright photographs have been used, with permission, from the following sources: Planet Earth Pictures (p.23); Science Photo Library (pp. 38, 98)

ISBN 0 340 66388 X

First published 1997
Impression number   10 9 8 7 6 5 4 3 2 1
Year   2001 2000 1999 1998 1997

The 'Teach Yourself' name and logo are registered trade marks of Hodder & Stoughton Ltd.

Copyright © 1997 Eileen Ramsden, Jim Breithaupt, David Applin
Introduction ('Revision made easy') copyright © 1997 Tony Buzan

Designed and produced by Gecko Ltd, Bicester, Oxon
Printed in Great Britain for Hodder & Stoughton Educational, a division of Hodder Headline Plc, 338 Euston Road, London NW1 3BH by Scotprint Ltd, Musselburgh, Scotland.

Mind Maps: Patrick Mayfield
Illustrations: Peter Bull, Simon Cooke, Chris Etheridge, Ian Law, Joe Little, Andrea Norton, Mike Parsons, John Plumb, Dave Poole, Chris Rothero, Anthony Warne
Cover design: Amanda Hawkes
Cover illustration: Paul Bateman

Contents

Revision made easy

The four pages that follow contain a gold mine of information on how you can achieve success both at school and in your exams. Read them and apply the information, and you will be able to spend less, but more efficient, time studying, with better results. If you already have another *Hodder & Stoughton Revision Guide*, skim-read these pages to remind yourself about the exciting new techniques the books use, then move ahead to page 8.

This section gives you vital information on how to remember more *while* you are learning and how to remember more *after* you have finished studying. It explains

- how to use special techniques to improve your memory

- how to use a revolutionary note-taking technique called Mind Maps that will double your memory and help you to write essays and answer exam questions

- how to read everything faster while at the same time improving your comprehension and concentration

All this information is packed into the next four pages, so make sure you read them!

Your *amazing* memory

There are five important things you must know about your brain and memory to revolutionise your school life.

1. how your memory ('recall') works *while* you are learning

2. how your memory works *after* you have finished learning

3. how to use Mind Maps – a special technique for helping you with all aspects of your studies

4. how to increase your reading speed

5. how to zap your revision

1 Recall during learning – the need for breaks

When you are studying, your memory can concentrate, understand and remember well for between 20 and 45 minutes at a time. Then it *needs* a break. If you carry on for longer than this without one, your memory starts to break down! If you study for hours non-stop, you will remember only a fraction of what you have been trying to learn, and you will have wasted valuable revision time.

So, ideally, *study for less than an hour*, then take a five- to ten-minute break. During the break listen to music, go for a walk, do some exercise, or just daydream. (Daydreaming is a necessary brain-power booster – geniuses do it regularly.) During the break your brain will be sorting out what it has been learning, and you will go back to your books with the new information safely stored and organised in your memory banks. We recommend breaks at regular intervals as you work through the *Revision Guides*. Make sure you take them!

2 Recall after learning – the waves of your memory

What do you think begins to happen to your memory straight *after* you have finished learning something? Does it immediately start forgetting? No! Your brain actually *increases* its power and carries on remembering. For a short time after your study session, your brain integrates the information, making a more complete picture of everything it has just learnt. Only then does the rapid decline in memory begin, and as much as 80 per cent of what you have learnt can be forgotten in a day.

However, if you catch the top of the wave of your memory, and briefly review (look back over) what you have been revising at the correct time, the memory is stamped in far more strongly, and stays at the crest of the wave for a much longer time. To maximise your brain's power to remember, take a few minutes and use a Mind Map to review what you have learnt at the end of a day. Then review it at the end of a week, again at the end of a month, and finally a week before the exams. That way you'll ride your memory wave all the way to your exam – and beyond!

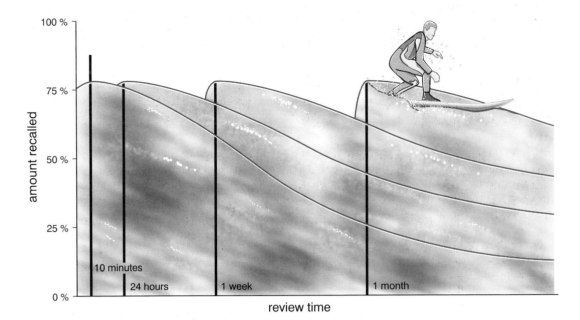

Amazing as your memory is (think of everything you actually do have stored in your brain at this moment) the principles on which it operates are very simple: your brain will remember if it (a) has an image (a picture or a symbol); (b) has that image fixed and (c) can link that image to something else.

3 The Mind Map® – a picture of the way you think

Do you *like* taking notes? More importantly, do you like having to go back over and learn them before exams? Most students I know certainly do not! And how do you take your notes? Most people take notes on lined paper, using blue or black ink. The result, visually, is *boring*! And what does your brain do when it is bored? It turns off, tunes out, and goes to sleep! Add a dash of colour, rhythm, imagination, and the whole note-taking process becomes much more fun, uses more of your brain's abilities, *and* improves your recall and understanding.

A Mind Map mirrors the way your brain works. It can be used for note-taking from books or in class, for reviewing what you have just studied, for revising, and for essay planning for coursework and in exams. It uses all your memory's natural techniques to build up your rapidly growing 'memory muscle'.

You will find Mind Maps throughout this book. Study them, add some colour, personalise them, and then have a go at drawing your own – you'll remember them far better! Put them on your walls and in your files for a quick-and-easy review of the topic.

How to draw a Mind Map

1 Start in the middle of the page with the page turned sideways. This gives your brain the maximum room for its thoughts.

2 Always start by drawing a small picture or symbol. Why? Because a picture is worth a thousand words to your brain. And try to use at least three colours, as colour helps your memory even more.

3 Let your thoughts flow, and write or draw your ideas on coloured branching lines connected to your central image. These key symbols and words are the headings for your topic. The Mind Map at the top of the next page shows you how to start.

4 Then add facts and ideas by drawing more, smaller, branches on to the appropriate main branches, just like a tree.

5 Always print your word clearly on its line. Use only one word per line. The Mind Map at the foot of the

next page shows you how to do this.

6 To link ideas and thoughts on different branches, use arrows, colours, underlining, and boxes.

How to read a Mind Map

1 Begin in the centre, the focus of your topic.

2 The words/images attached to the centre are like chapter headings, read them next.

3 Always read out from the centre, in every direction (even on the left-hand side, where you will have to read from right to left, instead of the usual left to right).

Using Mind Maps

Mind Maps are a versatile tool – use them for taking notes in class or from books, for solving problems, for brainstorming with friends, and for reviewing and revising for exams – their uses are endless! You will find them invaluable for planning essays for coursework and exams. Number your main branches in the order in which you want to use them and off you go – the main headings for your essay are done and all your ideas are logically organised!

4 Super speed reading

It seems incredible, but it's been proved – the faster you read, the more you understand and remember! So here are some tips to help you to practise reading faster – you'll cover the ground more quickly, remember more, *and* have more time for revision!

★ First read the whole text (whether it's a lengthy book or an exam paper) very quickly, to give your brain an overall idea of what's ahead and get it working. (It's like sending out a scout to look at the territory you have to cover – it's much easier when you know what to expect!) Then read the text again for more detailed information.

★ Have the text a reasonable distance away from your eyes. In this way your eye/brain system will be able to see more at a glance, and will naturally begin to read faster.

★ Take in groups of words at a time. Rather than reading 'slowly and carefully' read faster, more enthusiastically. Your comprehension will rocket!

★ Take in phrases rather than single words while you read.

★ Use a guide. Your eyes are designed to follow movement, so a thin pencil underneath the lines you are reading, moved smoothly along, will 'pull' your eyes to faster speeds.

5 Helpful hints for exam revision

Start to revise at the beginning of the course. Cram at the start, not the end and avoid 'exam panic'!

Use Mind Maps throughout your course, and build a Master Mind Map for each subject – a giant Mind Map that summarises everything you know about the subject.

Use memory techniques such as mnemonics (verses or systems for remembering things like dates and events, or lists).

Get together with one or two friends to revise, compare Mind Maps, and discuss topics.

And finally...

★ *Have fun while you learn* – studies show that those people who enjoy what they are doing understand and remember it more, and generally do it better.

★ *Use your teachers* as resource centres. Ask them for help with specific topics and with more general advice on how you can improve your all-round performance.

★ *Personalise your Revision Guide* by underlining and highlighting, by adding notes and pictures. Allow your brain to have a conversation with it!

Your brain is an amazing piece of equipment – learn to use it, and you, like thousands of students before you will be able to master 'B's and 'A's with ease. The more you understand and use your brain, the more it will repay you!

GCSE Science: Double Award and this Revision Guide

Tailor-made for *Science: Double Award*

This Revision Guide covers all the syllabuses for GCSE *Science: Double Award* for the different Examining Groups. It is not intended to replace your textbooks. As tests and examinations approach, however, many students feel the need to revise from something a good deal shorter than their usual textbook. This Revision Guide is intended to fill that need.

Getting the most out of the guide

We have tried to depart from the textbook style by presenting material in the form of charts, tables, concept maps and Mind Maps. Tony Buzan's advice on 'Revision made easy' will help you.

Each topic begins with a set of Test Yourself questions to give you an idea of how well you have already grasped the topic. You should work through the questions again after you have revised the topic. The improvement should be encouraging. There is a set of Round-up questions at the end of each topic. You can work out your Improvement Index from your score on the Round-up questions compared with your first score on the Test Yourself questions.

Revision tips

Here is some important advice for each stage of your revision:

- **Leading up to the exam**, make a timetable for homework and revision and stick to it. Be realistic and make sure you include all your subjects, and leave time for leisure activities. Planned use of time and concentrated study will give you time for recreation as well as revision.

- **When exam arrives,** make sure you have everything you need the night before, such as your pen, spare cartridge, pencils, rubber and calculator (in working order). Decide what to wear and get everything ready. Avoid last minute dithering. Be optimistic and be confident. Don't sit up late at night trying to cram. Looking through your Mind Maps is as much as your brain can take in at the last minute.

- **In the examination room**, read the instructions on the front of the paper before you set pen to paper. Don't spend more time than you should on a question. Attempt all the questions you are supposed to answer and make sure you turn every page over. If you suffer a panic attack, breathe deeply and slowly to get lots of oxygen into your system to clear your thoughts. Above all, keep your examination in perspective – it is not a matter of life or death! Finally, don't agonise over an examination afterwards.

We hope our Revision Guide leads you to success.

Eileen Ramsden, Jim Breithaupt, David Applin

Introducing biology

How much do you already know?
Work out your score on page 107.

Test yourself

1 What would happen to the ground temperature if Earth were **a)** nearer to the Sun **b)** further from the Sun? [2]

2 **a)** List the processes which tell you that something is living. $[7 \times \frac{1}{2}]$
   b) Put a tick (✔) next to the processes which you think apply to animals. $[7 \times \frac{1}{2}]$
   c) Put a cross (✗) next to the processes which you think apply to plants. $[6 \times \frac{1}{2}]$
   d) Do plants and animals have the same characteristics? If not, how are they different? [1]

3 Using the forget-me-not and oak tree as examples, explain the meaning of the words 'annual' and 'perennial'. [3]

4 **a)** What is a biological key used for? [1]
   b) Why are features like exact colour, size and mass not suitable for including in a biological key? [3]

5 List the physical features of soil which make it a suitable place for earthworms to live. [4]

1.1 Living on Earth

preview

At the end of this section you will:
- understand why Earth is a suitable place for living things (organisms)
- know that soil, air and water are the physical environments in which organisms live.

Why the Earth can support life

Earth is a planet in orbit round a star we call the Sun. It is the only planet we know of that supports life.

★ Earth is close enough to the Sun for its surface temperature to be in the range in which life can exist. The temperature at the Earth's surface varies between −70 and 55°C.

★ Earth is massive enough to have sufficient gravity to hold down an atmosphere of different gases essential for living organisms.

★ The layer of ozone which surrounds Earth reduces the amount of ultraviolet light from the Sun reaching the planet's surface. Too much ultraviolet light destroys living things.

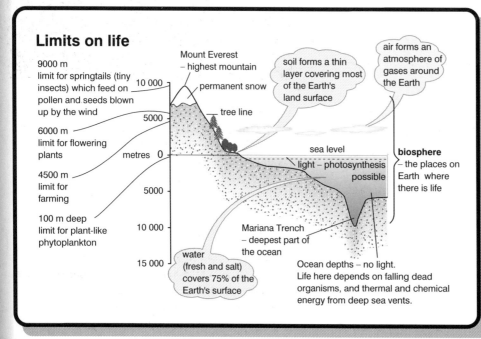

Limits on life

9000 m limit for springtails (tiny insects) which feed on pollen and seeds blown up by the wind

6000 m limit for flowering plants

4500 m limit for farming

100 m deep limit for plant-like phytoplankton

Mount Everest – highest mountain

permanent snow

tree line

sea level

light – photosynthesis possible

Mariana Trench – deepest part of the ocean

soil forms a thin layer covering most of the Earth's land surface

air forms an atmosphere of gases around the Earth

biosphere – the places on Earth where there is life

water (fresh and salt) covers 75% of the Earth's surface

Ocean depths – no light. Life here depends on falling dead organisms, and thermal and chemical energy from deep sea vents.

Earth's physical environment

The diagram on the opposite page shows that soil, air and water form Earth's environment:

★ **Soil** is formed when the weather, the roots of plants and the different activities of animals break down rocks into small particles.

★ **Air** consists of: 78% nitrogen; 21% oxygen; 0.03% carbon dioxide; and less than 1% water vapour, argon, xenon and other gases.

★ **Water** fills the seas, oceans, rivers and lakes. About 2% of the Earth's water is locked up as ice, in the soil, in the bodies of living things or is vapour in the atmosphere.

1.2 Characteristics of life

preview

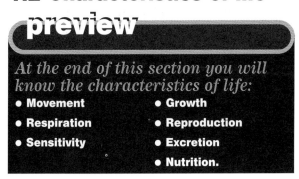

At the end of this section you will know the characteristics of life:
- ● Movement
- ● Respiration
- ● Sensitivity
- ● Growth
- ● Reproduction
- ● Excretion
- ● Nutrition.

Handy hint

The mnemonic **Mrs Gren** will help you remember the characteristics of living things.

More about MRS GREN

The characteristics of life are the features that are common to all living things:

★ **Movement**: animals are able to move from place to place because of the action of **muscles** which pull on the **skeleton**. Plants do not usually move from place to place; they move mainly by **growing**.

★ **Respiration** occurs in cells, and releases energy from food for life's activities. **Aerobic** respiration uses oxygen to release energy from food. **Anaerobic** respiration releases energy from food without using oxygen.

★ **Sensitivity** allows living things to detect changes in their surroundings and respond to them.

★ **Growth** leads to an increase in size. **Development** occurs as young change and become adult in appearance.

★ **Reproduction** produces new individuals.

★ **Excretion** removes the waste substances produced by the chemical reactions (called **metabolism**) taking place in cells.

★ **Nutrition** makes food (by the process of photosynthesis) or takes in food for use in the body.

Remember
- **Respiration** releases energy from food.
- **Gaseous exchange** takes in oxygen for respiration and removes carbon dioxide produced by respiration.
- **Excretion** removes wastes produced by metabolism.
- **Defecation** (or egestion) removes the undigested remains of food.

1.3 Grouping living things

preview

At the end of this section you will:
- ● understand that groups of living things are named according to Linnaeus' system of classification
- ● know the major groups of plants and animals
- ● understand binomial names.

Classification

Living things which have features in common are grouped together. Organising living things into groups is called **classification**. Some characteristics are unique to the group; other characteristics are shared with other groups. Groups therefore combine to form larger groups. The largest group of all is the **kingdom**. Each:

- kingdom contains a number of **phyla**
- phyl**um** (singular) contains a number of **classes**
- class contains a number of **orders**
- order contains a number of **families**
- family contains a number of **genera**
- gen**us** (singular) contains one or more **species**.

Arachnids
- The body is made up of two parts.
- There are 8 legs.
- Scorpions, mites and harvestmen are close relatives of spiders.

Cnidarians
- The body has no front or rear. Its parts are arranged evenly in the round.
- Tentacles surround an opening which is both mouth and anus.
- Stinging cells are used to capture prey.

Crustacea
- The body is made up of two parts.
- There are 14 legs.
- Woodlice are the only crustacea that live on land.
- Crabs, lobsters and prawns are close relatives of woodlice.

Reptiles
- Skin is dry and covered with scales that restrict water loss from the body.
- Lay eggs, each protected by a hard shell.
- As a result, water is not necessary for breeding.

Insects
- The body is made up of three parts: head, thorax and abdomen.
- There are six legs.
- There are usually two pairs of wings, but flies have one pair.

ANIMAL KINGDOM

Phylum Arthropoda

| Class Crustacea woodlouse | Class Arachnida spider |

| Class Insecta fly |

Phylum Cnidaria sea anemone

Phylum Chordata

| Class Pisces stickleback | Class Reptilia lizard |

| Class Aves thrush | Class Amphibia frog |

| Class Mammalia human |

Phylum Annelida earthworm

Worms
- The body is long and thin.
- The body is made up of many segments.

Birds
- The body is covered with feathers which:
  make flying possible
  keep in heat
  keep out water.
- The beak is specialised (adapted) differently in different species to deal with different foods.
- Birds lay eggs, protected by a hard shell.

Amphibians
- Live on land but breed in water.
- Young are swimming tadpoles.
- Development of young into adult is called a metamorphosis.
- Soft skin loses water easily in dry air.

Fish
- The body is covered with scales.
- Fins control the position of the body in water.
- Gills are surfaces for gaseous exchange.

Mammals
- Hair helps conserve body heat.
- Young feed on milk produced by the female's breasts (mammary glands).
- Have a small tail bone called the coccyx.

Groups within groups – the major groups of the Animal kingdom and the Plant kingdom, with an example of each. Each major group of plants is called a Division rather than a Phylum.

Mosses

- Mosses quickly lose water in dry air. As a result, mosses live in damp places.
- Roots are absent.
- As a result, water is soaked up by capillary movement over the leaves.
- Stalks grow from moss plants, each carrying a spore capsule filled with spores.
- Each spore is able to develop into a new plant.

REPRODUCE BY MEANS OF SPORES

PLANT KINGDOM

Division (= Phylum)
Mosses

Division (= Phylum)
Ferns

Division (= Phylum)
Seed plants

Class
conifers

Class
flowering plants

Ferns

- A waxy layer waterproofs the plant's surfaces, reducing water loss in a dry atmosphere.
- Roots draw water from the soil.
- Spore capsules containing spores grow in patches on the undersides of leaves.
- Each spore is able to grow into a new fern plant.

REPRODUCE BY MEANS OF SEEDS

Forget-me-not: annual – flowers and produces seed in one growing season. The plant then dies.

Oak tree: perennial – produces seeds year after year. The plant survives for many years.

Conifers

- Seeds are contained in cones.
- Covered with leaves all year round ('evergreens').
- Roots draw water from the soil.
- Waxy layer waterproofs plant surfaces.

Flowering plants

- Seeds are contained in fruits.
- Leaves of trees/shrubs fall once a year ('deciduous').
- Roots draw water from the soil.
- Waxy layer waterproofs plant surfaces.

The genus and the species identify the individual living thing, rather like your first name and surname identify you. For example, humans belong to the genus *Homo* and have the species name *sapiens*; barn owls are called *Tyto alba*.

Since the name of each living thing is in two parts, the method of naming is called the **binomial system**. Notice that the genus name begins with a capital letter, the species name begins with a small letter, and the whole name is printed in italics.

The Swedish naturalist Carolus Linnaeus (the Latin version of his name) published *Systema Naturae* in 1735. The book established the system of naming organisms that we use today.

The five kingdoms

There are five kingdoms. Living things in each kingdom obtain food in different ways. Their structure and body chemistry are different. Each kingdom, therefore, represents a way of life which all its members share. Pages 12–13 show the major groups in the Animal kingdom and Plant kingdom. The other kingdoms are:

Kingdom Fungi – organisms made up of cells that form thread-like structures called **hyphae**.

Kingdom Protista – single-celled organisms.

Kingdom Bacteria – single-celled organisms. The cell body is simple in structure compared with the cell body of protists.

(not to scale)

1.4 Identifying living things

preview

At the end of this section you will:
- know that a key is a set of clues that help identify a particular organism or group of organisms
- understand how to use a dichotomous key
- know that a dichotomous key can be written in different ways.

What is a key?

A **key** is a means of identifying an unfamiliar organism from a selection of specimens. A key consists of a set of descriptions. Each description is a clue that helps in the identification. A set of clues makes the key.

The easiest type of key to use is called a **dichotomous** key. 'Dichotomous' means branching into two. Each time the key branches, you have to choose between alternative statements. The alternative statements may be presented diagrammatically as a chart, or written in pairs or **couplets**. For example, a key to amphibians would begin:

		yes	no
1	The animal has a tail.	**newts**	go to **2**
2	The animal has no tail.	**frogs and toads**	go to **3**
	and so on …		

By comparing the pairs of statements with the organisms, you will eventually find one that fits. This identifies the organism. A key is therefore the route to a name. Different keys are used to name different living things.

When making a key, it is important to choose features that are characteristic of the type of organism rather than of the individual itself. For example, shape or proportions and patterns of colour are fairly constant in a type of organism and are therefore useful clues in a key. Size and shades of colour vary from individual to individual and are of limited use.

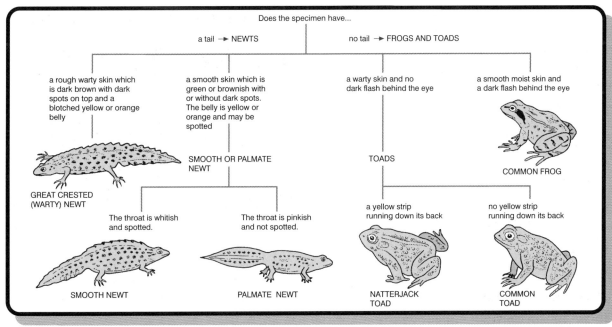

Does the specimen have...

a tail → NEWTS   no tail → FROGS AND TOADS

a rough warty skin which is dark brown with dark spots on top and a blotched yellow or orange belly

a smooth skin which is green or brownish with or without dark spots. The belly is yellow or orange and may be spotted

a warty skin and no dark flash behind the eye

a smooth moist skin and a dark flash behind the eye

SMOOTH OR PALMATE NEWT

TOADS

COMMON FROG

GREAT CRESTED (WARTY) NEWT

The throat is whitish and spotted.

The throat is pinkish and not spotted.

a yellow strip running down its back

no yellow strip running down its back

SMOOTH NEWT   PALMATE NEWT   NATTERJACK TOAD   COMMON TOAD

Different ways of writing a key to amphibians

round-up

How much have you improved?
Work out your improvement index on page 107.

1 What would happen to Earth's water if Earth were
a) nearer to **b)** further from the Sun?   [2]

2 a) Which gas is used during aerobic respiration to release energy from food?   [1]
b) Which gas is produced during aerobic respiration?   [1]

3 a) Distinguish between respiration and gaseous exchange.   [3]
b) Distinguish between excretion and defecation.   [2]

4 In the 1890s, when people saw cars for the first time, many thought that the cars were alive. Imagine that you are a reporter writing a short article for the local newspaper reassuring the populace that although cars seem to move under their own steam, they are not alive.   [8]

5 Match each characteristic of life in column **A** with its description in column **B**.

A characteristics	B descriptions
movement	making or obtaining food
respiration	responding to stimuli
sensitivity	removing waste substances produced by cells
growth	producing new individuals
reproduction	releasing energy from food
excretion	changing position
nutrition	increasing in size [7]

6 Different types of animal are listed in column **A**. Match each type with the correct description in column **B**.

A animals	B descriptions
insect	no legs
worm	eight legs
spider	two legs
bird	six legs [4]

7 Briefly describe how a biological key is used.   [4]

8 Briefly explain how the binomial system of biological names works.   [4]

9 A key can be written in couplets. What are 'couplets'?   [1]

Organisms in the environment

How much do you already know?
Work out your score on pages 107–8.

Test yourself

1 Match each term in column **A** with the correct description in column **B**.

A terms	B descriptions
biosphere	the place where a group of organisms lives
community	all the ecosystems of the world
habitat	a group of individuals of the same species
population	all the organisms that live in a particular ecosystem [4]

2 a) Why is a food web a more accurate description of feeding in a community than a food chain? [2]

b) Why do food chains and food webs always begin with plants? [4]

3 a) Why is the pyramid of biomass usually a better description of a community than the pyramid of numbers? [2]

b) Why is the pyramid of energy the best description of the feeding relationships within a community? [3]

4 Give reasons for the rapid increase in the human population. [4]

5 Weigh up the benefits in food production of intensive farming against the costs to the environment. [5]

2.1 Introducing ecology

preview

At the end of this section you will understand that:

- an ecosystem is a self-contained part of the biosphere, such as a pond or an oak wood
- the community consists of the organisms that live in a particular ecosystem
- the habitat is the place where a group of organisms live
- a niche is the role each species has in its habitat
- a population is a group of organisms of the same species living in a particular place at the same time.

Some ecological terms

Ecology involves studying the relationships between organisms and between organisms and the environment.

The diagram on page 10 shows how all the places on Earth where there is life form the **biosphere**. Each organism is suited (**adapted**) to the place where it lives. This place consists of

- an **environment** of air, soil or water
- a living **community** of plants, animals, fungi and microorganisms.

Environment and community together form an **ecosystem**, which is a more or less self-contained part of the biosphere. 'Self-contained' means that each ecosystem has its own characteristic organisms not usually found in other ecosystems. These organisms are the living (**biotic**) community of the ecosystem. The physical environment is the non-living (**abiotic**) part, consisting of air, soil or water. The diagram opposite shows the different components of an oak wood ecosystem.

The flow chart below shows the hierarchy of ecological terms.

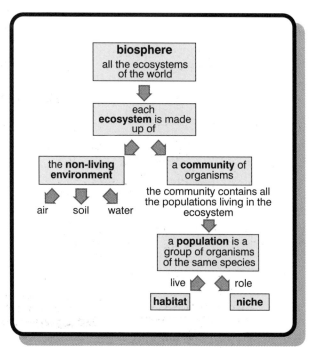

COMMUNITY

key
1 oak tree
2 hazel
3 holly
4 bluebell
5 wood anemone
6 primrose
7 moss on tree trunk
8 pigeons, rooks living in canopy
9 bluetits, woodpeckers living further down tree
10 great tits, warblers living in shrubs
11 wrens, blackbirds living on ground
12 toadstools on rotting log
13 woodlice in detritus
14 earthworm pulling leaf into burrow
✓ falling leaves

HABITATS

canopy layer

shrub layer
field layer
ground layer
detritus layer

THE ECOSYSTEM

PHYSICAL ENVIRONMENT

There may be up to 90% less light inside the wood than outside when the canopy is fully developed.

* canopy fully developed
**leaf fall

light outside wood

light

light passing through canopy

*   **

J F M A M J J A S O N D
month

EXAMPLE HABITAT

decomposers (which break down dead organic matter) at work on dead wood

decomposed dead material

FUNGI
Page 14.

NICHE: Fungal hyphae decompose dead wood, releasing minerals into the environment.

Woodlice and other wood-eating animals break up the tree into pieces called **frass**, increasing the surface area exposed to attack by fungi and bacteria.

Earthworms pull dead leaves into their burrows for food.

wall of hypha

wood

digested wood

food absorbed into hypha

enzymes secreted

enzymes

cytoplasm

digested wood

tip of hypha

Fungi and bacteria feed on the dead wood causing decomposition.

Nitrates and phosphates are absorbed in solution by the roots.

CARBON CYCLE
Page 156.
NITROGEN CYCLE
Page 154.

Decomposition releases gases and minerals into the soil.

nutrients essential for the growth of plants

The components of an oak wood ecosystem

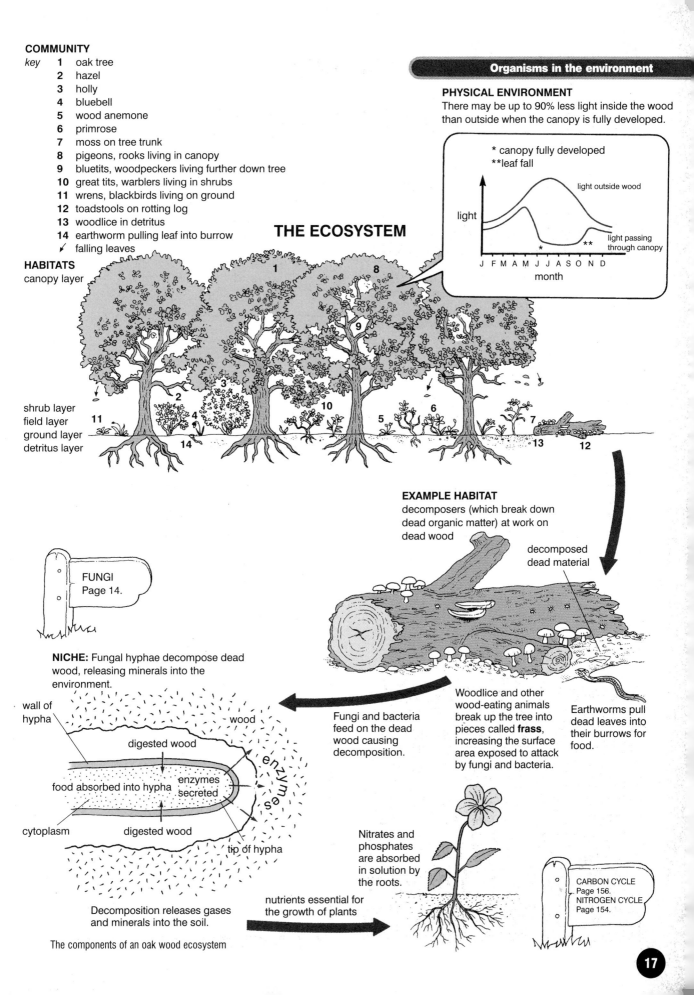

2.2 Food chains and webs

preview

At the end of this section you will:
- know the meaning of the terms producer, herbivore, carnivore and omnivore
- understand that energy is transferred along food chains
- be able to interpret diagrams of food chains and food webs.

Who eats whom?

Finding out 'who eats whom' is one way of describing how a community works. Looking at

- animals' teeth or mouthparts
- what is in the intestine
- animals feeding
- what food an animal likes best (a **food preference test**)

helps find out what animals feed on.

The working community

Animals fall into three categories according to what they eat.

★ **Herbivores** eat plants.

★ **Carnivores** eat meat.

★ **Omnivores** eat both plants and meat. (Most human beings are omnivorous.)

Most carnivores are **predators** – they catch and eat other animals. The animals caught are called their **prey**, and are often herbivores.

Scavengers are carnivores that feed on the remains of prey left by predators, or on the bodies of animals that have died for other reasons such as disease or old age.

A **food chain** shows the links between plants, prey, predators and scavengers. Some examples of food chains are shown opposite.

Notice in each example that

- the arrows represent the transfer of food between different organisms

- the arrows point from the eaten to the eater
- the number of links in a food chain is usually four or less.

A **food web** is usually a more accurate description of feeding relationships in a community because most animals eat more than one type of plant or other animal. Some examples of food webs are shown opposite.

Notice in each example that

- several food chains link up to form a food web
- plants produce food by photosynthesis
- different types of animal eat the same type of food.

Producers

Plants, algae and some bacteria (see page 14) are called **producers** because they can use sunlight to produce food by photosynthesis. This is why food chains and food webs always begin with plants (or algae or photosynthetic bacteria). Animals use this food when they eat plants. Even when they eat other animals, predators depend on plant food indirectly since somewhere along the line the prey has been a plant eater. Because they eat food, animals are called **consumers**.

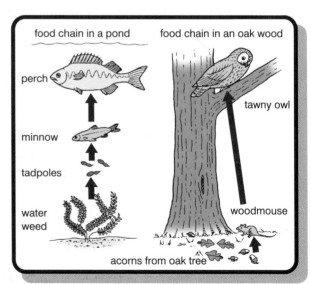

Food chains

food web in a pond

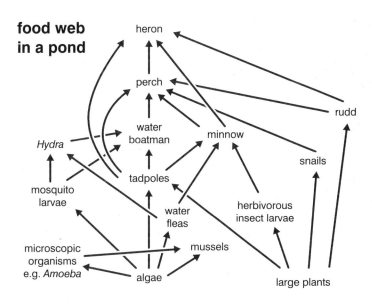

Energy flow

Sunlight underpins life on earth. Without sunlight, and the photosynthesis which depends on it, communities would cease to exist.

Through photosynthesis plants convert light energy into the chemical energy of food. A food chain represents one pathway of food energy through the community of an ecosystem. A food web represents many pathways. The diagram below shows the idea.

At each link in the food chain, energy is lost in the waste products of each living thing.

food web in an oak wood

insect-eating birds e.g. woodpecker

fruit- and seed-eating insects

owl   fox

woodmouse

wood-boring beetles

woodlice

beetles

nectar-feeding insects

fruit- and seed-eating birds e.g. finches

wood   bark   flowers   fruits and seeds   roots

woodland plants

Food webs

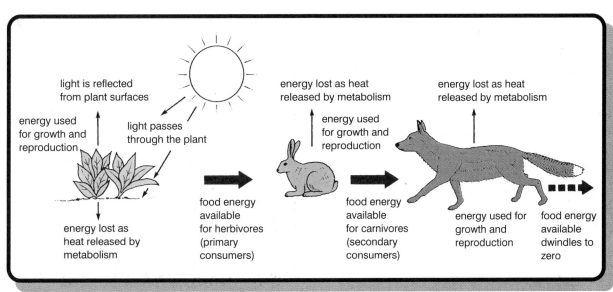

The flow of energy through a food chain

2.3 Ecological pyramids

preview

At the end of this section you will:
- understand the term **trophic level**
- know how to build a **pyramid of numbers**
- be able to interpret **pyramids of numbers and pyramids of biomass**
- understand that the **pyramid of energy** gives the best picture of the relationships between producers and consumers.

How many?

Food chains and food webs describe the feeding relationships within a community. However, they do not tell us about the numbers of individuals involved. Many plants support a limited number of herbivores which in turn support fewer carnivores.

Trophic levels

Below is a diagram of an ecological pyramid.

key **P** = plants   **H** = herbivores
C₁ = first carnivores   **C₂** = second carnivores

Ecological pyramid

★ The pyramid has several feeding levels called **trophic levels**.

★ Producers (plants/algae/some bacteria) occupy the base of the pyramid.

★ Other trophic levels are made up of consumers:
- **primary** consumers are herbivores (H) that feed on plants
- **secondary** consumers or first/primary carnivores (C_1) are carnivores that feed on herbivores
- **tertiary** consumers or second/secondary carnivores (C_2) are carnivores which feed on first/primary carnivores.

Each trophic level groups together organisms that have similar types of food. For example, a snail and a sheep are herbivores. Both belong to the second (H) trophic level.

The group of organisms in each trophic level is smaller than the one below it. This gives the pyramid its shape.

Pyramids of numbers

Pyramids of numbers show the number of organisms in each trophic level. The table shows the numbers of insects and spiders collected from grass with a sweep net.

sample	number of insects	number of spiders
1	135	5
2	150	10
3	110	10
4	115	5
5	120	15
	630	45
	average $= \dfrac{630}{5}$ $= 126$ insects in each sample	average $= \dfrac{45}{5}$ $= 9$ spiders in each sample

Samples of insects and spiders collected with a sweep net. Each sample was collected with 10 sweeps while walking around an area of $10\,m^2$

Data like that in the table can be used to plot a pyramid of numbers, as shown below. Half the number of organisms in each trophic level is plotted on one side of the vertical line, the other half is plotted on the other side of the vertical line.

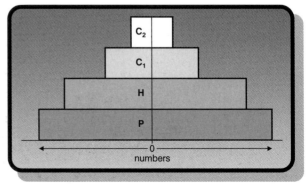

How to plot a pyramid of numbers

In grassland, the producers (grasses) and consumers (mainly insects and spiders) are small and numerous. A lot of plants support many herbivores (mostly insects) which in turn support fewer carnivores (mostly spiders). Plotting the number of organisms in each trophic level of the grassland community gives an upright pyramid that tapers to a point.

Problems with numbers...

Example 1: the pyramid of numbers for a woodland below has a point at the bottom as well as the top. This is because relatively few producers (trees) support a large number of herbivores and carnivores. You might think that woodland consumers are in danger of starvation! However, each tree is large and can meet the food needs of many different organisms.

Pyramid of numbers for a woodland community

Example 2: pyramids of numbers including parasites appear top-heavy, as shown below. Many parasites feed on fewer secondary consumers.

In both these examples, number pyramids are not an accurate description of the feeding relationships in the different communities. Why? Because the pyramid of numbers does not take into account differences in size of the different producers and consumers.

Pyramid of numbers including parasites of the secondary consumers (ladybirds)

... and the solution

A **pyramid of biomass** allows for differences in the size of organisms, because the pyramid shows the *amount of organic material* in each trophic level.

- A representative sample of the organisms at each trophic level is weighed.
- The mass is then multiplied by the estimated number of organisms in the community.

In practice, dry mass is used because fresh mass varies greatly as organisms contain different amounts of water. The sample is dried out in an oven at 110°C until there is no further change in mass. The dry mass data is plotted as kilograms of dry mass per unit area (m²) of the community.

Pyramid of biomass for a woodland community

Problems with biomass...

Example 1: the biomass of an organism can vary during the year. For example, an oak tree in full leaf during the summer will have a much greater biomass than in winter without the leaves.

Example 2: some organisms reproduce so quickly that sampling misses the rapid fluctuations in population. For example, here is an upside-down pyramid of biomass for the English Channel. Microscopic algae (producers) only live for a few days but reproduce millions of offspring very quickly. Collecting them over a short period misses this rapid turnover of living material and results in a pyramid which suggests that the biomass of herbivores (H) is greater than that of the producers (P) they feed on.

Pyramid of biomass for the English Channel, grams per unit volume (m³) of water

... and the solution

A **pyramid of energy** gives information about the *amount of energy* at each trophic level over a certain period of time. In other words, the energy pyramid shows the amount of food being produced and consumed in a given time. Its shape therefore is not affected by differences in size, or changes in numbers of individuals.

The food energy in each trophic level is measured by incinerating samples of organisms in a **bomb calorimeter**. The heat given off is a measure of the energy value of the samples and is therefore representative of the food energy in the trophic level to which the sample of organisms belongs. The diagram below shows you the idea.

Notice that

★ feeding transfers food energy from one trophic level to the next

METABOLISM
Page 11.

★ energy is lost from each trophic level through life's activities, mostly in the form of heat released by the metabolism of cells.

As a result, the amount of food energy in a trophic level is less than the one below it.

As a result, the amount of living material (biomass) in a trophic level is less than the one below it.

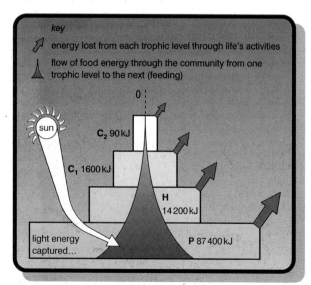

key

↗ energy lost from each trophic level through life's activities

△ flow of food energy through the community from one trophic level to the next (feeding)

0

sun

C_2 90 kJ

C_1 1600 kJ

H 14 200 kJ

light energy captured...

P 87 400 kJ

Pyramid of energy for a stream in kJ/m²/year

2.4 Distribution of organisms

preview

At the end of this section you will:

● **understand the effect of environmental factors on the distribution of plants**

● **know that competition affects the distribution of organisms**

● **understand that different adaptations enable plants and animals to survive.**

Competition between organisms

The distribution of organisms (where living things are found in the environment) is affected by different factors.

★ Physical factors include
  • the amount of light
  • the abundance of water.

★ Biological factors include
  • **intraspecific competition** – competition between individuals of the same species
  • **interspecific competition** – competition between individuals of different species
  • **interactions** between predators and prey
  • **adaptations** of organisms for survival in different environments.

Fact file

★ **Competition:** in nature organisms that are rivals for something that is in limited supply are competitors. The 'something' is a resource like water, light, space, food or mates.

★ **Adaptation:** organisms are adapted (suited) for the environment in which they live and for their role (niche – see page 16) in that environment.

Different factors affect the distribution of organisms. Some examples follow.

Example 1: intraspecific competition for light

In a wood, the branches of full-grown trees spread in all directions. They touch the branches of neighbouring trees, forming a continuous layer. This is the **canopy** which shades out plants beneath. When a tree is blown over, light floods through the gap in the canopy, stimulating vigorous plant growth on the woodland floor. This sunlit clearing becomes an arena for intense competition between tree seedlings sprouting from thousands of seeds, and then forming saplings (young trees). Many competitors start out but there is limited space for spreading branches, which also overshadow slower-growing rivals. Many young trees perish along the way. Only the one that grows the fastest will fill the gap in the canopy, finally cutting off the sunlight that signalled the start of the race many years previously.

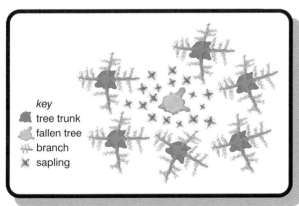

key
🌲 tree trunk
🌿 fallen tree
🌿 branch
✳ sapling

Which sapling will survive to fill the gap? The length of the branches determines the distance between neighbouring trees, producing a continuous canopy and a regular pattern of tree trunks. The sunlit clearing caused by the fallen tree breaks the pattern and provides opportunities for new plant growth and competition between saplings to complete the canopy once more.

Example 2: intraspecific competition for water

The cacti in the photograph are widely spaced apart, and they look as if they have been planted out in a regular arrangement. The pattern appears because although many tiny cactus seedlings sprout in a particular area, there is only enough water for some of them to grow into a mature plant. Growing cacti are the competitors and water is the resource in short supply.

Example 3: interspecific competition

Competition between different species is usually greatest among individuals that occupy the same trophic level. This competition for the same resource often leads to one species replacing another (called **competitive exclusion**). For example, when two species of clover (both producers) were grown separately, they grew well. However, when grown together one species eventually replaced the other. The reason was that the successful species grew slightly taller than its competitor and overshadowed it.

Example 4: predator and prey

Predators are adapted to catch prey, and prey are adapted to escape predators. The table summarises their different strategies.

predator	prey
eats a variety of prey species, reducing the risk of starvation should one prey species decline in numbers	large groups (e.g. herds of antelope, shoals of fish) distract predators from concentrating on a particular individual
catches young, old and sick prey	stings and bitter taste deter predators
catches large prey which provides more food per kill	warning coloration tells predators to avoid particular prey
moves to areas where prey is plentiful	camouflage conceals prey
	shock tactics startle predators
	prey tries to run/swim/fly faster than pursuing predator

Strategies for predator success and prey survival

Cacti in the Arizona Desert, south-western United States, where rainfall is erratic and infrequent

2.5 Population size

preview

At the end of this section you will:
- **know how populations increase in size**
- **understand that the impact of human activity on the environment is related to population size**
- **be able to identify specific effects of human activity on the environment.**

The size of a population

★ A **population** is a group of individuals of the same species living in a particular place at the same time.

★ **Births** and **immigration** increase the size of a population.

★ **Deaths** and **emigration** decrease the size of a population.

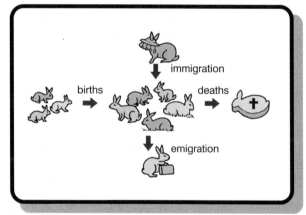

Factors affecting the size of a population

Population growth

The following graph shows that populations grow in a particular way. **Limiting factors** stop populations from growing indefinitely. They include:

shortages of
- food
- water
- oxygen
- light
- shelter

build-up of
- poisonous wastes
- predators
- disease
- social factors.

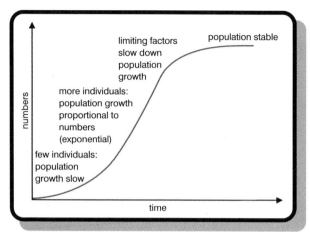

Population growth curve

Predator and prey populations

Predation affects the number of the prey population. The number of prey affects the predator population: if prey is scarce, then some of the predators will starve. The graphs below show the relationships between the numbers of predators and prey.

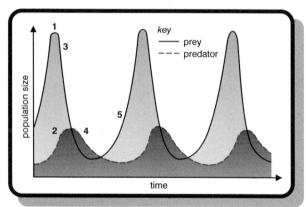

Predator–prey relationships

1 Prey breed and increase in numbers if conditions are favourable (e.g. food is abundant).

2 Predators breed and increase in numbers in response to the abundance of prey.

3 Predation pressure increases and the number of prey declines.

4 Predator numbers decline in response to the shortage of food.

5 Predation pressure decreases and so prey numbers increase ... and so on.

Notice that

- fluctuations in predator numbers are *less* than fluctuations in prey numbers
- fluctuations in predator numbers *lag* behind fluctuations in prey numbers.

Why is this? There are fewer predators than prey, and predators tend to reproduce more slowly than prey.

The human population

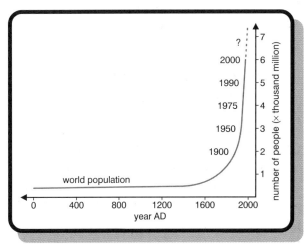

World population growth over the past 2000 years showing predicted future increase based on present trends

This graph shows that the human population has grown dramatically since the beginning of the nineteenth century. Although the populations of Europe, North America and Japan (developed countries) are levelling off, the populations of Latin America, Asia and Africa (developing countries) are still growing rapidly as a result of

- improvements in food production
- more drugs for the treatment of disease
- improved medical care
- improved public health.

The rate of population growth is affected by the number of young people in the population, particularly women of child-bearing age. The table summarises the problem.

A large proportion of the world's population is young so the problems listed in the table are global. The problems are particularly acute in developing countries.

problem	result
present birth rate high	adding to the rate of population increase
future birth rate high	as children in the population 'bulge' grow older and have their own children, adding further to the rate of population increase
social services inadequate	large numbers of children put strain on the educational system, medical services and housing

Problems of a young population

In Britain (and other developed countries) the problems are more to do with a population that has an increasing proportion of old people. The diseases of old age (cancer, arthritis, dementia) take up an increasing proportion of the resources available for medical care.

Human impact on the environment

1.5 million years ago: early humans probably moved from place to place in search of food. They hunted animals and gathered plants. Their impact on the environment was no more than that of other medium-sized animals.

10 000 years ago: about 12 million people lived in the world. In the Middle East they harvested wild wheat and other grains. When the grain was ripe, a family could probably gather over a year's supply in just a few weeks. People had little impact on the environment beyond their village.

2000 years ago: people had started to farm. Skills in crafts and tool-making developed. Villages became larger and some grew into towns. People had a much greater impact on the environment – farming the land, using raw materials.

Today: about 6 billion (thousand million) people live in the world. In developed countries, food is produced by relatively few people. Industry and technology use raw materials, often obtained from developing countries where environments may be stripped of resources. Pages 26–7 show the impact of human activities on today's environment.

HUMAN IMPACT ON THE ENVIRONMENT

RESOURCES

Resources are the raw materials needed to satisfy human demands for food, homes, hospitals, schools and manufactured goods.

- **Renewable resources** are replaced as fast as plants and animals can reproduce and grow. If a resource is over-used it will decline. Damage to the environment also limits the production of renewable resources.

CASE STUDY: Fishing in the North Sea

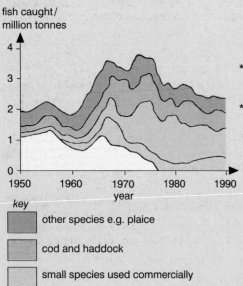

fish caught / million tonnes

key

other species e.g. plaice

cod and haddock

small species used commercially

mackerel

herring

Catches of fish are reduced because of:

* **overfishing:** increased efficiency of fishing methods catches more fish than are replaced by reproduction

* **pollution:**
  - nutrients (e.g. nitrogen and phosphorus) from sewage works and surplus artificial fertilisers enter rivers which discharge into the North Sea
  - pesticides used to protect crops enter rivers which discharge into the North Sea
  - metals (e.g. mercury, cadmium, copper) from different industrial processes

- **Non-renewable resources** cannot be replaced when used up. For example, there are only limited amounts of fossil fuels (coal, oil, natural gas) and metals.

CASE STUDY: World reserves of metals

The table shows estimated world reserves of some metals vital for the manufacture of goods and technological development. Work out how long reserves of each metal will last at present rates of use.

iron ore	annual use	1.6 billion tonnes
	reserves	216.4 billion tonnes
copper	annual use	10 million tonnes
	reserves	570 million tonnes
tin	annual use	226 thousand tonnes
	reserves	4.2 million tonnes

Answers (to the nearest whole number)
Iron ore: 135 years
Copper: 57 years
Tin: 19 years

FARMING Page 28.

How human activities exploit resources and land and produce pollution

Land use destroys habitats, driving thousands of species of plants and animals to the verge of extinction. The pressures are
• economic development
• growing human populations   } increase the use of land
• the increasing need for food to feed people.

CASE STUDY 1: Land use in the United Kingdom
Out of 24 million hectares of land in the UK:
• 19 million hectares are used for agriculture
• 1.7 million hectares are used for housing.
Quarrying (gravel, limestone, sand and sandstone) for building materials and the disposal of household waste account for some of the rest.

CASE STUDY 2: Exploiting tropical rainforest
Rainforests girdle the equator covering 14.5 million km^2 of land. The vegetation recycles carbon dioxide and oxygen through photosynthesis.
Moisture absorbed by the forest evaporates back into the atmosphere, to fall as rain thousands of miles away. Rainforest is being cleared at a rate of 100 000 km^2 each year for:

cheap beef is exported to be made into hamburgers

Beef: about 20 000 km^2 of Brazilian forest are cleared each year for cattle ranches.

Opencast mining for metals causes much damage to rainforest.

After clearing, nutrients disappear and soil is soon exhausted.
Semi-desert develops: the ranchers move on to clear a new area.

Logging: only 4% of trees are felled for timber, but another 40% are damaged or destroyed in the process.

POLLUTION

Pollution is the result of industry making goods that maintain our standard of living.
• **Air** is polluted by gases, dust and smoke from vehicles and industry.
• **Water** is polluted by wastes from factories and runoff of agrochemicals.
• **Land** is polluted by agrochemicals and the dumping of rubbish and waste.

CASE STUDY: Environmental problems caused by pollution

chemicals put into rivers and the sea

nuclear waste

destruction of wildlife

dirty beaches and bathing water

chemical sprays

rubbish and litter

loss of hedgerows

decay of inner cities and derelict land

acid rain

losing green belt land

oil slicks from ships

fumes and smoke from factories

car exhaust fumes

noise from traffic, aircraft, radios, etc.

27

2.6 Food production

preview

At the end of this section you will:
- **understand why a short food chain makes more food energy available to the consumer than a long food chain**
- **know that intensive farming produces food in great quantities.**

Fact file

★ **Intensive farming** means that farmers use different methods to produce as much food as possible from the land available for raising crops (**arable** farming) and the land available for raising animals (**livestock** farming).

★ **Productivity** means the amount of food produced (crops or livestock) per unit area of land (e.g. per hectare (ha)).

Energy and farming

Farms are ecosystems with people as consumers in a food chain of crops and livestock. The amount of food a farm produces depends on

- the amount of energy entering the farm ecosystem
- the efficiency with which energy is converted into plant and animal tissue.

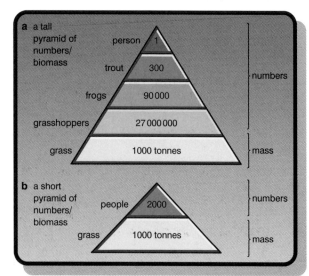

Eating trout and eating vegetables

Do you like trout? The pyramid that supports one person's appetite for trout is shown, along with another pyramid showing the number of people supported who are vegetarian. (Remember that cereals are varieties of cultivated grass.)

Shortening the food chain

The inefficiency of energy transfer between trophic levels accounts for the difference between pyramids **a** and **b**. The *fewer* the trophic levels (links in a food chain), the *less* food energy is lost and so the *more* food is available to consumers.

Energy transfer between producers and consumers is inefficient because

- some of the plant material is not digested and passes out of the herbivore body as faeces
- the herbivore uses energy to stay alive
- when the herbivore dies, its body represents 'locked up' energy, some of which transfers to decomposers.

Eating meat is therefore wasteful in terms of food energy.

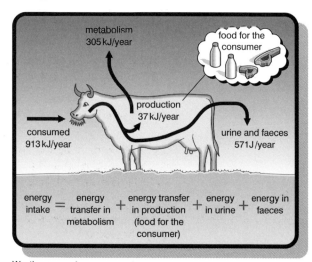

Wasting energy

Farming

The concept map for **food production** on page 30 shows different technologies at work on the modern intensive farm. The checklist points opposite summarise the benefits for food production but also highlight the impact on the environment and the possible risks to public health.

Checklist for intensive farming

checklist	benefits	impact
1 pesticides	kill pests which damage crops	spray is carried in the wind (drift) which can harm wildlife
	food production increases	pesticide runoff seeps into groundwater, eventually draining into ponds and river systems, possibly contaminating drinking water and harming wildlife
2 irrigation	brings water to land	salination: the Sun's heat evaporates water, increasing the concentration of mineral salts in soil. Eventually land is too 'salty' for crops to grow, reducing crop yields
	food production increases	overwatering: land becomes waterlogged, reducing crop yields. In warm countries the threat to public health increases because habitats are created for the spread of water-borne diseases such as malaria and schistosomiasis
3 mechanisation	powerful machinery needs few people to work it, cutting wage costs	land is cleared of woods and hedges to make fields larger – large machinery is most efficient in big fields
	more land can be used for farming	habitats are destroyed with loss of wildlife
	harvests crop more quickly	soil is packed, causing waterlogging
4 manure	spreading manure on land adds humus which improves soil structure	water is needed to wash manure into lagoon
		slurry leaks from lagoon, seeping into streams and rivers, kill fish and other wildlife
5 monoculture	efficient use of expensive machinery	crop provides unlimited food for consumer populations, which increase to pest proportions
	reduces labour costs	costs are high because crops must be sprayed with pesticides
	high yields mean farmer can take advantage of selling in bulk to obtain best prices for produce	soil loses its nutrients which are replaced with expensive artificial fertilisers
		soil is left bare between crops, risking erosion
6 artificial fertilisers	land can be used continuously for growing crops	manufacture of fertilisers uses a lot of fuel
	farmers do not need to keep animals for manure	soil structure deteriorates and soil erosion increases
	efficiency is increased by specialising in growing one or two crops each year	surplus fertiliser runs off into streams and rivers: this encourages population explosion of algae (called blooms) which use up oxygen in the water, killing wildlife. Surplus fertiliser may also put excess nitrates, a health hazard, into drinking water
	food production is increased, helping feed the world's growing population	

Pests are plants and animals that destroy crops and livestock or prevent land from being used for farming.

Pesticides are chemicals that kill pests. Pesticides are very poisonous if accidentally swallowed. Some can cause illnesses when eaten in food. There are three types of pesticide:

- insecticides kill insects
- herbicides kill weeds (plants that compete with crops for space, light and nutrients)
- fungicides kill fungi.

Farmers apply pesticides as sprays, dusts, dips, fogs or granules.

CHECK LIST 1

pesticide spray

PESTICIDES

Irrigation brings water to land that would otherwise be too dry to grow crops. It also improves yields where rainfall is low. Today, over 2 million km^2 of irrigated land produce about 30% of the world's food. Estimates predict that more than 3 million km^2 of land will be irrigated by the end of the twentieth century.

CHECK LIST 2

overhead irrigation system

IRRIGATION

INTENSIVE FARMING

MECHANISATION

Farm machinery works best in large fields without hedges, fences or other obstructions. Fuel oil powers the machinery, replacing the muscle power of humans and horses used for centuries previously.

CHECK LIST 3

Artificial fertilisers supply nutrients directly to crops. For example, nitrogen is supplied as ammonium salts and nitrates. Farmers apply artificial fertilisers either as sprays or granules.

ARTIFICIAL FERTILISERS

CHECK LIST 6

MONOCULTURE

MANURE

Growing a large area of a single crop is called monoculture. The same crop is often grown year after year. Intensive arable farms specialise in monocultures of a limited number of crops.

CHECK LIST 5

dung drops through slats in floor

manure

CHECK LIST 4

washed to lagoon

Large numbers of animals reared intensively indoors produce large amounts of manure. Washed into pits called lagoons, the manure forms a liquid slurry.

The intensive farm at work

round-up

How much have you improved?
Work out your improvement index on page 108.

1 Look at pages 16–17. List the different components of an ecosystem. [6]

2 a) Explain the meaning of the word 'abiotic'. [1]
b) Why is the amount of light an important abiotic influence on life inside a wood? [4]

3 Look at the pond food chain on page 18.
a) How many links are there in the food chain? [1]
b) Name the producers. [1]
c) Briefly explain why they are called producers. [1]
d) Name the herbivores. [1]
e) Briefly explain why they are called herbivores. [1]
f) Name the carnivores. [2]
g) Briefly explain why they are called carnivores. [1]

4 Why is the efficiency of energy conversion in photosynthesis less than 8%? [3]

5 In what circumstances is the pyramid of numbers an accurate description of the feeding relationships in a community? [1]

6 The diagram shows a pyramid of biomass for a rocky seashore.
a) Name the producers. [1]
b) Name the secondary consumers. [1]
c) Severe weather conditions virtually wipe out the periwinkles. What will be the effect on the biomass of dog whelks and saw wrack? [2]

5.8 g/m² dog whelks

71 g/m² periwinkles

3987 g/m² saw wrack

7 Explain the differences between
a) intraspecific competition and interspecific competition
b) adaptation and survival
c) camouflage and warning coloration. [6]

8 The graph shows long-term changes in the numbers of snowshoe hare and its predator the Canadian lynx.

key
-------- snowshoe hare
———— lynx

number / thousands

time / years

a) Why do the highs and lows in the numbers of lynx lag behind the highs and lows in the numbers of snowshoe hare? [3]
b) Although the numbers of snowshoe hare and lynx fluctuated between 1850 and 1940, what do you think is the *overall* trend in the population growth of each species between these years? [1]
c) In 1890, if disease had virtually wiped out the lynx population, what do you think would have happened to the numbers of snowshoe hare? [1]
d) If the lynx population had recovered from the effects of disease by 1910, what then do you think would have happened to the numbers of snowshoe hare? [2]
e) If the lynx population had never recovered from the effects of disease, what then do you think would have happened to the numbers of snowshoe hare? Briefly explain your answer. [2]

9 The terms in column **A** refer to different aspects of intensive farming. Match each term with its correct description in column **B**.

A terms	B descriptions
fertiliser	kills plants
herbicide	an unwanted plant
irrigation	supplies plants with nutrients
monoculture	supplies plants with water
weed	a crop plant grown over a large area [5]

Well done if you've improved. Don't worry if you haven't. Take a break and try again.

Cell activity

Work out your score on page 108.

Test yourself

1 Match each of the structures in column **A** with its function in column **B**.

A structures	B functions
mitochondrion	partially permeable to substances in solution
cell membrane	where energy is released from the oxidation of glucose
chloroplast	fully permeable to substances in solution
cell wall	contains the chromosomes
nucleus	where light energy is captured [5]

2 Why do you think the process of active transport requires more energy than diffusion? [1]

3 Explain the difference between
   a) a plasmolysed cell and a turgid cell [4]
   b) a fully permeable membrane and a partially permeable membrane. [3]

4 What is a clone? [1]

5 What is formed by the replication of DNA? [2]

6 a) Why do the cells of a tissue undergo mitosis?
   b) In mitosis, what is the relationship between the number and type of chromosomes in the parent cell and in the daughter cells? [5]

7 Briefly explain the meaning of 'haploid' and 'diploid'. [4]

8 Complete the following paragraph using the words below. Each word may be used once, more than once or not at all.

   types organism tissues organs cells an organ

   Living things are made of _____ . Groups of similar _____ with similar functions form _____ that can work together as _____ . A group of _____ working together form _____ system. [6]

9 Cellulose and chitin are important building materials in living things. Give an example of the use of each. [2]

10 Briefly explain the difference between saturated and unsaturated fats. [2]

11 What is a nucleotide? [4]

3.1 Cells at work

preview

At the end of this section you will know that:

- all living things are made of cells
- plant cells and animal cells have structures in common but are also different from one another
- mitochondria and chloroplasts are structures in cells which convert energy from one form to another
- different types of cells are each specialised to perform a particular biological task.

Cell functions

The structures that make up a cell are organised in a way that depends on the **functions** of the cell (the way it works).

Fact file

★ Most cells are too small to be seen with the naked eye.

★ The light microscope helps us see the structure of cells.

★ The transmission electron microscope reveals cell structures too small to be seen under the light microscope. It enables us to see the fine structure of cells in great detail.

★ The human body is constructed from more than 200 different types of cell.

How cells work

The diagram on pages 34–5 is the concept map for **cells at work**. The numbers on the diagram refer to the checklist of points.

3.2 Into and out of cells

preview

Moving molecules

Cells need a non-stop supply of water and the substances dissolved in it to stay alive. Substances therefore move inside and into and out of cells. They move in one of three ways.

★ **diffusion** – the movement of a substance through a solution or gas *down* a concentration gradient (that is, from a region of high concentration to a region of low concentration)

★ **osmosis** – the movement of **water** *down* a concentration gradient through a **partially permeable** membrane

★ **active transport** – the movement of a substance through a solution *up* (against) a concentration gradient (that is, from a region of low concentration to a region of high concentration).

Fact file

★ Why does sugar sprinkled onto strawberries turn pink? Because it makes the juice come out of the strawberries.

In and out of cells

On page 36 is the concept map for **Movement into and out of cells**. The numbers on the concept map refer to the checklist of points below.

Checklist for movement in and out of cells

1 ★ The molecules of a substance move at random, but there is a better than even chance that some molecules will spread from where they are highly concentrated to where they are fewer in number.

As a result, there is a net movement of molecules from where the substance is in high concentration to where it is in low concentration.

★ Diffusion continues until the concentration of the substance is the same throughout the gas or solution.

★ The greater the difference in concentration between the regions, the steeper the concentration gradient and the faster the substance diffuses.

2 ★ In active transport, the molecules of a substance move in the reverse direction to normal diffusion.

As a result, cells may build up stores of a substance which would otherwise be spread out by diffusion.

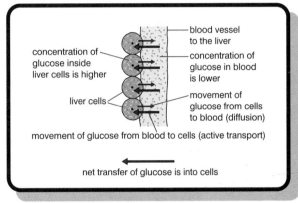

Glucose is stored in the liver by active transport

★ Active transport requires more energy than normal diffusion.

3 ★ The flow of water from a more dilute solution to a more concentrated solution is called osmosis.

★ A partially permeable membrane allows some substances to pass through but stops others. The passage of substances across such a membrane depends on the
- size of the molecules
- size of the membrane pores
- surface area of the cell membrane
- rate of diffusion.

★ The changes happening inside plant cells due to osmosis bring about visible changes in the plant.
- Plasmolysis causes a plant to **wilt** through lack of water.
- The plant recovers following watering, which restores turgor to its cells.

★ Osmosis through a partially permeable membrane continues until the concentrations of water on either side of the membrane are equal.

3

Checklist for cells at work

1 ★ During photosynthesis, oxygen is released into the environment.

★ During aerobic respiration, oxygen is used to release energy from food.

As a result, photosynthesis and aerobic respiration are stages in a cycle, the by-products of one forming the starting point of the other.

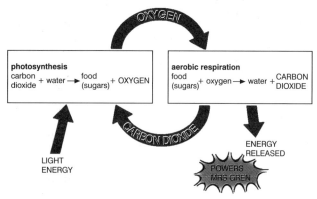

The oxygen–carbon dioxide cycle

2 ★ There are different types of cell for different functions.

★ Each type of cell is suited (**adapted**) for its function in the animal body or plant body.

★ A sheet of cells which covers a body surface is called an **epithelium**.

★ Red blood cells do not have nuclei.

Ciliated cells – cilia are rows of fine hairs which sway to and fro. Ciliated cells line the windpipe. They sweep a covering layer of mucus, which traps bacteria, viruses and other particles, into the pharynx. The mucus is either swallowed, sneezed out or coughed up.

cilia

Cells at work

Root hair cell absorbs water from the soil. The hair-like extension of the cell increases the surface area available for the absorption of water.

root hair

root tissue cells

Red blood cells transport oxygen around the body. They contain haemoglobin which combines with oxygen.

flattened disc shape increases surface area for the absorption of oxygen

VARIETY OF CELLS

sperm – the male sex cell which swims to the egg

tail-like flagellum lashes from side to side

ovum (egg) – the female sex cell which is fertilised when a sperm fuses with it

The **leaf palisade cell** contains numerous chloroplasts.

chloroplasts

Xylem cells form tubes in the stem, roots and leaves, transporting water to all parts of the plant.

SUNLIGHT
ENERGY

chloroplast

captured by
chlorophyll

PHOTO-
SYNTHESIS
Page 48.

**PLANT CELLS
TRANSFORM
ENERGY**

CONVERTED TO CHEMICAL ENERGY
$$6CO_2 + 6H_2O \rightarrow C_6H_{12}O_6 + 6O_2$$
carbon   water   sugar   oxygen
dioxide   (glucose)

CELL STRUCTURE

chloroplasts
contain chlorophyll
which captures light
energy

mitochondria where
energy is released
from the oxidation of
glucose

nucleus contains
the chromosomes
which carry genes

cell wall
made of
cellulose, fully
permeable to
substances in
solution

cytoplasm is jelly-like
material which fills the
cell, giving it shape

vacuole
contains cell sap
– a solution of
sugar and salts

ANIMAL CELL

PLANT CELL

cell membrane is
partially permeable to
substances in solution

SUGAR

CHECK
LIST
☑
☑ **1**
☑

STRUCTURES FOUND IN
ANIMAL *AND* PLANT CELLS

STRUCTURES FOUND
ONLY IN PLANT CELLS

**ANIMAL AND
PLANT CELLS
TRANSFORM
ENERGY**

MRS GREN
Page 11.

mitochondrion

OXYGEN

oxidation
of sugar
(glucose)

MOVEMENT
RESPIRATION
SENSITIVITY

POWERS

ENERGY

CHEMICAL ENERGY RELEASED
$$C_6H_{12}O_6 + 6O_2 \rightarrow 6CO_2 + 6H_2O$$
sugar   oxygen   carbon   water
(glucose)   dioxide

GROWTH
REPRODUCTION
EXCRETION
NUTRITION

AEROBIC
RESPIRATION
Page 67.

molecules of substance

water molecules

CONCENTRATION

GRADIENT

CHECK 1 LIST

net movement of molecules

DIFFUSION

high concentration of substance ⊙ in solution

low concentration of substance ⊙ in solution

REMEMBER: [higher ⊙] diffusion [lower ⊙]

ACTIVE TRANSPORT

CHECK 2 LIST

sugar

ENERGY aerobic respiration

CONCENTRATION

GRADIENT

net movement of molecules

high concentration of substance ⊙ in solution

low concentration of substance ⊙ in solution

REMEMBER: [higher ⊙] active transport [lower ⊙]

AEROBIC RESPIRATION Page 67.

MOVING MOLECULES

OSMOSIS

CHECK 3 LIST

HIGH CONCENTRATION OF WATER (dilute solution)

LOW CONCENTRATION OF WATER (concentrated solution)

net movement of water molecules

partially permeable membrane

molecule of substance

water molecule

pore in membrane

CONCENTRATION

GRADIENT OF WATER

turgid plant cell

plasmolysed plant cell

TURGOR

PLASMOLYSIS

more water molecules on this side of membrane, so more water molecules pass from left to right

fewer water molecules on this side of membrane, so fewer water molecules pass from right to left

REMEMBER: [higher ·] osmosis [lower ·]

cell membrane – partially permeable

nucleus

cell wall – fully permeable

concentrated solution in the cytoplasm and vacuole [lower ·]

vacuole

dilute solution outside the cell [higher ·]

cell wall

dilute solution in cytoplasm and vacuole [higher ·]

cell membrane

vacuole shrinks

concentrated solution outside the cell [lower ·]

As the cytoplasm is pulled away from the cell wall, the cell becomes limp (flaccid).

key

➤ net movement of water molecules

→ increased pressure of water in the vacuole presses the cytoplasm against the cell wall

➤ net movement of water molecules

→ decreased pressure of water in the vacuole decreases pressure on the cytoplasm until the cytoplasm pulls away from the cell wall

3.3 Cell division

preview

At the end of this section you will:
- **know that new cells (daughter cells) are formed when old cells (parent cells) divide into two**
- **understand that the cytoplasm and nucleus divide during cell division**
- **know that a cell may divide in two ways: mitosis and meiosis.**

How cells divide

On pages 38–9 is the concept map for **cell division**. Study it carefully.

Remember

★ The **cells of the body** divide by **mitosis**.

★ The **cells of the sex organs** that give rise to the sex cells (**gametes**) divide by **meiosis**. Sex cells are produced in the sex organs:
- the testes of the male and the ovaries of the female in mammals
- the anthers (male) and the carpels (female) in flowering plants.

SEXUAL REPRODUCTION Pages 91–3.

Mitosis and meiosis

The nucleus contains **chromosomes**, each consisting of **deoxyribonucleic acid (DNA)** wound round a core of protein. In cell division, the chromosomes are passed from the **parent** cell to the new **daughter** cells. 'Daughter' does not mean that the cells are female. It means that they are the new cells formed as a result of cell division.

CHROMOSOMES AND DNA Pages 45–7.

Mitosis produces daughter cells with the same number of chromosomes as the parent cell. The daughter cells are described as **diploid** (or $2n$).

Meiosis produces daughter cells with only half the number of chromosomes in the parent cell. The daughter cells are described as **haploid** (or n).

The importance of mitosis

The daughter cells each receive an identical full (diploid) set of chromosomes from the parent cell.

ASEXUAL REPRODUCTION Pages 94–5.

As a result, the parent cell and its daughter cells are genetically identical. They form a **clone**.

As a result, mitosis is the way in which living things

- **repair damage:** for example, mitosis replaces damaged skin cells with identical new skin cells
- **grow:** for example, the root of a plant grows because root tip cells divide by mitosis to form new root tissue

DEVELOPMENT Page 91.

- **reproduce asexually:** for example, parts of stems can sprout roots and grow into new plants. The new individuals are genetically identical to the parents and are therefore clones.

The importance of meiosis

The daughter cells each receive a half (haploid) set of chromosomes from the parent cell.

As a result, during fertilisation (when sperm and egg join together), the chromosomes from each cell combine.

As a result, the fertilised egg (**zygote**) is diploid but inherits a new combination of genes contributed (50:50) from the parents.

As a result, the new individual inherits characteristics from both parents, not just from one parent as in asexual reproduction.

VARIATION Pages 101–2.

PARENT CELL

four chromosomes per cell: the **diploid** number

cell membrane

chromosome

cytoplasm

nuclear membrane

The chromosomes shorten, fatten and become visible under the light microscope.

replication

chromatids

centromere

Each chromosome divides into a pair of identical (replica) **chromatids** joined to one another by the **centromere**.

equator of the cell

The chromosomes line up on the equator (middle) of the cell. The nuclear membrane has disappeared.

direction of movement of the chromatids

The chromatids separate and move to the opposite ends of the cell, which begins to divide.

The chromatids are now the new chromosomes of the two daughter cells. A nuclear membrane forms around each group of chromosomes.

four chromosomes per cell: the **diploid** number

TWO DAUGHTER CELLS

MITOSIS

Plant cells

A thin slab-like structure called the **cell plate** extends outwards until it meets the sides of the cell. The cell plate divides the cytoplasm into two.

CELL DIVISION

Animal cells

A furrow develops. It pinches the cell membrane in. As the furrow deepens the cell divides into two.

Cell division

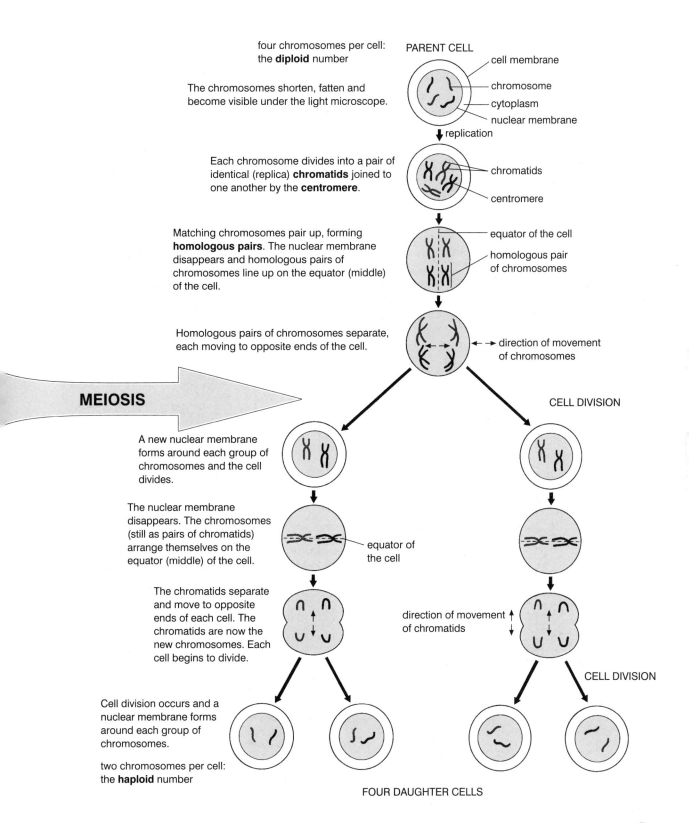

four chromosomes per cell: the **diploid** number

PARENT CELL

cell membrane
chromosome
cytoplasm
nuclear membrane

The chromosomes shorten, fatten and become visible under the light microscope.

replication

Each chromosome divides into a pair of identical (replica) **chromatids** joined to one another by the **centromere**.

chromatids

centromere

Matching chromosomes pair up, forming **homologous pairs**. The nuclear membrane disappears and homologous pairs of chromosomes line up on the equator (middle) of the cell.

equator of the cell

homologous pair of chromosomes

Homologous pairs of chromosomes separate, each moving to opposite ends of the cell.

direction of movement of chromosomes

MEIOSIS

CELL DIVISION

A new nuclear membrane forms around each group of chromosomes and the cell divides.

The nuclear membrane disappears. The chromosomes (still as pairs of chromatids) arrange themselves on the equator (middle) of the cell.

equator of the cell

The chromatids separate and move to opposite ends of each cell. The chromatids are now the new chromosomes. Each cell begins to divide.

direction of movement of chromatids

CELL DIVISION

Cell division occurs and a nuclear membrane forms around each group of chromosomes.

two chromosomes per cell: the **haploid** number

FOUR DAUGHTER CELLS

3.4 Cells, tissues and organs

At the end of this section you will:
- **understand that cells are organised into tissues, tissues into organs, and organs into organ systems**
- **know about the importance of the surface area to volume ratio for living processes**
- **understand that organ systems are specialised for exchanging materials.**

Building an organ system

Here is the concept map which revises **cells**, **tissues** and **organs**.

Plants and animals are **multicellular**: they are made of many types of cells. Each type of cell is specialised to perform a particular biological task.

★ A group of similar cells makes a **tissue**.

★ Different tissues together make up an **organ**.

★ Different organs combine to make an **organ system**.

VARIETY OF CELLS Page 34.

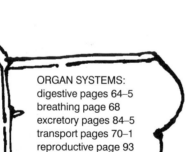

ORGAN SYSTEMS:
digestive pages 64–5
breathing page 68
excretory pages 84–5
transport pages 70–1
reproductive page 93
nervous pages 74–5

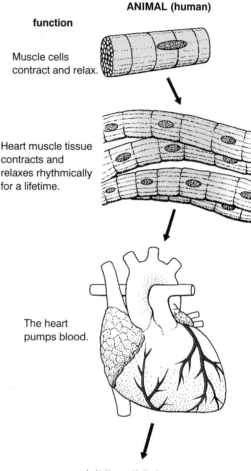

ANIMAL (human)

function

Muscle cells contract and relax.

Heart muscle tissue contracts and relaxes rhythmically for a lifetime.

The heart pumps blood.

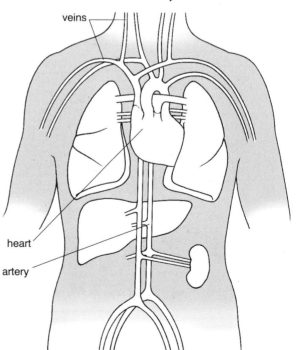

veins

heart

artery

The heart and blood vessels transport blood to all parts of the body.

BUILDING AN ORGAN SYSTEM

PLANT

function

Leaf palisade cells are filled with chloroplasts.

CELLS

Cells are the building blocks of which living things are made.

Photosynthesis occurs in leaf palisade tissue.

TISSUE

A **tissue** is a group of similar cells with a similar function.

The leaf makes and stores food.

ORGAN

A tissue may combine with other tissues to form an **organ**. For example, muscle tissue, nerve tissue and blood work together in the heart; palisade tissue and vascular tissue (xylem and phloem) work together in the leaf.

phloem vessel

Phloem vessels carry food away from the leaf and transport it to all parts of the plant.

phloem vessels

ORGAN SYSTEM

The heart, arteries and veins make up an **organ system** in humans. The leaf and vascular tissue make up an **organ system** in plants.

leaf

leaf stalk (petiole)

phloem vessels

midrib

Surface area to volume ratio

All cells (tissues, organs, organisms) exchange gases, food and other materials with their environment. The exchanges occur mostly by diffusion across surfaces. Look at the calculations for surface area (SA), volume (V) and surface area to volume ratio (SA/V) here.

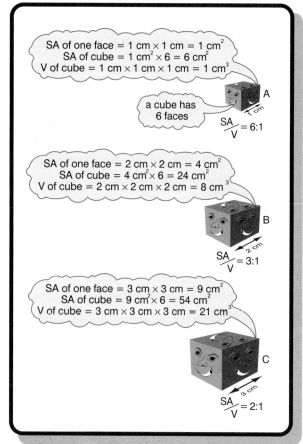

Cubic arithmetic

SA of one face = 1 cm × 1 cm = 1 cm^2
SA of cube = 1 cm^2 × 6 = 6 cm^2
V of cube = 1 cm × 1 cm × 1 cm = 1 cm^3

a cube has 6 faces

A

$\frac{SA}{V}$ = 6:1

SA of one face = 2 cm × 2 cm = 4 cm^2
SA of cube = 4 cm^2 × 6 = 24 cm^2
V of cube = 2 cm × 2 cm × 2 cm = 8 cm^3

B

$\frac{SA}{V}$ = 3:1

SA of one face = 3 cm × 3 cm = 9 cm^2
SA of cube = 9 cm^2 × 6 = 54 cm^2
V of cube = 3 cm × 3 cm × 3 cm = 21 cm^3

C

$\frac{SA}{V}$ = 2:1

- The SA/V of cube B is half that of cube A.
- The SA/V of cube C is two-thirds that of cube B and one-third that of cube A.

Remember
The LARGER the cube becomes, the SMALLER its SA/V.

★ Surface area increases with the **square** (power^2) of the side.

★ Volume increases with the **cube** (power^3) of the side.

Cells (tissues, organs, organisms) are not cube shaped, but the calculations apply to any shape. For example, as a cell grows it

- takes in more food and gases
- produces more waste substances.

After the cell reaches a certain size, its surface area becomes too small to meet the needs of the larger volume of living matter inside.

At this point, the cell divides into two smaller daughter cells. This restores the ratio of surface area to volume because the surface area to volume ratio of a daughter cell is greater than that of the parent cell.

As a result, sufficient food and gases can pass across the cell surface into the cell.

As a result, wastes can pass across the cell surface out of the cell.

Organ systems specialised for exchanging materials

We all exchange gases, food and other materials between our body and the environment. The exchange happens slowly by diffusion across body surfaces. Different organs and organ systems are specialised to increase the available surface area for the exchange of materials with their surroundings. They make the SA/V as large as possible.

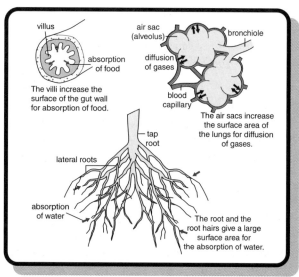

villus

air sac (alveolus)

bronchiole

absorption of food

diffusion of gases

The villi increase the surface of the gut wall for absorption of food.

blood capillary

The air sacs increase the surface area of the lungs for diffusion of gases.

tap root

lateral roots

absorption of water

The root and the root hairs give a large surface area for the absorption of water.

Increasing surface area

3.5 Chemicals in living things

preview

At the end of this section you will:
- **understand that living things are made from the same elements as other types of matter**
- **know that carbohydrates, lipids, proteins and nucleic acids are important chemicals in living things**
- **understand that atoms of carbon are able to combine to form long chains.**

Elements for life

All matter is made of chemical elements. Of these elements, six make up more than 95% by mass of living matter. They are:

- carbon (C)
- hydrogen (H)
- nitrogen (N)
- oxygen (O)
- phosphorus (P)
- sulphur (S).

The symbols of the elements arranged in order of abundance in living matter make the mnemonic **CHNOPS**.

Compounds for life

Important compounds in living things are

- **carbohydrates**: a major source of energy and structural materials
- **lipids**: stores of energy
- **proteins**: for building bodies
- **nucleic acids**: carry a code which tells cells how to make proteins.

Fact file

Carbon is the most common element in the substances that make up living things. Carbon atoms can combine to form long chains. Many of the carbon compounds in living things have large molecules (**macromolecules**) formed by small molecules combining.

Carbohydrates

Carbohydrates are compounds containing the elements carbon, hydrogen and oxygen. There are three categories:

Monosaccharides are simple sugars. Sweet-tasting **fructose** and **glucose** are examples. Both have the formula $C_6H_{12}O_6$. The six carbon atoms form a ring. Sugars (especially glucose) are an important source of energy in all living things.

RESPIRATION
Page 66.

fructose   glucose

The formula of fructose and glucose in shorthand form

Disaccharides are more complex sugars. They are formed when two monosaccharides combine. For example, two molecules of glucose combine to form one molecule of **maltose**:

2 glucose → maltose + water
$2C_6H_{12}O_6 \rightarrow C_{12}H_{22}O_{11}(aq) + H_2O$

The formula for maltose in shorthand form

A molecule of fructose and a molecule of glucose combine to form one molecule of **sucrose**:

glucose + fructose → sucrose + water

Polysaccharides are carbohydrates whose molecules contain hundreds of sugar rings. For example, **starch**, **cellulose** and **glycogen** are polysaccharides. Their molecules consist of long chains of glucose rings.

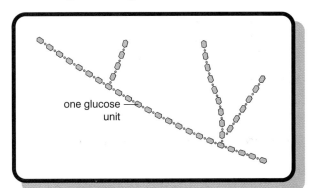
one glucose unit

Part of a starch molecule

3

Polysaccharides differ in the length and structure of their chains. They are important storage and structural materials in living things.

★ **Starch** is a food substance stored in plants. Their cells convert the starch into glucose, which is oxidised (respired) to release energy.

★ **Glycogen** is a food substance stored in animals. Liver cells convert glycogen into glucose, which is oxidised (respired) to release energy.

CELLS
Page 33.

★ **Cellulose** is an important component of the cell walls of plants.

★ **Chitin** is an important component of the exoskeleton of insects.

Lipids

Lipids are compounds containing the elements carbon, hydrogen and oxygen. There are two types of lipids: **fats**, which are solid at room temperature; and **oils**, which are liquid at room temperature.

Fats and oils are compounds formed between two constituents: **fatty acids** and **glycerol**. A molecule of glycerol can combine with three fatty acid molecules to form a **triglyceride** molecule and three molecules of water. Fats and oils are mixtures of triglycerides.

glycerol + fatty acid $\longrightarrow$ triglyceride + water

$$\begin{array}{c|c} \text{OH} \\ \text{OH} + 3HA \\ \text{OH} \end{array} \longrightarrow \begin{array}{c|c} \text{A} \\ \text{A} + 3H_2O \\ \text{A} \end{array}$$

Making a triglyceride

Saturated and unsaturated fats and oils

Fatty acids (and therefore the fats and oils of which they are a part) may be

• **saturated** – the carbon atoms are joined by single bonds, *or*

• **unsaturated** – the carbon atoms have double bonds between them (see page 199). If there is one double bond in the molecule, the compound is **monounsaturated**. If there is more than one double bond in the molecule, the compound is **polyunsaturated**.

HEART DISEASE
Page 73.

Fats and oils are important as

• components of cell membranes
• sources of energy
• sources of the fat-soluble vitamins A, D and E
• insulation which helps keep the body warm
• protection for delicate organs.

Proteins

Proteins are compounds containing the elements carbon, hydrogen, oxygen, nitrogen and sometimes sulphur.

Amino acids are the building blocks which combine to make proteins. Two or more amino acids can combine to form a **peptide**, which can combine with more amino acids to form a **protein**.

Fact file

★ **Peptides** have molecules with up to 15 amino acids.

★ **Polypeptides** have molecules with 15–100 amino acids.

★ **Proteins** have still larger molecules.

There are 20 different amino acids that combine to form proteins. The protein made depends on the type and number of amino acids joining together.

How amino acids combine to form peptides and proteins. Each shape represents a particular type of amino acid.

Proteins are important because

- they are the materials from which new tissues are made during growth and repair
- **enzymes** are proteins which control the rates of chemical reactions in cells
- **hormones** are proteins which control the activities of organisms.

HORMONES
Pages 82–3.

Enzymes in action

CATALYST
Pages 188–9.

Enzymes are made by living cells. They are **catalysts** which control the speeds of chemical reactions in cells. There are thousands of different enzymes in a cell. Enzymes also speed up the digestion of food in the gut.

Enzymes are

- **specific** in their action – each enzyme catalyses a certain chemical reaction or type of chemical reaction

- sensitive to changes in **pH**
- sensitive to changes in **temperature**.

The substance that the enzyme helps to react is called the **substrate**. The substances formed in the reaction are called **products**.

The features of enzymes are shown below.

Nucleic acids

There are two important nucleic acids – **deoxyribonucleic acid (DNA)** and **ribonucleic acid (RNA)**.

★ DNA makes up the chromosomes in the nucleus of the cell. The **genes** that carry information from parents to offspring are lengths of DNA. They carry the **genetic code** which tells cells how to assemble amino acids in the correct order to make proteins.

★ RNA occurs in the nucleus and cytoplasm of the cell. It transfers the information in the genes to the places in the cell where proteins are made.

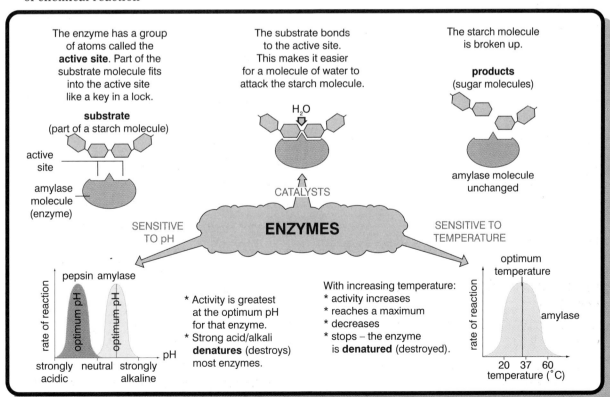

Enzymes in action

The structure of DNA

DNA and RNA are large complex molecules made from lots of smaller molecules called **nucleotides**.

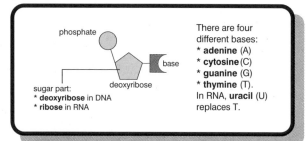

There are four different bases:
* **adenine** (A)
* **cytosine** (C)
* **guanine** (G)
* **thymine** (T).
In RNA, **uracil** (U) replaces T.

phosphate
base
sugar part:
* **deoxyribose** in DNA
* **ribose** in RNA
deoxyribose

A nucleotide molecule

★ Many nucleotides join together, sugar to phosphate, to form a long strand.

★ Two of these strands link together by **base pairing** to form a molecule of DNA.

★ The double strand twists into a spiral called a **double helix** – two intertwined spiral strands.

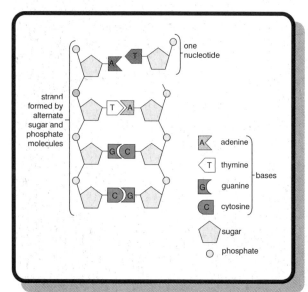

one nucleotide

strand formed by alternate sugar and phosphate molecules

bases:
A adenine
T thymine
G guanine
C cytosine

sugar
○ phosphate

Part of a molecule of DNA

two strands intertwined

base pairing holds the strands together

The double helix: two spiral strands connected by their bases

★ A **chromosome** consists of folded strands of DNA coiled round a protein core. The DNA part of the structure controls the inheritance of characteristics.

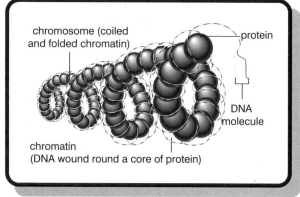

chromosome (coiled and folded chromatin)
protein
DNA molecule
chromatin (DNA wound round a core of protein)

The structure of a chromosome

DNA replication

In cell division, the chromosomes **replicate** – they form an identical copy of themselves. This means the DNA molecule must make a copy of itself. The diagram below shows how this happens.

CELL DIVISION Pages 38–9.

Now you can see why the daughter cells formed by mitosis are genetically identical to each other and to their parent cell. The two new molecules of DNA are each a replica of the original because of the base pairing. A always pairs with T, and G always pairs with C. All the cells in the body that die are replaced by mitosis, so they stay the same.

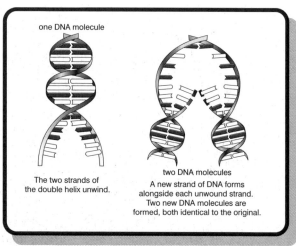

one DNA molecule

The two strands of the double helix unwind.

two DNA molecules
A new strand of DNA forms alongside each unwound strand. Two new DNA molecules are formed, both identical to the original.

DNA replication

Mutation

Hundreds of thousands of nucleotides a second can be adding to the replicating DNA. Occasionally the wrong base adds by mistake. Then the new DNA formed is slightly different from the original. The change is called a **mutation**.

The genetic code

★ A **codon** is the length of a DNA molecule that codes for one amino acid. It is three nucleotides long.

★ A **gene** is the length of a DNA molecule that codes for one complete protein.

★ So a gene is a long line of codons in a particular order.

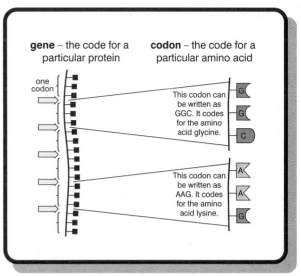

gene – the code for a particular protein   **codon** – the code for a particular amino acid

one codon

This codon can be written as GGC. It codes for the amino acid glycine.

This codon can be written as AAG. It codes for the amino acid lysine.

The genetic code

round-up

How much have you improved? Work out your improvement index on page 109.

1 Which of the structures listed below are found in **a)** animal cells and plant cells **b)** plant cells only?

nucleus   cell membrane   cell wall   large vacuole   mitochondria   chloroplasts   cytoplasm [7]

2 Describe what happens in the cells of a plant deprived of water which is then watered. How will the appearance of the plant change? [5]

3 Complete the following paragraph using the words below. Each word may be used once, more than once or not at all.

osmosis   faster   gains   down   slower   partially   energy   against

The movement of a substance _____ a concentration gradient is called diffusion. The steeper the concentration gradient, the _____ is the rate of diffusion. Active transport occurs _____ a concentration gradient. The process requires more _____ than diffusion. The diffusion of water through a _____ permeable membrane is called _____ . [6]

4 Why is mitosis important for maintaining the health of the tissues of the body? [1]

5 Compare and contrast the processes of mitosis and meiosis by listing the similarities and the differences in different columns. [8]

6 Below is a series of words that describe the organisation of living matter. Arrange the words in the correct sequence, beginning with the simplest level of organisation and ending with the most complex.

organs   cells   organisms   organ systems   tissues [5]

7 Match each substance in column **A** with its function in column **B**.

A substances	B functions
fat	carries the genetic code
cellulose	insulates the body
DNA	a component of the plant cell wall
polypeptide	a food substance stored in the liver
glycogen	enzymes are made of this substance
protein	made of about 40 amino acids

[6]

8 a) The following is a sequence of bases for a length of DNA. How many codons are there in the sequence, assuming the first codon begins at the left-hand side and there is no overlap?

T T A G G A C T G A T C

b) If each codon codes for one amino acid, how many amino acids are coded for in this length of DNA? [2]

Green plants as organisms

4

How much do you already know?
Work out your score on page 109.

Test yourself

1 a) Name the inorganic substances that are the raw
materials for photosynthesis. [2]
b) Name the gas given off during photosynthesis. [1]

2 Minerals are needed for healthy growth. Match each
substance in column **A** with its function in column **B**.

A substances	B functions
nitrogen	used to make cell membranes
phosphorus	used to make chlorophyll
magnesium	used to make protein [3]

3 Complete the following paragraph using the words below.
Each word may be used once, more than once or not at
all.

transpiration   active transport   evaporation   increase
translocation   osmotic   stomata   xylem   osmosis

Root hairs _____ the surface area available for the
_____ uptake of water. _____ also
transports water across the root into the _____ .
The uptake of minerals in solution is by _____ .
Water moves through the _____ tissue in unbroken
columns connecting the root with the leaves of the plant.
Water is lost from the leaves by _____ through the
_____ . [8]

4 Different types of tropisms are listed in column **A**. Match
each type with the correct description in column **B**.

A tropisms	B descriptions
phototropism	growth movement in response to gravity
geotropism	growth movement in response to touch
hydrotropism	growth movement in response to light
thigmotropism	growth movement in response to water [4]

sugars — used in respiration (see page 34)
used as building molecules to make starch which is a store of food (see pages 43–4)
used as building molecules to make cellulose which is a component of cell walls (see pages 43–4)
react with nitrates to form proteins (see page 44)

The uses of sugar in plants

4.1 Photosynthesis

and mineral nutrients

preview

At the end of this section you will:
- **understand that leaves are adapted for photosynthesis**
- **know that limiting factors affect the rate of photosynthesis**
- **be able to identify the minerals that plants need for healthy growth.**

Photosynthesis

Photosynthesis is a chemical process that traps
the energy of sunlight and uses it to convert
carbon dioxide and water into sugars. A summary
of the process is:

$$\text{carbon dioxide} + \text{water} \xrightarrow{\text{catalysed by chlorophyll}} \text{glucose} + \text{oxygen}$$
$$6CO_2(g) + 6H_2O(l) \longrightarrow C_6H_{12}O_6(aq) + 6O_2(g)$$

There are lots of different
chemical reactions that
make up the process of
photosynthesis. The
reactions happen inside
chloroplasts, in the leaves and other green parts
of plant cells.

CELLS CONVERT
ENERGY
Page 35.

Leaves

A leaf is a food-making factory. It is **adapted** for
photosynthesis.

Carbon dioxide and water
circulate within the leaf. Light is
captured by the pigment
chlorophyll, which is packaged in
the chloroplasts that pack the cells
of the leaf. On pages 50–1 is the
concept map for **photosynthesis**,
and its checklist of points. The
diagram on the left shows you how
the plant uses sugars.

48

Limiting factors

The rate at which plants make sugar by photosynthesis is affected by supplies of **carbon dioxide** and **water**, **temperature** and the **intensity of light**. These factors are called **limiting factors** because if any one of them falls to a low level, photosynthesis slows down or stops. The diagram below illustrates the point. At low concentrations of carbon dioxide, the carbon dioxide limits the rate of photosynthesis, whatever the light level is. Carbon dioxide is the limiting factor. At higher concentrations of carbon dioxide, the rate of photosynthesis increases if the light is bright enough. Light is now the limiting factor.

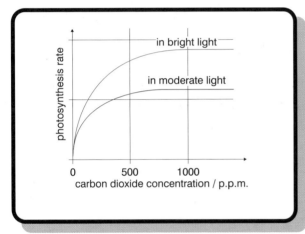

Effect of carbon dioxide concentration on the rate of photosynthesis

The higher the temperature, the faster the chemical reactions of photosynthesis, within limits. Extreme cold (below 0°C) and extreme heat (above 45°C) denature the enzymes which control the chemical reactions of photosynthesis.

Water is a raw material for photosynthesis. However, water is also the solvent in which the reactions of metabolism occur within cells. Singling out the direct effect of the availability of water on photosynthesis is therefore very difficult.

In a greenhouse, conditions are controlled so that limiting factors are eliminated.

Fact file

★ Bottles of 'plant food' sold at garden centres contain solutions of some of the important minerals needed for healthy plant growth.

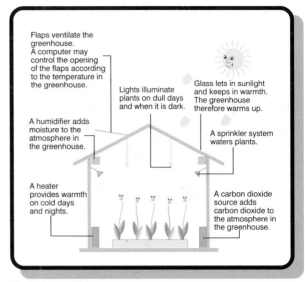

The maximum-efficiency greenhouse

Mineral nutrients

Plants grow using the food (sugars) they make by photosynthesis. Healthy plant growth also depends on **minerals** which are absorbed from the soil through the roots as solutions of salts.

Major elements are needed in quite large amounts.

★ **Nitrogen (N)** is used by plants to make protein.

★ **Phosphorus (P)** is used by plants to make cell membranes.

★ **Potassium (K)** is needed for photosynthesis.

Plants deprived of any of the major elements grow less well. Most artificial fertilisers are NPK fertilisers.

Trace elements (micronutrients) are needed in much smaller amounts than major elements.

★ **Magnesium (Mg)** is a component of the chlorophyll molecule.

★ **Iron (Fe)** is also a component of the chlorophyll molecule.

If magnesium and iron are in short supply then leaves become mottled and pale. **Copper (Cu)**, **sodium (Na)** and **manganese (Mn)** are also trace elements. Absence of any one of them from the soil leads to poor plant growth.

Checklist for photosynthesis

1 ★ Leaves are arranged so that the lower ones are not overshadowed by those above. The arrangement is called the **leaf mosaic**.

As a result, more leaves are exposed to direct sunlight.

★ The leaf blade is flat.

As a result, a large surface area is exposed for the absorption of light.

★ The leaf blade is thin.

As a result, light reaches the lower layers of cells in the leaf.

2 ★ Water moves up to leaves in the **transpiration stream**.

TRANSPIRATION
Pages 52–5.

★ Carbon dioxide enters leaves through the **stomata**.

3 ★ The cells of the upper leaf surface do not contain chloroplasts and are transparent.

★ **Palisade cells** beneath the upper epidermis are column shaped, tightly packed and filled with chloroplasts.

As a result, many chloroplasts are exposed to bright light, maximising the rate of photosynthesis.

★ **Spongy mesophyll cells** contain fewer chloroplasts and are more loosely packed.

As a result, there are air spaces between the spongy mesophyll cells.

★ The spaces allow carbon dioxide and water vapour to circulate freely within the leaf, bringing the raw materials for photosynthesis to the leaf cells.

STOMATA
Page 52.

★ Each **stoma** is flanked by guard cells which control the size of the opening of the stoma.

As a result, the rate of diffusion of gases into and out of the leaf through the stomata is controlled.

★ The cells of the lower leaf surface lack chloroplasts, except the guard cells.

4 ★ Chloroplasts pack the inside of each palisade cell.

★ Chloroplasts stream in the cytoplasm (**cyclosis**) to the region of the palisade cell where light is brightest.

As a result, the rate of photosynthesis is maximised.

5 ★ Membranes inside the chloroplasts are covered with the green pigment **chlorophyll**.

★ Chlorophyll absorbs light, especially wavelengths in the red and blue parts of the spectrum.

★ The membranes are arranged like stacks of pancakes, maximising the surface area of chlorophyll exposed to light.

6 ★ During photosynthesis, light energy is converted into the energy of chemical bonds of glucose (sugar).

★ Chlorophyll makes light energy available for the synthesis (making) of sugar.

★ The region between membranes contains enzymes which convert water and carbon dioxide into sugar. The energy needed for conversion comes from the light absorbed by chlorophyll.

membrane of chloroplast

PHOTOSYNTHESIS IN ACTION
Water molecules and carbon dioxide molecules combine to form sugar. The chemical reactions produce oxygen.

CHECK **6** LIST

carbon dioxide + water ⟶ sugar + oxygen

INSIDE THE CHLOROPLAST

membranes covered with chlorophyll

CHLOROPLAST ×50 000

lining of chloroplast cut away

Track the route of water molecules and carbon dioxide molecules into the chloroplast.

CHECK **5** LIST

Photosynthesis

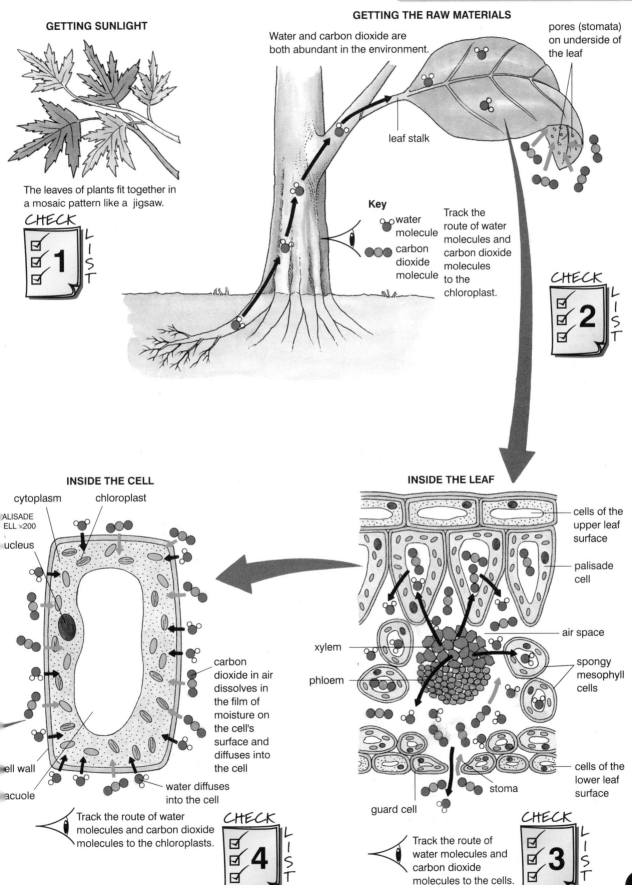

GETTING SUNLIGHT

The leaves of plants fit together in a mosaic pattern like a jigsaw.

CHECK **1** LIST

GETTING THE RAW MATERIALS

Water and carbon dioxide are both abundant in the environment.

leaf stalk

pores (stomata) on underside of the leaf

Key
- water molecule
- carbon dioxide molecule

Track the route of water molecules and carbon dioxide molecules to the chloroplast.

CHECK **2** LIST

INSIDE THE CELL

cytoplasm   chloroplast

PALISADE CELL ×200

nucleus

carbon dioxide in air dissolves in the film of moisture on the cell's surface and diffuses into the cell

cell wall

vacuole

water diffuses into the cell

Track the route of water molecules and carbon dioxide molecules to the chloroplasts.

CHECK **4** LIST

INSIDE THE LEAF

cells of the upper leaf surface

palisade cell

air space

xylem

phloem

spongy mesophyll cells

cells of the lower leaf surface

guard cell

stoma

Track the route of water molecules and carbon dioxide molecules to the cells.

CHECK **3** LIST

4.2 Transport in plants

preview

At the end of this section you will:

- know that xylem tissue transports water and that phloem tissue transports food
- understand the processes of transpiration and translocation
- know that xylem tissue and phloem tissue form vascular bundles which reach all parts of the plant.

Transport systems in plants

On pages 54–5 is the concept map for **transport in plants**, and its checklist. Study them carefully.

Factors affecting transpiration

Think of the ways plants lose and gain water.

★ Loss of water is through transpiration.

★ Gain is through the uptake of water by the roots.

If the loss of water is greater than the gain, then the stomata close.

As a result, transpiration is reduced.

If the loss of water is still more than the gain, then the cells of the plant lose turgor and the plant **wilts**.

The graphs show the effect of other factors on the rate of transpiration. Light stimulates the stomata to open wide. The rate of transpiration is therefore greater during the day than at night.

Factors affecting the rate of transpiration

Controlling the size of stomata

Two sausage-shaped **guard cells** surround the opening which forms the stoma. The guard cells contain chloroplasts. Think of the sequence:

★ During the day, photosynthesis increases the concentration of sugar in the guard cells. There is a net flow of water by osmosis into the guard cells making them turgid. The guard cells bow out, opening the stoma.

★ At night, photosynthesis stops and the concentration of sugar in the guard cells falls. There is a net outflow of water and the guard cells lose turgor. The guard cells bow in, closing the stoma.

4.3 Plant responses

preview

At the end of this section you will know that:

- plants grow in response to stimuli
- there are two sorts of growth movement – nastic movements and tropic movements (tropisms)
- plant hormones (growth substances) affect the growth of plants
- auxin is an example of a plant hormone
- commercial applications of plant hormones include weed control and the production of 'seedless' fruits.

Nastys and tropisms

Plants move by growing in response to stimuli. One part of the plant grows faster than another. There are two types of growth movement.

★ **Nastic movements** are responses to stimuli that come from all directions. For example, flowers open and close in response to changes in temperature.

★ **Tropic movements** (tropisms) are responses to stimuli which come mainly from one direction. For example, shoots bend towards light.

How plants respond

The diagram below and its checklist are your revision guide to **plant responses**. Study them carefully.

Checklist for plant responses

1 ★ Tropisms are **positive** if the plant grows towards the stimulus and **negative** if it grows away.

As a result of different positive and negative tropisms, the different parts of the plant grow in a way that increases the plant's chances of survival. For example, the roots 'find' water, leaves receive as much light as possible for photosynthesis.

★ The growing tips (shoot/root) of a plant are receptors for different stimuli.

2 ★ Auxin makes the cellulose wall of plant cells more elastic.

As a result, the cells elongate rapidly.

As a result, the cells on the shady side of the shoot tip grow *more* rapidly than the cells on the brightly lit side.

As a result, the shoot tip bends towards the light.

3 ★ The effect of the hormone produced by the root cap is different from auxin produced by the shoot tip. It *slows down* growth in the underside of the root tip.

As a result, the root bends down.

Fact file

★ The stems of some types of plant respond to the touch of an object by growing in a spiral around the object. The response is called thigmotropism. Sweet peas and runner beans show thigmotropism. They spiral round canes stuck into the ground to support them.

★ Does it matter which way up a seed is planted? Positive phototropism means that the shoot will always grow upwards. Positive geotropism means that the roots will always grow downwards. So no matter which way up a seed is, its shoot and roots will always grow in the right direction.

★ Auxin sometimes prevents growth. It diffuses down the stem and prevents the growth of side shoots. Lopping the top off a plant removes the source of auxin and side branches then develop. This is why a gardener trims a hedge to make it more bushy.

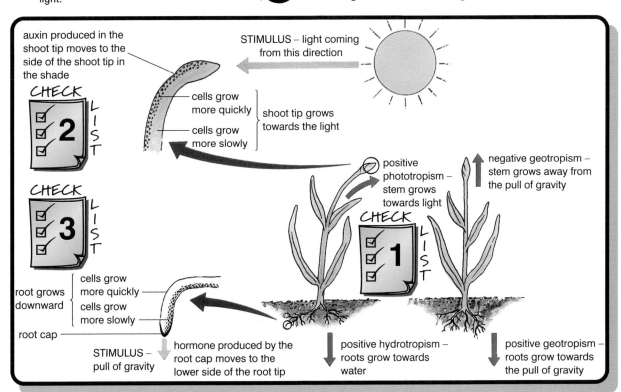

Tropisms – the response of the shoot tip to light and the root tip to gravity and water

4

TRANSPORT OF FOOD

strands of xylem and phloem branch from midrib

waxy cuticle – waterproof layer which reduces water loss from leaf surfaces

The vascular tissue forms a thick vein (midrib) which runs through the middle of the leaf

xylem

phloem

ACTIVE TRANSPORT Page 36.

cells of a bud

B

companion cells support the function of sieve cells

phloem tissue

sieve cells form tubes by joining end to end

A

leaf cell

leaf stalk (petiole)

midrib

xylem

phloem

form a bundle of vascular tissue

stem

Key

⋰ sugar concentration

→ movement of sugar and other dissolved substances

A Sugar passes from the leaf cells into the sieve cells by **active transport**.

B Sugar and other substances are transported through the sieve cells to where they are needed in the plant. The process is called **translocation**.

C Sugar passing to the root moves out of the sieve cells into the root cells, where it is converted to starch and stored.

sieve plate formed by a perforated cross wall

B

xylem

phloem

form a core of vascular tissue

C

CHECK LIST 1

root cells

root

TRANSPORT OF WATER

leaf

stomata – gaps through which gases diffuse

upper leaf surface

G

phloem

xylem

D

E

air space

lower leaf surface

F

guard cell

stoma

TRANSPIRATION

Xylem cells join end to end. Cross walls separating a cell from neighbouring cells are broken down forming a continuous tube, rather like a drinking straw.

CHECK LIST 2

C

B

A

root cells

soil particles

root hair cell

Checklist for transport in plants

CHECK LIST

1 ★ Phloem consists of living cells.

★ The concentration of sugar in the leaf is often lower than the concentration of sugar in the upper ends of the sieve tubes.

As a result, sugar has to move from the leaf into the sieve cells by **active transport**.

★ Osmosis draws water from the xylem and increases the pressure in the sieve tubes.

As a result, sugar solution moves to all parts of the plant.

★ Pressure in the sieve tubes drops as cells use sugar or store it as starch.

2 ★ Xylem consists of dead cells.

★ The walls of xylem tubes are waterproofed with a substance called **lignin**.

★ As water transpires, more is drawn from the xylem in the leaf.

As a result, water is 'sucked' upwards through the xylem of the stem.

As a result, more water is supplied to the bottom of the xylem by the roots.

As a result, there are unbroken moving columns of water from the roots to the leaves.

Key

→ movement of water

Ⓐ Root hairs absorb water from the soil by **osmosis**. Mineral ions are **actively transported** into the root.

Ⓑ Water passes through the root tissue into the xylem by **osmosis**.

Ⓒ Water travels through the xylem of the root and stem in unbroken columns – the **transpiration stream**.

Ⓓ Water moves through the xylem of the leaf stalk and veins of the leaf.

Ⓔ Water evaporates into the large air spaces within the leaf. The air spaces are saturated with water vapour.

Ⓕ The concentration of water vapour in the atmosphere is lower than that in the air spaces. Water vapour therefore diffuses from the leaf through the stomata. The process is called **transpiration**.

Ⓖ Water lost by cells through evaporation is replaced with water drawn through the cells by osmosis. Cells next to the xylem draw water from the xylem by osmosis.

The shoot tip

The diagram below shows the sorts of experiments carried out by scientists investigating the response of plants to light. These experiments suggest that there is a growth substance (auxin) which

- is produced in the shoot tip
- diffuses to the region behind the shoot tip
- stimulates growth so that the shoot bends towards light.

Using plant hormones

★ **Ripening** – fruit is quickly ripened in sheds in an atmosphere which contains one part of **ethene** per million parts of air.

★ **Weedkillers** – 2,4-D (2,4-dichlorophenoxyethanoic acid) is a synthetic auxin which kills plants by making them grow too fast. Broad-leaved weed plants like docks, daisies and dandelions are more sensitive to 2,4-D than narrow-leaved crop plants like wheat and barley.

★ **Seedless fruit** – an auxin paste smeared over the carpels of some crop species produces fruit without fertilisation. Seedless cucumbers and seedless tomatoes are produced in this way.

★ **Rooting** – gardeners use 'rooting powder' which contains auxin to encourage root growth from stem cuttings.

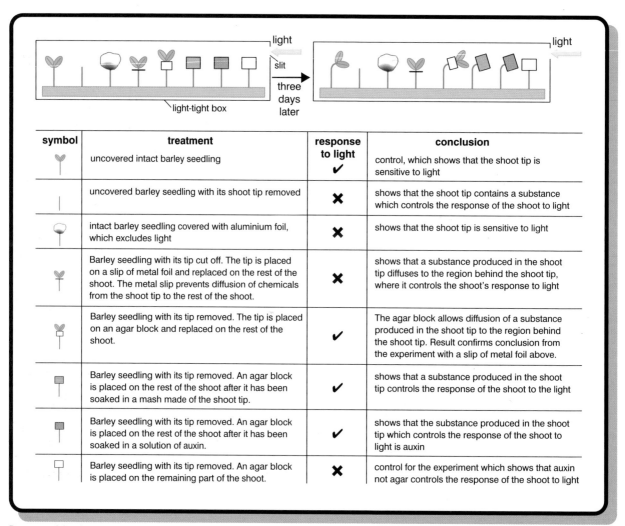

symbol	treatment	response to light	conclusion
	uncovered intact barley seedling	✔	control, which shows that the shoot tip is sensitive to light
	uncovered barley seedling with its shoot tip removed	✘	shows that the shoot tip contains a substance which controls the response of the shoot to light
	intact barley seedling covered with aluminium foil, which excludes light	✘	shows that the shoot tip is sensitive to light
	Barley seedling with its tip cut off. The tip is placed on a slip of metal foil and replaced on the rest of the shoot. The metal slip prevents diffusion of chemicals from the shoot tip to the rest of the shoot.	✘	shows that a substance produced in the shoot tip diffuses to the region behind the shoot tip, where it controls the shoot's response to light
	Barley seedling with its tip removed. The tip is placed on an agar block and replaced on the rest of the shoot.	✔	The agar block allows diffusion of a substance produced in the shoot tip to the region behind the shoot tip. Result confirms conclusion from the experiment with a slip of metal foil above.
	Barley seedling with its tip removed. An agar block is placed on the rest of the shoot after it has been soaked in a mash made of the shoot tip.	✔	shows that a substance produced in the shoot tip controls the response of the shoot to the light
	Barley seedling with its tip removed. An agar block is placed on the rest of the shoot after it has been soaked in a solution of auxin.	✔	shows that the substance produced in the shoot tip which controls the response of the shoot to light is auxin
	Barley seedling with its tip removed. An agar block is placed on the remaining part of the shoot.	✘	control for the experiment which shows that auxin not agar controls the response of the shoot to light

Response of the shoot tip to light

round-up

How much have you improved?
Work out your improvement index on pages 109–10.

1 Name the different cells in the leaf that contain chloroplasts. [3]

2 Briefly explain why most chloroplasts are found in palisade cells lying just beneath the upper surface of the leaf. [4]

3 List the major limiting factors for photosynthesis. Briefly explain how a greenhouse overcomes the effect of limiting factors on the growth of plants. [8]

4 Complete the following paragraph using the words below. Each word may be used once, more than once or not at all.

**xylem   transport   sugar   translocation
transpiration   phloem   pressure
active transport   water**

Leaves produce _____ by photosynthesis. The concentration of _____ in leaf cells is often less than that in nearby _____ tissue. _____ therefore moves from the leaf cell into the _____ by _____ . Osmosis draws _____ into the _____ tissue increasing _____ which helps transport sugar. The transport of sugar is called _____ . Storage of _____ as starch in the root cells reduces _____ in the _____ . [13]

5 Describe the probable climate on a day when the transpiration rate of a plant is at a maximum. [4]

6 Briefly explain what happens if a plant loses more water through transpiration than it gains through absorption of water by its roots. [3]

7 Compare the characteristics of xylem tissue with those of phloem tissue. List the comparisons in two columns headed 'xylem' and 'phloem' respectively. [5]

8 Complete the following paragraph using the words below. Each word may be used once, more than once or not at all.

**weedkiller   ripens   plant hormone
unfertilised   tip   seedless   slowly**

Auxin is a _____ produced in the _____ of the shoot. Synthetic auxin is used as a _____ to kill unwanted plants. Auxin paste applied to the _____ carpels of some crop species produces _____ fruits. Fruit stored in an atmosphere containing ethene _____ more quickly. [6]

9 The diagram shows an experiment on the shoots of growing seedlings. In experiment A a thin piece of metal was placed between the tip of the shoot and the rest of the stem. In experiment B a thin piece of metal was placed further down, separating the shoot into an upper part and a lower part.

The growing seedlings were placed in a box which was light-tight except for a slit on one side. The seedlings were illuminated for three days.

a) What hypothesis was the scientist trying to test? [2]

b) In each case, what do you think the response of the seedling will be to the light source? (Assume the seedlings survived the treatment for the time of the experiment.) [2]

Explain your answer. [4]

Well done if you've improved. Don't worry if you haven't. Take a break and try again.

Humans as organisms

How much do you already know?
Work out your score on page 110.

Test yourself

1 The nutrients in food are listed below. Use these nutrients to answer the following questions.

 carbohydrates fats proteins vitamins minerals

 a) Which nutrients give food its energy content? [3]
 b) Which nutrient is a source of energy, but is most important in the body for growth and repair? [1]
 c) Which nutrient releases the most energy per gram? [1]
 d) Which nutrients are needed only in small amounts, but play an important role in the control of metabolism? [2]

2 Match each term in column **A** with its correct description in column **B**.

A terms	B descriptions
ingestion	the removal of undigested food through the anus
digestion	digested food passes into the body
absorption	food is taken into the mouth
egestion	food is broken down [4]

3 Explain the differences between
 a) bronchi and bronchioles [2]
 b) lungs and alveoli [2]
 c) aerobic respiration and anaerobic respiration [4]
 d) breathing and gaseous exchange. [3]

4 Explain how the heart functions as a double pump. [4]

5 The different components of blood are listed in column **A**. Match each component with its correct description in column **B**.

A components	B descriptions
plasma	contain haemoglobin
red blood cells	promote the formation of blood clots
white blood cells	contains dissolved food substances
platelets	produce antibodies [4]

6 The components of the reflex arc are listed as follows: sensory neurone, effector, relay neurone, receptor, motor neurone. Write the components in their correct order. [4]

7 What is the function of each of these parts of the ear?
 a) the eardrum   b) the bones of the middle ear
 c) the pinna   d) the hair cells [8]

8 What are hormones and how are they transported around the body? [2]

9 Distinguish between the roles of the hormones insulin and glucagon in keeping the blood glucose level steady. [2]

10 The structures of the kidney tubule and its blood supply are listed below. Rewrite them in the order in which a molecule of urea passes from the renal artery to the outside of the body.

 **tubule urethra bladder glomerulus
 Bowman's capsule ureter collecting duct** [7]

11 Match each body structure in column **A** with its role in the defence of the body against disease in column **B**.

A body structures	B roles
tear gland	produces sebum which kills bacteria and fungi
blood	white cells produce antibodies which destroy antigens
skin	produce hydrochloric acid which kills bacteria
cilia lining the upper respiratory tract	produce the enzyme lysozyme which destroys bacteria
glands in the stomach wall	sweep away mucus containing trapped microorganisms and particles [5]

5.1 Food and diet

preview

At the end of this section you will:
● **understand that different foods contain different amounts of energy**
● **be able to identify the components of a diet**
● **know the role of different foods in the body.**

Nutrients in food

The **nutrients** in food are **carbohydrates**, **fats**, **proteins**, **vitamins** and **minerals**. **Water** and **fibre** are also components of food. Different foods contain nutrients, water and fibre in different proportions. Our **diet** is the food and drink we take in. Remember the sequence:

$$\left.\begin{array}{l}\text{nutrient}\\ +\text{ water}\\ +\text{ fibre}\end{array}\right\} \xrightarrow{\text{components of}} \text{food} \xrightarrow{\text{eaten}} \text{diet}$$

All living things (including us) need food. The nutrients in food are a source of

- **energy** which powers life's activities
- materials for the **growth** and **repair** of bodies
- substances which control the **metabolism** of cells.

On pages 60–1 is a Mind Map for **food and diet**. The checklist of points gives you more information.

Checklist for food and diet

1 ★ The **energy value** of food is measured using an instrument called a bomb calorimeter, shown below.

labels:
- combustion gases out
- stirrer to distribute heat evenly through the water
- cover plate
- heat exchange coil made of copper, which conducts heat very well
- known volume of water in water jacket
- thermometer
- combustion chamber filled with oxygen
- known mass of food
- electrically heated wire to set the food alight
- oxygen in
- electricity supply

A bomb calorimeter

The burning food heats the surrounding water. The change in temperature of the water is used to work out the energy value of the food:

$$\frac{\text{energy released}}{\text{per gram}} = \frac{\dfrac{\text{volume of water}}{\text{in water jacket}} \times \dfrac{\text{temperature}}{\text{rise}} \times 4.2}{\text{mass of food}}$$

★ The energy released from food depends on the nutrients it contains.
- 17.2 kJ/g for carbohydrate
- 22.2 kJ/g for protein
- 38.5 kJ/g for fat

Although protein is an 'energy nutrient', its most important use in the body is for growth and repair.

★ People have different energy requirements depending on their
- **age** – on average young people have greater energy requirements than older people
- **gender** (male or female) – pregnancy and lactation (milk production) increase the energy requirements of women
- **activities** – any kind of activity increases a person's energy requirements.

★ The rate at which the body uses energy is called the **metabolic rate**. It is lowest (called the **basal metabolic rate**) when the body is at rest.

★ If a person eats more food than is necessary for his/her energy needs, the excess is turned into fat.

As a result, the person puts on weight.

★ To lose weight, a person can
- take more exercise, which increases energy output
- eat less high-energy food, decreasing energy input.

2 ★ **Additives** are put into food to
- make it tastier
- make it more attractive
- improve its texture
- prevent it from spoiling.

★ Some additives can make some people unwell.

3 ★ A **balanced diet** is a mixture of foods which together provide sufficient nutrients for healthy living.

★ The 'basic four' food groups help us choose a balanced diet.

4 ★ The amount of **alcohol** people consume is measured in units, as shown below.

unit of alcohol = one measure of whisky = one glass of sherry = one glass of table wine = half a pint of beer or lager

Units of alcohol

★ How much alcohol is too much? It depends on a person's age, size, gender (male or female) and metabolic rate.

5 ★ Vitamin C helps cells to join together. It also controls the use of calcium by bones and teeth.

★ Vitamin D helps the body to absorb calcium.

★ Deficiency of iron is a common cause of anaemia.

GRAIN FOODS

ANTIOXIDANTS

PRESERVATIVES

CHECK LIST ②

ADDITIVES

COLOUR

+ FLAVOUR

EMULSIFIER

MIX: OIL WATER

CHECK LIST ③

FOODS

VARIETY IS BEST!

daily each choose 4

GROUPS

BALANCED

HELP HEALTHY EATING

D E T

ALCOHOL SENSIBLE

ABUSE DRUNKENNESS

DRINK RISK ? UNITS ♂ 28 per week ♀ 21

DISEASE

CHECK LIST ④

FAT

EXCESS OVERWEIGHT RISK

RISK DISEASE

ADDICTION

+ LIVER DISEASE

SUGAR EXCESS OVERWEIGHT

BLOOD CHOLESTEROL: SATURATED RISK

+ UNSATURATED RISK PLANT

ANIMAL

CHOLESTEROL DISEASE

SEE 44 PAGE

TOOTH DECAY

OUCH!

ENAMEL DENTINE PULP CAVITY

RISK DISEASE

⬇ = decreased risk

⬆ = increased risk

61

5.2 The digestive system

preview

At the end of this section you will:

- **know that the digestive system is a muscular tube through which food moves**
- **understand that as food moves through the digestive system it is processed (digested) into substances which the cells of the body can absorb and use**
- **be able to identify enzymes responsible for digesting food.**

Testing your understanding

The terms:

gut
intestine   all refer to the digestive
alimentary canal   system.

Digesting food

Food is processed through the digestive system in the following sequence:

ingestion
food is taken
into the mouth

↓

digestion
large molecules of
food are broken down
into smaller molecules

↓

absorption
the small molecules
of digested food
pass into the body

↓

egestion
undigested food is
removed from the body
through the anus

The digestive system is a muscular tube through which food moves. It processes food.

★ **Mechanical processes** break up food and mix it with digestive juices.

★ **Chemical processes** digest food using different enzymes in the digestive juices. The body cannot absorb the large molecules of carbohydrate, protein and fat in food. They are broken down into smaller molecules which the body can absorb.

On pages 64–5 is the concept map for **the digestive system**. The **liver** and **pancreas** are connected by ducts to the digestive system. They play an important role in the digestion of food. The numbers on the concept map refer to the checklist below.

Checklist for the digestive system

(M) = mechanical processes of digestion

(C) = chemical processes of digestion

1 ★ **(M) Teeth** chew food, breaking it into small pieces.

As a result, the surface area of food exposed to the action of digestive enzymes is increased.

As a result, food is digested more quickly.

2 ★ **(C) Saliva**, produced by the salivary glands, contains the enzyme **amylase**.

As a result, the digestion of starch begins in the mouth.

★ **(M)** Saliva moistens the food.

As a result, the food is made slippery for easy swallowing.

3 ★ **(M)** Muscles of the **stomach** wall and **small intestine** mix food thoroughly with different juices containing digestive enzymes.

As a result, a liquid paste called **chyme** is formed.

As a result, food and digestive enzymes are brought into intimate contact.

★ **(C)** Gastric juice, produced by **pits** in the stomach wall, contains **hydrochloric acid** and the enzymes **pepsin** and **renin**.

Hydrochloric acid
- increases the acidity of the stomach contents.

As a result, bacteria in the food are killed.

As a result, the action of salivary amylase is stopped.

Pepsin
- begins the digestion of protein.

Renin
- clots milk, making it semi-solid.

As a result, milk stays in the gut long enough to be digested.

4 ★ **(C) Bile**, produced by the **liver**, is a green alkaline liquid which is stored in the gall bladder before release into the small intestine through the bile duct. It
- neutralises acid from the stomach
- breaks fat into small droplets (**emulsification**).

As a result, the surface area of fat exposed to the action of the enzyme **lipase** is increased.

As a result, fat is digested more quickly.

5 ★ **(C) Pancreatic juice**, produced by the **pancreas**, is released into the small intestine through the pancreatic duct. It contains
- **sodium carbonate** which neutralises stomach acid
- **carbohydrases**, **proteases** and **lipases** (see table below) which digest carbohydrate, protein and fat.

6 ★ **(C) Intestinal juice**, produced by glands in the wall of the **duodenum** and **ileum**, contains
- **carbohydrases** and **lipases** that complete the digestion of carbohydrates and fats.

Chemistry of digestion

Digestive enzymes catalyse the breakdown of food by **hydrolysis**. Water splits large molecules of food into smaller molecules which are suitable for absorption into the body. The table below summarises the process.

What happens to digested food?

Digested food is carried away from the ileum in the blood of the hepatic portal vein and in the fluid of the lymph vessels.

VEINS Page 69.
LYMPH VESSELS Page 72.

★ Blood transports water, sugars, glycerol and amino acids to the liver.

★ Lymph transports fats and fat-soluble vitamins to a vein in the neck where the substances enter the bloodstream.

The **liver** plays a major role in the metabolism of food substances after they have been absorbed into the body.

★ Glucose may be converted to **glycogen** and stored in the liver. Glycogen may be hydrolysed to glucose and released back into the blood in response to the body's needs.

★ Iron, obtained from destroyed red blood cells, is stored in the liver.

★ Amino acids in excess of the body's needs are broken down (a process called **deamination**) in the liver. Urea is formed and excreted in urine.

★ Amino acids are converted from one type into another in the liver (a process called **transamination**) according to the body's needs.

enzyme group	example	where found	food component	after digestion
carbohydrases (catalyse the digestion of carbohydrates)	amylase maltase	mouth small intestine	starch maltose	maltose glucose
proteases (catalyse the digestion of proteins)	pepsin chymotrypsin dipeptidase	stomach small intestine	protein polypeptides dipeptides	polypeptides dipeptides amino acids
lipases (catalyse the digestion of fats)	lipase	small intestine	fat	fatty acids + glycerol

Enzymes that digest carbohydrates, proteins and fats

5

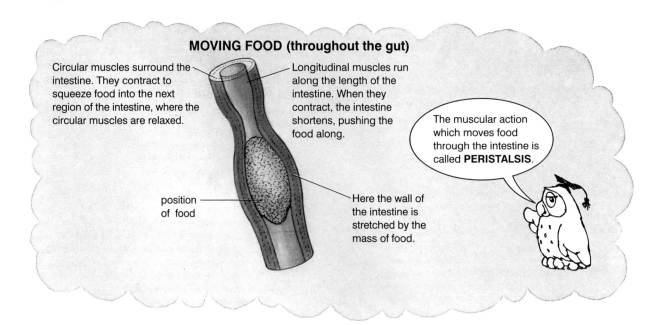

MOVING FOOD (throughout the gut)

Circular muscles surround the intestine. They contract to squeeze food into the next region of the intestine, where the circular muscles are relaxed.

Longitudinal muscles run along the length of the intestine. When they contract, the intestine shortens, pushing the food along.

The muscular action which moves food through the intestine is called **PERISTALSIS**.

position of food

Here the wall of the intestine is stretched by the mass of food.

ABSORPTION (ileum and colon)

outer layer

longitudinal muscles

circular muscles

villi

MAGNIFIED ×50

microvilli – tiny projections from each cell of the villus surface

MAGNIFIED ×10 000

surface cells

network of capillary blood vessels

a **villus**

The ileum is adapted for the absorption of food by having an increased surface area.

• The intestine is **folded** and packed into the abdominal cavity.
• **Villi** project from the lining of the ileum.
• **Microvilli** project from the surface of each cell lining the villus.

fats are absorbed into the lymph vessel

blood vessels carrying blood to each villus

digested food – sugars, glycerol, fatty acids and amino acids – are absorbed into the blood

lymph vessel

circular muscle

longitudinal muscle

MAGNIFIED ×200

lymph vessels carry fats away from the villus

branch of the hepatic portal vein carries blood with its load of digested food to the liver (see page 63)

The digestive system – its structure and functions (checklist on pages 62–3)

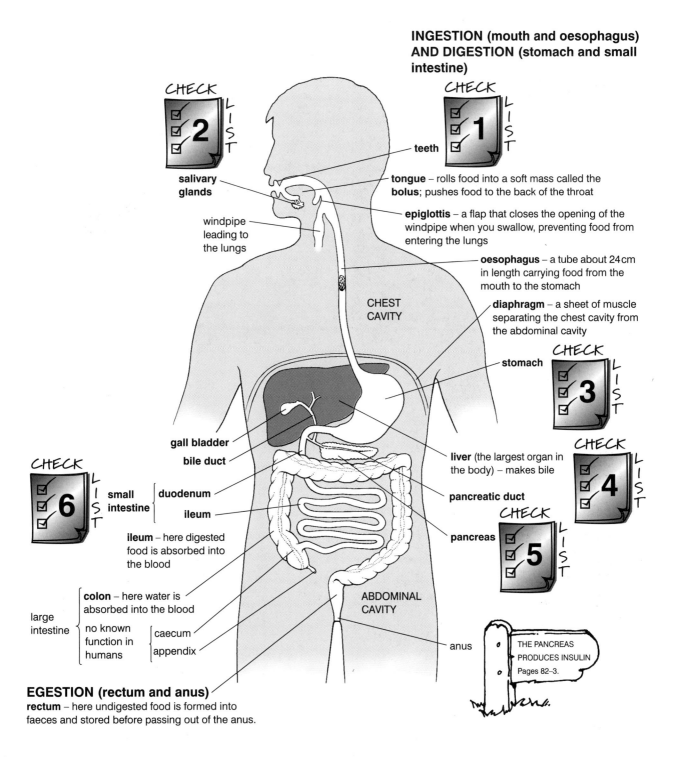

INGESTION (mouth and oesophagus) AND DIGESTION (stomach and small intestine)

CHECK LIST **2**

CHECK LIST **1**

teeth

salivary glands

tongue – rolls food into a soft mass called the **bolus**; pushes food to the back of the throat

windpipe leading to the lungs

epiglottis – a flap that closes the opening of the windpipe when you swallow, preventing food from entering the lungs

oesophagus – a tube about 24 cm in length carrying food from the mouth to the stomach

diaphragm – a sheet of muscle separating the chest cavity from the abdominal cavity

CHEST CAVITY

stomach

CHECK LIST **3**

CHECK LIST **4**

gall bladder

bile duct

liver (the largest organ in the body) – makes bile

pancreatic duct

CHECK LIST **6**

small intestine

duodenum

ileum

pancreas

CHECK LIST **5**

ileum – here digested food is absorbed into the blood

colon – here water is absorbed into the blood

large intestine

no known function in humans

caecum

appendix

ABDOMINAL CAVITY

anus

THE PANCREAS PRODUCES INSULIN Pages 82–3.

EGESTION (rectum and anus)
rectum – here undigested food is formed into faeces and stored before passing out of the anus.

5.3 Breathing, gaseous exchange and respiration

preview

At the end of this section you will:

- **know that breathing in (inhalation) takes air into the lungs and that breathing out (exhalation) pushes air out from the lungs**
- **be able to describe how breathing movements take place**
- **know that the exchange of gases (oxygen and carbon dioxide) happens in the lungs, between the air sacs (alveoli) and the capillary blood vessels**
- **understand that the blood transports oxygen to cells which use it for aerobic respiration**
- **be able to distinguish between aerobic respiration and anaerobic respiration.**

Respiration

Remember the distinction between respiration and gaseous exchange. Oxygen is used by cells to oxidise digested food substances (glucose) to release energy. The process is called **aerobic respiration**. The energy released from the oxidation of glucose powers the activities which define the characteristics of life. The table shows that there is less oxygen in exhaled air than in inhaled air. This is because some of the oxygen is used by cells for aerobic respiration. There is more carbon dioxide in exhaled air than in inhaled air because carbon dioxide is produced by the chemical reactions of aerobic respiration.

gas	amount in inhaled air / %	amount in exhaled air / %
nitrogen	78	78
oxygen	21	16
noble gases	1	1
carbon dioxide	0.03	4
water vapour	0	1

Differences between inhaled and exhaled air

★ How does oxygen reach cells?

★ How does carbon dioxide leave cells?

The answer is by gaseous exchange.

Now you can see the link between breathing air, gaseous exchange and aerobic respiration.

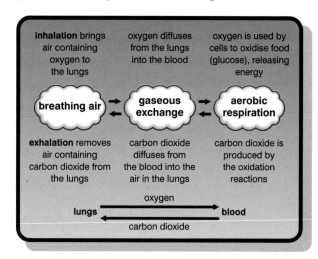

inhalation brings air containing oxygen to the lungs

oxygen diffuses from the lungs into the blood

oxygen is used by cells to oxidise food (glucose), releasing energy

breathing air → gaseous exchange → aerobic respiration

exhalation removes air containing carbon dioxide from the lungs

carbon dioxide diffuses from the blood into the air in the lungs

carbon dioxide is produced by the oxidation reactions

oxygen

lungs → blood

carbon dioxide ←

On page 68 is the concept map for **breathing, gaseous exchange and respiration**. The numbers on the concept map refer to the checklist below.

Checklist for breathing, gaseous exchange and respiration

1 ★ The **upper respiratory tract** is a tube from the nostrils and mouth to the lungs.
- It is well supplied with blood.

As a result, inhaled air is warmed to body temperature.

- Hairs in the nasal passage filter out large dust particles.
- The lining of **mucus** traps bacteria, viruses and dust particles.
- Hair-like **cilia** sweep the mucus into the **pharynx**, where it is either swallowed, sneezed out or coughed up.

As a result, the air entering the lungs is cleaned and freed of disease-causing microorganisms.

2 ★ The network of **bronchioles** in the lungs form the **bronchial tree**.

★ The millions of **alveoli** in a pair of human lungs form a surface area of about 90 m^2.

As a result, gaseous exchange is very efficient.

3 ★ The chemical reactions of aerobic respiration take place inside the mitochondria of cells.

MITOCHONDRIA
Page 35.

★ Cells do not use the energy from aerobic respiration as soon as it is released. It is converted into the energy of chemical bonds in a substance called **adenosine triphosphate** (**ATP**). ATP is the link between the cell's energy-releasing activities and its energy-using activities.

Breathing movements

The **ribs** and **diaphragm** form an elastic cage around the lungs. As they move, the pressure in the lungs changes. This change in pressure causes **inhaling** (breathing in) and **exhaling** (breathing out).

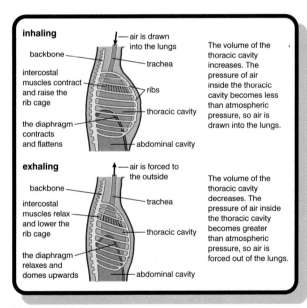

inhaling
- air is drawn into the lungs
- backbone
- trachea
- intercostal muscles contract and raise the rib cage
- ribs
- thoracic cavity
- the diaphragm contracts and flattens
- abdominal cavity

The volume of the thoracic cavity increases. The pressure of air inside the thoracic cavity becomes less than atmospheric pressure, so air is drawn into the lungs.

exhaling
- air is forced to the outside
- backbone
- trachea
- intercostal muscles relax and lower the rib cage
- thoracic cavity
- the diaphragm relaxes and domes upwards
- abdominal cavity

The volume of the thoracic cavity decreases. The pressure of air inside the thoracic cavity becomes greater than atmospheric pressure, so air is forced out of the lungs.

Inhaling and exhaling

Remember

★ **All** cells respire – animal cells, plant cells and the cells of fungi and single-celled organisms.

★ **Most** cells respire aerobically.

★ **Some** cells, such as muscle cells, the cells of plant roots, yeast cells and some types of bacteria, are able to respire anaerobically when supplies of oxygen are low.

★ **Some** cells, such as the bacterium that causes tetanus, can *only* respire anaerobically.

Mutual friends!

The muscles of the man and dog are working hard. At first, aerobic respiration in their muscle cells gives them a flying start.

glucose + oxygen → carbon dioxide + water

$$C_6H_{12}O_6(aq) + 6O_2(g) \rightarrow 6CO_2(g) + 6H_2O(l)$$

energy released = 16.1 kJ/g glucose

The man and dog are both panting. However, in spite of rapid breathing and strenuous pumping by the heart, oxygen cannot reach the muscles fast enough to supply their needs.

The muscles then switch from aerobic respiration to **anaerobic respiration** which does *not* use oxygen. **Lactic acid** is produced, which collects in the muscles.

glucose → lactic acid

$$C_6H_{12}O_6(aq) \quad 2CH_3CHOHCO_2H(aq)$$

energy released = 0.83 kJ/g glucose

Notice that the energy released per gram of glucose is less than in aerobic respiration. As lactic acid accumulates, the muscles stop working. The man and dog will be unable to run any further until the lactic acid has been removed from their muscles. This removal process uses oxygen. Lactic acid stimulates the body to pant vigorously, bringing a rush of oxygen to the muscles. During the recovery period, the lactic acid is oxidised and the **oxygen debt** is repaid. Aerobic respiration can then start again.

The chemical reactions of anaerobic respiration provide us with food, drink and a range of other products.

BIOTECHNOLOGY
Pages 98–100.

LUNG detail

air moves in and out

bronchiole

alveoli

blood vessels from the pulmonary arteries bring blood without much oxygen from the heart to the alveoli

blood vessels to the pulmonary veins take blood enriched with oxygen from the alveoli to the heart

ALVEOLUS detail

blood with a low [O₂] and a high [CO₂]

air moves in and out

blood with a high [O₂] and a low [CO₂]

red blood cells absorb oxygen

CO₂ diffuses out of blood

O₂ diffuses into blood

gases dissolve in layer of moisture

wall of capillary – only one cell thick

wall of alveolus – only one cell thick

The alveolus is adapted for the efficient diffusion of gases. It is:
• thin walled • moist
• well supplied with blood vessels.

CHECK 3 LIST

eustachian tube

middle ear

nasal passage

pharynx

epiglottis – prevents food from entering the larynx

larynx (voice box)

oesophagus

nostril through which air passes to the nasal passage

palate – separates the nasal passages from the mouth

mouth through which air passes

CHECK 1 LIST

UPPER RESPIRATORY TRACT detail

mucus produced by a goblet cell

cilia sweep mucus along

sheet of mucus

membrane cells

larynx

incomplete rings of cartilage support the trachea and bronchi

left lung
left bronchus

bronchial tree { bronchiole
alveolus

trachea

right lung

right bronchus

intercostal muscles (between ribs)

heart

cut end of rib

pleural fluid stops the lungs from sticking to the chest wall

diaphragm – a sheet of muscle that separates the thoracic (chest) cavity from the abdominal cavity

CHECK 2 LIST

bronchial tree

pleural membranes line the rib cage and cover the lungs

Breathing, gaseous exchange and respiration (checklist on pages 66–7)

5.4 Blood and the circulatory system

preview

At the end of this section you will:
- be able to identify the different components of blood
- understand the functions of blood
- understand why the heart is a double pump
- know that capillary blood vessels link arteries and veins
- understand how different factors (diet, exercise and stress) affect the circulatory system.

Fact file

★ The **heart** is a pump.

★ **Blood** is a liquid containing different cells.

★ **Arteries, veins** and **capillaries** are tube-like vessels through which blood flows.

$$\text{heart} \xrightarrow{\text{pumps}} \text{blood} \xrightarrow{\text{through}} \text{blood vessels}$$

Moving blood around

The circulatory system consists of tubes (arteries, veins and capillaries) through which blood is pumped by the heart. Blood carries oxygen, digested food, hormones and other substances *to* the tissues and organs of the body that need them. Blood also carries carbon dioxide and other waste substances produced by the metabolism of cells *from* the tissues and organs of the body. On pages 70–1 is the concept map for **blood and the circulatory system**. The numbers on the concept map refer to the checklist below.

Checklist for blood and the circulatory system

1 ★ Red blood cells are made in the **marrow** of the limb bones, ribs and vertebrae.

★ Old red blood cells are destroyed in the liver.

LIVER
Page 63.

★ **White blood cells** originate in the **bone marrow** and **spleen**.

★ **Antibodies** produced against a particular **antigen** will attack only that antigen. The antibody is said to be **specific** to that antigen.

2 ★ **Arteries** carry blood *from* the heart.

Veins carry blood *to* the heart.

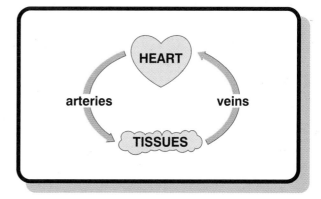

3 ★ Heart (**cardiac**) muscle contracts and relaxes rhythmically for a lifetime.

★ **Valves** direct the flow of blood through the heart.

★ The heartbeat is a two-tone sound:
- **diastole** – the heart muscles are relaxed
- **systole** – the heart muscles contract. During **auricular systole**, contraction of the auricles (atria) forces blood into the ventricles. During **ventricular systole**, contraction of the ventricles forces blood into the pulmonary artery (from the right ventricle) and aorta (from the left ventricle)

★ The heart is a **double pump**.

★ The beating of the heart is controlled by a **pacemaker**.

As a result, the heart beats on average 72 times a minute.

4 ★ The arteries and veins in the human body form two circuits:
- the lung circuit
- the head and body circuit.

Testing your understanding

Examinations test your understanding of ideas and important principles. Be sure you have grasped the arrangement of the **hepatic portal vein** and the role of the **pulmonary artery** and **pulmonary vein** – see page 72.

BLOOD

Plasma – transports heat released by metabolism in the liver, muscles and body fat. Plasma consists of 90% water with 10% of materials dissolved in it:
- **blood proteins** including antibodies that defend the body against disease, fibrinogen which helps stop bleeding, and enzymes
- **foods, vitamins** and **enzymes**
- **wastes**
- **hormones** which help co-ordinate different bodily functions.

balancing tube

The sample of human blood has been spun in a centrifuge. The plug of blood cells is examined under a microscope.

plug smeared on to a slide

types of white cells

phagocyte   lymphocyte   red cells

CHECK LIST 1

platelets

Red blood cells do not have a nucleus, but white cells do. Red cells are packed with the pigment haemoglobin which gives cells their red colour. Notice the characteristic shapes of the nuclei of phagocytes and lymphocytes. Platelets look like fragments of red cells.

Blood and the circulatory system (checklist on page 69)

BLOOD SYSTEM

HEAD
oxygen goes to tissues from blood: carbon dioxide and wastes go to blood from tissues

LUNGS
oxygen goes to blood: carbon dioxide goes from blood

HEART
right atrium
valves
right ventricle
left atrium
valves
left ventricle

LIVER
food stored: wastes changed to urea: oxygen goes to tissues from blood: carbon dioxide and urea go to blood from tissues

BODY / INTESTINE
food absorbed into blood: oxygen goes to tissues from blood: carbon dioxide and wastes go to blood from tissues

KIDNEYS
urea removed: oxygen goes to tissues from blood: carbon dioxide and wastes go to blood from tissues

BODY MUSCLES
oxygen goes to tissues from blood: carbon dioxide and wastes go to blood from tissues

jugular vein carries blood from head to heart

pulmonary artery carries blood to the lungs from the heart

vena cavae into which veins drain blood from the head and body

carotid artery carries blood from heart to head

aorta from which arteries branch to the organs and tissues of the body

hepatic portal vein brings blood rich in digested food from the intestine to the liver

→ direction of blood flow

CHECK LIST 4

CHECK LIST 3

VALVES

Valves ensure that blood flows in one direction only. Inside the veins, where blood is at a lower pressure than in the arteries, valves stop blood flowing backwards.

n valve

of vein

eezing by
y muscles
es blood up
ugh the vein

ed valve

vein squeezed by body muscles

wall of vein

valve

Enlarged cut-away diagram showing pocket-like valves set in the wall of vein. If blood flows back, it fills the pockets closing the valve

CHECK LIST 2

BLOOD VESSELS

ARTERIES

thick outer wall

thick layer of muscles and elastic fibres withstand pressure of blood

narrow diameter

smooth lining

- carry blood away from the heart to organs and tissues
- blood at high pressure
- have a pulse because the vessel walls expand and relax as blood spurts from the heart

VEINS

fairly thin outer wall

thin layer of muscles and elastic fibres easily expand reducing resistance to the flow of blood returning to the heart

smooth lining

large diameter

- return blood to the heart from organs and tissues (except hepatic portal vein)
- blood at low pressure
- working body muscles squeeze the veins, helping push blood to the heart
- do not have a pulse since blood flows smoothly
- have valves

Understanding the hepatic portal vein

Veins carry blood to the heart. The **hepatic portal vein** is the exception. Notice on page 71 that it carries blood with its load of digested food from the intestine to the liver.

ABSORPTION OF FOOD Page 64.

Understanding the pulmonary artery and the pulmonary vein

Arteries are often described as carriers of oxygenated blood (often coloured red on diagrams), and veins as carriers of deoxygenated blood (often coloured blue on diagrams). However, the **pulmonary artery** carries deoxygenated blood from the heart to the lungs. The **pulmonary vein** carries oxygenated blood from the lungs to the heart.

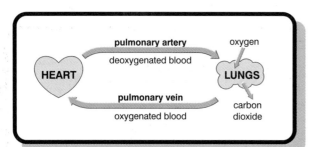

Capillaries – fact file

Capillaries are tiny blood vessels, 0.001 mm in diameter.

★ The walls of capillary blood vessels are one cell thick.

As a result, substances easily diffuse between blood in the capillaries and the surrounding tissues.

★ Capillaries form dense networks called **beds** in the tissues of the body.

As a result, no cell is very far away from a capillary.

★ The blood in capillaries supplies nearby cells with oxygen, food molecules and other substances. It also carries away carbon dioxide and other wastes produced by the cells' metabolism.

★ **Tissue fluid** carries oxygen, food and other substances to the cells. This fluid is blood plasma that has been forced out through the thin capillary walls by the pressure of the blood inside.

★ Red blood cells squeeze through the smallest capillaries in single file.

As a result, the pressure drops as blood passes through the capillaries from the artery to the vein.

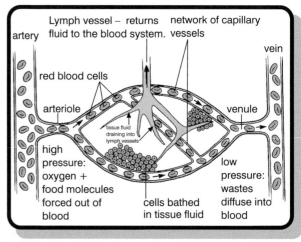

Capillaries at work

Disorders of the blood

★ **Leukaemia** is the overproduction of abnormal white blood cells.

As a result, there are too few red blood cells.

Treatment is with drugs that slow the production of white blood cells, and radiotherapy which kills the abnormal cells.

★ **Haemophilia** is a genetic disease which runs in families. The blood does not clot properly because factor VIII, one of the substances in the blood needed for blood clots to form, is missing.

As a result, **haemophiliacs** (people suffering from haemophilia) lose a lot of blood if they injure themselves.

Treatment is by injections of factor VIII.

GENETIC DISEASES Page 87.

AIDS

AIDS (**A**cquired **I**mmune **D**eficiency **S**yndrome) is caused by the **H**uman **I**mmunodeficiency **V**irus (**HIV**). The virus attacks a particular type of lymphocyte (see page 87).

As a result, a person infected with HIV has reduced protection from disease-causing microorganisms.

Once HIV has destroyed a number of lymphocytes, the diseases of AIDS develop. Common diseases include:

* pneumonia – a disease of the lungs
* thrush – a fungal infection
* Kaposi's sarcoma – a skin cancer.

Understanding heart disease

The **coronary arteries** supply blood to the heart muscle, as shown in the diagram. The lining of blood vessels can be damaged and roughened by a fatty deposit called **atheroma**. The build-up of atheroma in the coronary arteries is one cause of **heart disease**. It increases the risk of blood clots forming. A blood clot in the coronary arteries can interrupt the blood supply to the heart, and the person suffers a **heart attack**.

The symptoms are

* severe pain in the chest, neck and arms
* sweating
* faintness and sickness.

The clot is called a **thrombus**, and the blockage a **thrombosis**.

The diagram shows some of the factors affecting the risk of a person developing heart disease.

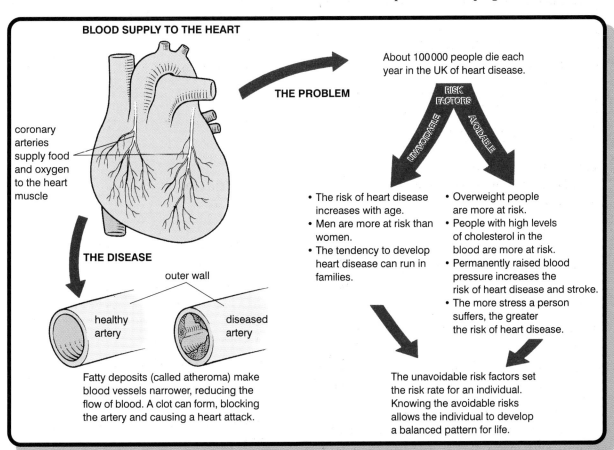

The risk of heart disease

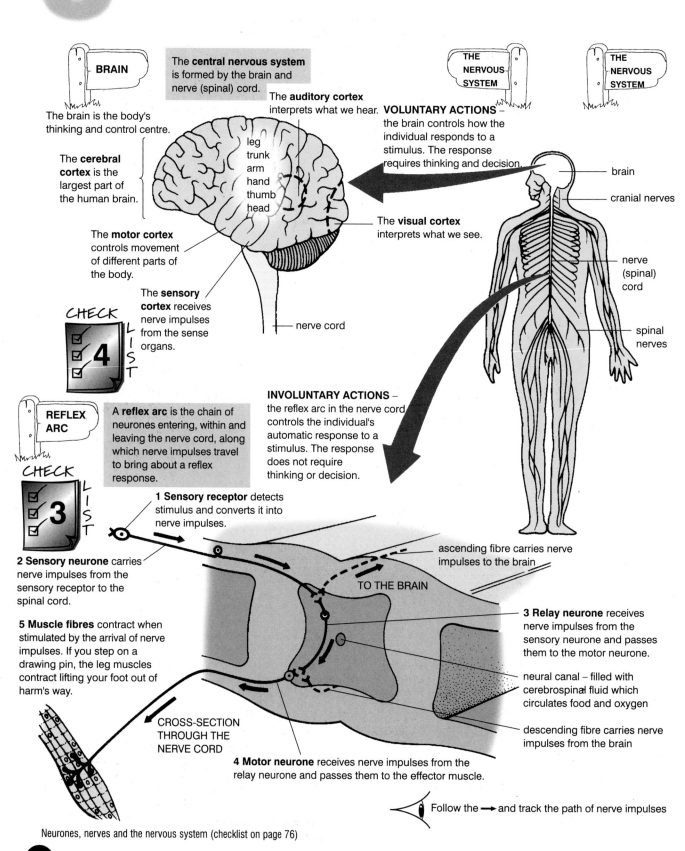

BRAIN

The brain is the body's thinking and control centre.

The **cerebral cortex** is the largest part of the human brain.

The **motor cortex** controls movement of different parts of the body.

The **sensory cortex** receives nerve impulses from the sense organs.

The **central nervous system** is formed by the brain and nerve (spinal) cord.

The **auditory cortex** interprets what we hear.

leg
trunk
arm
hand
thumb
head

The **visual cortex** interprets what we see.

nerve cord

THE NERVOUS SYSTEM

THE NERVOUS SYSTEM

VOLUNTARY ACTIONS – the brain controls how the individual responds to a stimulus. The response requires thinking and decision.

brain

cranial nerves

nerve (spinal) cord

spinal nerves

CHECK **4** LIST

REFLEX ARC

A **reflex arc** is the chain of neurones entering, within and leaving the nerve cord, along which nerve impulses travel to bring about a reflex response.

INVOLUNTARY ACTIONS – the reflex arc in the nerve cord controls the individual's automatic response to a stimulus. The response does not require thinking or decision.

CHECK **3** LIST

1 Sensory receptor detects stimulus and converts it into nerve impulses.

2 Sensory neurone carries nerve impulses from the sensory receptor to the spinal cord.

5 Muscle fibres contract when stimulated by the arrival of nerve impulses. If you step on a drawing pin, the leg muscles contract lifting your foot out of harm's way.

ascending fibre carries nerve impulses to the brain

TO THE BRAIN

3 Relay neurone receives nerve impulses from the sensory neurone and passes them to the motor neurone.

neural canal – filled with cerebrospinal fluid which circulates food and oxygen

descending fibre carries nerve impulses from the brain

CROSS-SECTION THROUGH THE NERVE CORD

4 Motor neurone receives nerve impulses from the relay neurone and passes them to the effector muscle.

Follow the ➝ and track the path of nerve impulses

Neurones, nerves and the nervous system (checklist on page 76)

The **peripheral nervous system** is formed by the cranial nerves and spinal nerves that join the central nervous system.

NERVES

Neurones are grouped together into bundles called **nerves** which pass to all parts of the body, forming a nervous system.

CHECK **1** LIST

single neurones

covering around the nerve

NEURONE

× magnified

Neurones are cells specialised to transmit nerve impulses. They build the nervous system.

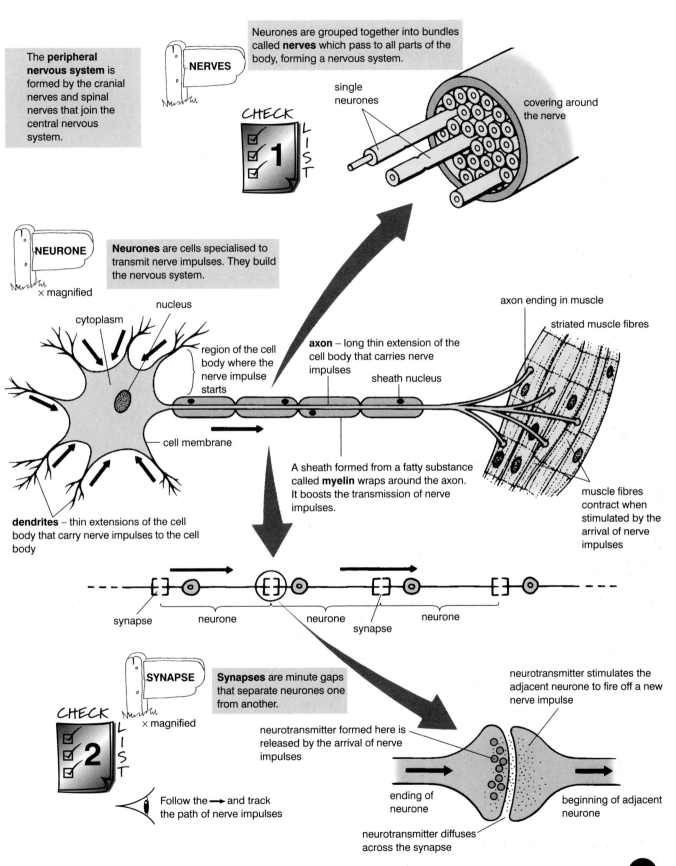

cytoplasm

nucleus

region of the cell body where the nerve impulse starts

axon – long thin extension of the cell body that carries nerve impulses

sheath nucleus

axon ending in muscle

striated muscle fibres

cell membrane

A sheath formed from a fatty substance called **myelin** wraps around the axon. It boosts the transmission of nerve impulses.

muscle fibres contract when stimulated by the arrival of nerve impulses

dendrites – thin extensions of the cell body that carry nerve impulses to the cell body

synapse

neurone

neurone

synapse

neurone

SYNAPSE

× magnified

Synapses are minute gaps that separate neurones one from another.

CHECK **2** LIST

Follow the ➤ and track the path of nerve impulses

neurotransmitter stimulates the adjacent neurone to fire off a new nerve impulse

neurotransmitter formed here is released by the arrival of nerve impulses

ending of neurone

beginning of adjacent neurone

neurotransmitter diffuses across the synapse

75

5.5 Senses and the nervous system

preview

At the end of this section you will know that:

- **stimuli are converted by receptors into signals called nerve impulses, to which the body can respond**
- **neurones (nerve cells) conduct nerve impulses to muscles, which respond by contracting**
- **muscles are called effectors**
- **nerves are formed from bundles of neurones and are the link between stimulus and response.**

The process runs:

stimulus → receptor → nerves → effector → response

Stimulus and response

A **stimulus** is a change in the environment which causes a living organism to take action. A **response** is the action that the living organism takes. The **nervous system** links stimuli and responses. This is the sequence of events:

- ★ **Sensory receptor cells** detect stimuli and convert them into **nerve impulses**, to which the body can respond.

- ★ Nerve impulses are minute electrical disturbances.

- ★ **Neurones** (nerve cells) conduct nerve impulses to **effectors** (muscles or glands). Muscles respond to nerve impulses by HORMONES Pages 80–3. contracting; glands respond by secreting substances. For example, the adrenal glands respond to nerve impulses by producing the hormone adrenaline, which helps the body cope with sudden stress.

The nervous system

On pages 74–5 is the concept map for **the nervous system**. The numbers on the concept map refer to the checklist.

Checklist for the nervous system

1. ★ Each **nerve** of the nervous system consists of a bundle of **neurones**.

   ★ Each neurone transmits nerve impulses to an **effector** (muscle or gland).

   ★ Nerve impulses are minute electrical disturbances which carry information about stimuli.

   ★ Nerve impulses stimulate effectors to respond to stimuli in a useful way.

   ★ A nerve impulse takes just milliseconds to travel along a neurone.

2. ★ **Neurotransmitter** is a chemical substance released from the end of a neurone into the **synapse**.

   ★ Neurotransmitter is produced only from the end of the neurone before the synapse.

   As a result, nerve impulses always travel *from* the receptor *to* the effector.

3. ★ **Reflex responses** happen before the brain has had time to process the nerve impulses carrying the information about the stimulus.

   ★ When the brain catches up with events, it brings about the next set of reactions – such as a shout of pain.

   ★ **Ascending fibres** form synapses with sensory neurones. The ascending fibres carry nerve impulses to the brain.

   As a result, the brain receives information about the stimulus causing the reflex response.

   ★ Nerve impulses from the brain are transmitted to effectors by the **descending fibres**, which synapse with motor neurones.

   As a result, the reflex response is brought under conscious control.

4. ★ The human brain weighs approximately 1.3 kg and occupies a volume of about 1500 cm³.

   ★ Around 6 million neurones make up 1 cm³ of brain matter.

   ★ Memory and learning are under the brain's control.

   ★ Different drugs affect the brain. For example, ethanol (the alcohol in beers, wines and spirits) depresses the activity of the cerebral cortex, affecting judgement and the control of movement.

5.6 Sense organs

preview

At the end of this section you will know that:

● the sense organs consist of sensory cells which are adapted to detect a particular type of stimulus.

Handy hint

The sensory cells of the

- **S**kin detect heat and cold, touch and pain
- **N**ose detect chemicals
- **E**ye detect light
- **E**ar detect sound
- **T**ongue detect chemicals.

Thinking of the mnemonic **SNEET** will help you remember the major sense organs of the body.

Sensing the surroundings

On pages 78–9 is the concept map for **sense organs**. The numbers refer to the checklist below.

Checklist for sense organs

1 ★ **Tears** lubricate the surface of the eye. They contain the enzyme **lysozyme** which kills bacteria.

★ The **iris** of the eye is usually coloured brown, blue or green.

★ A pair of human eyes contains around 130 million **rods** and 7 million **cones**.

★ **Cone** cells are packed most densely in the region of the **fovea** and respond to bright light.

As a result, objects are seen most clearly if looked at straight on.

★ **Rod** cells occur mostly near the edges of the retina and respond to dim light.

As a result, objects are seen less clearly out of the corner of the eye.

2 ★ Loudness is measured in **decibels**. The faintest sound that the ear can hear is defined as zero decibels.

★ The response of the ear to different levels of loudness varies with frequency. The ear is most sensitive to frequencies around 3000 Hz, and can detect the

softest sounds. It is completely insensitive to sounds over 18 000 Hz and cannot detect them.

★ The walls of the ear tube produce wax, which keeps the eardrum soft and supple.

3 ★ The nerve impulses from **temperature receptors** are interpreted by the brain, enabling us to feel whether our surroundings are hot or cold.

★ Sensitivity to **touch** depends on which part of the body is stimulated. The tip of the tongue and the fingertips can distinguish between two pin pricks 1.0 mm apart. Two pinpricks on the thigh may have to be more than 60 mm apart before they are detected as separate stimuli.

4 ★ **Taste buds** help us to decide whether food is safe. A bitter taste is usually a warning signal not to swallow.

★ **Smell** is defined as the detection of substances carried in the air.

★ To be detected, substances which are tasted or smelt must first be dissolved in the watery environment covering the receptor cells.

Check the vibrations

In the concept map, notice the different structures in the ear vibrating in response to sound waves striking the eardrum. The sequence reads:

- eardrum
- bones of the middle ear
- oval window
- fluid in the cochlea
- basilar membrane
- stimulated hair cells (receptors) fire off nerve impulses to the brain along the auditory nerve

Fact file

★ The ear becomes less and less sensitive if it is regularly exposed to very loud sounds. At noisy discos, you can protect your ears by plugging them with cotton wool.

★ In most humans the ear lobe (pinna) is fixed. Cats and dogs, however, can adjust the pinna and turn it towards sources of sound.

★ A cat's tongue contains very few taste receptors which respond to sugar. Cats, therefore, are among the few animals that do not prefer substances with a sweet taste.

5

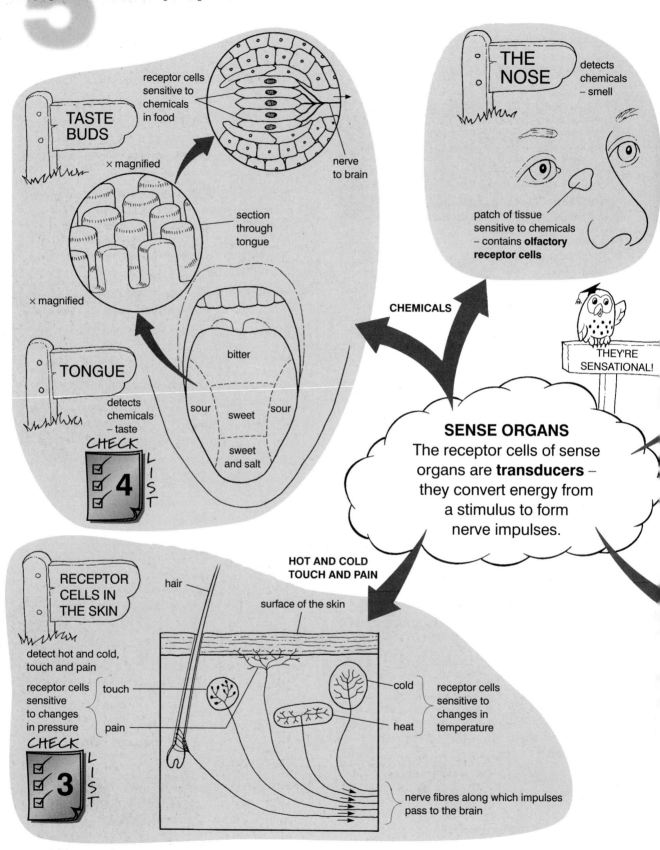

TASTE BUDS

receptor cells sensitive to chemicals in food

× magnified

× magnified

nerve to brain

section through tongue

TONGUE

detects chemicals – taste

bitter

sour

sour

sweet

sweet and salt

CHECK **4** LIST

THE NOSE

detects chemicals – smell

patch of tissue sensitive to chemicals – contains **olfactory receptor cells**

CHEMICALS

THEY'RE SENSATIONAL!

SENSE ORGANS
The receptor cells of sense organs are **transducers** – they convert energy from a stimulus to form nerve impulses.

RECEPTOR CELLS IN THE SKIN

hair

surface of the skin

detect hot and cold, touch and pain

receptor cells sensitive to changes in pressure

touch

pain

cold

heat

receptor cells sensitive to changes in temperature

HOT AND COLD TOUCH AND PAIN

nerve fibres along which impulses pass to the brain

CHECK **3** LIST

Sense organs (checklist on page 77)

THE EYE

detects light

lens – focuses light onto the retina

retina – the light-sensitive layer around the inside of the eye

iris – coloured ring of muscle that controls the amount of light entering the eye

cornea – helps to focus light on the retina

pupil – the central hole formed by the iris

ciliary muscles – change the thickness of the lens

fovea – region of the retina where the retinal cells are most dense

blind spot – region where the retina is not sensitive to light

optic nerve – along which nerve impulses travel from the retina to the brain

LIGHT

CHECK LIST **1**

RECEPTOR CELLS OF THE RETINA

× magnified

nerve fibres pass to the optic nerve

cone – each cone cell is sensitive to red, blue or green light

rod – rod cells are *not* sensitive to colour, only to the brightness of light

outer covering of eye

follow the → and track the path of nerve impulses

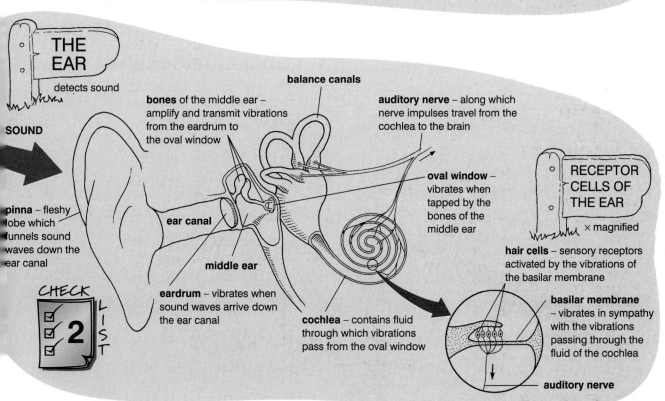

THE EAR

detects sound

SOUND

balance canals

bones of the middle ear – amplify and transmit vibrations from the eardrum to the oval window

auditory nerve – along which nerve impulses travel from the cochlea to the brain

pinna – fleshy lobe which funnels sound waves down the ear canal

ear canal

middle ear

eardrum – vibrates when sound waves arrive down the ear canal

oval window – vibrates when tapped by the bones of the middle ear

cochlea – contains fluid through which vibrations pass from the oval window

RECEPTOR CELLS OF THE EAR

× magnified

hair cells – sensory receptors activated by the vibrations of the basilar membrane

basilar membrane – vibrates in sympathy with the vibrations passing through the fluid of the cochlea

auditory nerve

CHECK LIST **2**

The eye at work

Look up from this page and gaze out of the window at some distant object. Your eye lens becomes thinner to keep your vision in focus. This change in lens shape to keep a nearby object and then a distant object in focus is called **accommodation**.

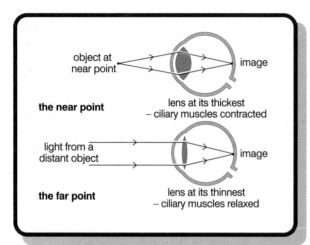

object at
near point
image

the near point

lens at its thickest
– ciliary muscles contracted

light from a
distant object
image

the far point

lens at its thinnest
– ciliary muscles relaxed

Accommodation keeps objects in focus

Fact file

★ Human eyes are damaged by ultraviolet light. However, insects' eyes can see in ultraviolet light.

★ A normal eye can see clearly any object from far away (at the **far point**) to 25 cm from the eye (the **near point**).

★ The image of an object on the retina is inverted, but the brain interprets it so you see it the right way up.

Light control

The **iris** controls the amount of light entering the eye. Bright light causes a **reflex response**:

★ The muscle of the iris contracts.

As a result, the pupil narrows.

As a result, the amount of light entering the eye is reduced.

In dim light:

★ the muscle of the iris relaxes.

As a result, the pupil widens.

As a result, the amount of light entering the eye is increased.

5.7 Hormones

preview

At the end of this section you will know that:

● chemicals called hormones regulate the activities of the body

● hormones are produced in the tissues of endocrine glands

● endocrine glands are ductless glands – they release their hormones directly into the bloodstream

● hormones circulate in the blood and cause specific effects on the body

● the tissue on which a particular hormone or group of hormones acts is called a target tissue.

The hormonal system

The blood system is the link between a hormone and its **target tissue**. The sequence reads:

$$\text{endocrine gland} \xrightarrow{\text{produces}} \text{hormone} \xrightarrow{\text{circulates}} \text{blood} \xrightarrow{\text{affects}} \text{target tissue}$$

Hormones affect many of the body's activities. For example, the hormones **insulin** and **glucagon** help regulate the level of glucose in the blood and cope with the surge of glucose at mealtimes and when you eat a snack, such as a bar of chocolate.

Fact file

Most hormones produce their effects rather slowly. They bring about long-term changes in the body such as growth and sexual development.

How hormones work

On pages 82–3 is the concept map which revises **hormones**. The numbers on the concept map refer to the checklist opposite.

Checklist for hormones at work

1 ★ If the pancreas does not produce enough insulin, a condition called **diabetes mellitus** occurs.

As a result, the glucose level in the blood becomes dangerously high and can cause kidney failure and blindness.

★ People suffering from diabetes (**diabetics**) are taught to inject themselves regularly with insulin to lower their blood glucose level.

★ Glycogen is a polysaccharide whose molecules consist of hundreds of glucose units.

2 ★ The human female usually produces one mature egg each month from the onset of **puberty** (age 11–14 years) to the approach of the **menopause** (age about 45 years). Egg production becomes more irregular and then stops at the menopause (average age around 51 years).

★ The contraceptive pill contains one or both of the hormones oestrogen and progesterone. The hormones stop the ovaries from producing eggs.

3 ★ **Diuresis** is the flow of urine from the body. Antidiuretic hormone counteracts diuresis.

As a result, less urine leaves the body.

★ Ethanol (the alcohol in beer, wine and spirits) increases diuresis.

4 ★ Unlike most hormones, adrenaline produces its effect very quickly.

As a result, the body is able to respond to sudden shock or danger.

Fact file – guys and gals

Secondary sexual characteristics are the physical features which distinguish boys from girls. Testosterone helps develop and maintain the secondary sexual characteristics of boys. Oestrogen and progesterone help develop and maintain the secondary sexual characteristics of girls.

guys	gals
pubic hair develops	pubic hair develops
penis gets larger	breasts develop and fat is laid down in the thighs
voice breaks	menstruation starts
hair grows on armpits, chest, face and legs	hair grows on armpits

Secondary sexual characteristics

5.8 Maintaining the internal environment

preview

At the end of this section you will:

● **understand that for cells to work efficiently, the composition of the tissue fluid which surrounds them should be kept fairly constant**

● **know about the important systems which maintain a constant environment in the body: the pancreas and liver (blood glucose), the kidneys (water content) and the skin (temperature).**

Conditions in the body

The cells of the body work efficiently when they are

• at an appropriate temperature
• supplied with an appropriate mixture and concentration of substances
• supplied with sufficient water
• at an appropriate acidity/alkalinity (pH).

These conditions are part of the body's **internal environment**. Different mechanisms help regulate the body, keeping its internal environment fairly constant. Keeping conditions constant is called **homeostasis**.

★ The **skin** regulates the body's temperature.

★ The **kidneys** regulate the concentration of salts in the blood, and the water content of the body.

LIVER AND PANCREAS Pages 82–3.

★ The **liver** and **pancreas** regulate the concentration of sugar in the blood.

Homeostasis

Homeostasis depends on **negative feedback** mechanisms, which enable different processes to correct themselves when they change. In other words, the processes of life are **self-adjusting**. A level of a chemical or a temperature that deviates from a **set point** (a normal value) is returned to

FLIGHT OR FIGHT

Adrenaline at work prepares the body for sudden action.

brain thinking quickly

muscles working hard

EFFECTS OF ADRENALINE
- Cells metabolise glucose faster. As a result, more energy is available for sudden action.
- The heart beats more rapidly. As a result, more blood with its load of glucose reaches tissues and organs more rapidly.
- Blood is diverted to tissues such as the muscles and brain

CHECK LIST **4**

HORMONE LIST
- adrenaline

BODY'S WATER CONTENT

Sensory receptors in the brain detect how much water is in the blood.

NOT ENOUGH
Antidiuretic hormone (ADH) is produced from the pituitary gland.
As a result, the walls of the collecting duct of the nephron are more permeable ('leaky') to water.
As a result water is absorbed back into the body.

brain

LOTS
Reduced production of antidiuretic hormone (ADH) from the pituitary gland.
As a result, most of the surplus water is excreted through the kidneys.

brain

pituitary gland

✕ ADH

full up!

iced water

kidney

ureter

pituitary gland
ADH ✓

DEAD MAN'S GULCH

water reabsorbed into the blood

CHECK LIST **3**

HORMONE LIST
- antidiuretic hormone (ADH)

THE NEPHRON
Page 84.

Excess water is excreted. As a result, large volumes of dilute urine are produced.

Very little water is excreted. As a result, the urine is scanty and concentrated.

Hormones at work (checklist on page 81)

BLOOD GLUCOSE

HORMONE LIST
• insulin
• glucagon

glycogen stored in the liver — LIVER

CHECK LIST **1**

insulin promotes conversion of glucose to glycogen

glucagon promotes conversion of glycogen to glucose

Thyroid gland produces **thyroxine** which affects cellular respiration (see page 66).

tuitary gland at the base of the
ain produces different hormones
hich affect:
water reabsorption from the
kidney tubules (ADH)
sperm and egg production
growth
release of hormones by other
endocrine glands.

glucose circulating in the blood — BLOODSTREAM

HOMEOSTASIS Page 81.

• High concentrations of blood sugar promote the release of insulin.
• Low concentrations of blood sugar promote the release of glucagon. As a result, the concentration of glucose is regulated at around 90 mg of glucose per 100 cm^3 of blood.

lung

heart

stomach

drenal gland
oduces **adrenaline**
hich prepares the
dy for sudden action.

kidney

stis (male) produces
stosterone which
lps to develop and
aintain secondary
xual characteristics.

Pancreas produces **insulin** and **glucagon** which regulate glucose levels in the blood.

Ovary (female) produces **oestrogen** and **progesterone** which regulate the menstrual cycle and help to develop and maintain secondary sexual characteristics.

FROM THE PITUITARY

brain

Surge of luteinising hormone is the stimulus for ovulation.

pituitary gland

Follicle-stimulating hormone and luteinising hormone promote growth and development of egg follicles.

developing follicles

FROM THE OVARY
Oestrogen stimulates division of cells lining the uterus, which thickens. Its blood supply increases.

ovary

FROM THE CORPUS LUTEUM
Progesterone maintains the thickening of the lining of the uterus.

THE MENSTRUAL CYCLE

ovulation – egg is released from its follicle

HORMONE LIST
follicle-stimulating
hormone
luteinising
hormone
oestrogen
progesterone

CHECK LIST **2**

lining of the uterus

0   14   28   days

Menstruation – lining of the uterus breaks down because of declining levels of progesterone. Blood and tissue pass through the vagina.

CONTROLLING WATER CONTENT

cortex

medulla

nephron

ureter

vena cava   aorta

diaphragm

left kidney

renal artery ⎫ the blood
renal vein   ⎬ supply to the
             ⎭ kidneys

ureter – urine passes through the ureter from each kidney to the bladder

bladder – stores urine

Sphincter muscle – keeps the bladder closed. It can relax to allow the bladder to empty.

urethra – tube through which urine passes to the outside

Section lengthways through a kidney. Two zones of tissue, the cortex and the medulla, can be seen. The horseshoe-shaped Bowman's capsule is in the cortex. The rest of the nephron dips downs into the medulla. (The nephron is drawn much larger than life.)

CHECK ✓ ✓ ✓ **1** LIST

THE NEPHRON AT WORK

branch from renal vein takes 'clean' blood away

glomerulus

→ direction of liquid through the nephron

branch from renal artery brings 'dirty' blood under high pressure

Bowman's capsule

cortex

medulla

1 Filtration – the horseshoe-shaped Bowman's capsule surrounds a knot of capillary blood vessels called the glomerulus. Blood reaching the glomerulus is under high pressure which forces waste materials, glucose, salts and other materials in solution through the walls of the capillaries into the Bowman's capsule.

2 Reabsorption – as the liquid travels through the nephron, glucose, salts and other useful substances pass in solution back into the blood. At the end of its journey, the liquid is called urine. Its composition is different because of reabsorption of useful substances since it started out in the Bowman's capsule.

collecting duct

3 Reabsorption – water passes from the collecting duct of the nephron into the blood. The amount of water reabsorbed depends on the amount of antiduiretic hormone (ADH) circulating in the blood – see page 82.

remaining liquid, called urine, flows into the ureter

MAINTAINING A CONSTANT INTERNAL ENVIRONMENT

CONTROLLING TEMPERATURE

CHECK
2
L
I
S
T

sebaceous gland

hairs

sweat duct

sweat pore – 3 million cover the human skin

epidermis

heat receptor

hair erector muscle – when the muscle contracts, it raises the hair

cold receptor

dermis

hair follicle

layer of fat cells

blood vessel

sweat gland – produces sweat which contains 99.5% water, 0.25% urea and 0.25% sodium chloride

Different mechanisms help to control the body's temperature:

- Hairs raised by erector muscles trap a layer of air which insulates the body in cold weather (air is a poor conductor of heat). In warm weather, the hair is lowered and no air is trapped.
- Fat insulates the body and reduces heat loss.
- Sweat cools the body because it carries heat energy away from the body as it evaporates.
- Millions of temperature-sensitive sense receptors cover the skin. Nerves connect them to the brain which controls the body's response to changes in temperature in the environment.
- When it is warm, blood vessels in the skin dilate (**vasodilation**). More blood flows through the vessels in the skin and loses heat to the environment. In cold weather, the blood vessels in the skin constrict (**vasoconstriction**) and less heat is lost to the environment.

5

that set point. The menstrual cycle pictured on page 83 illustrates the principles. Rising levels of follicle-stimulating hormone and luteinising hormone stimulate the ovaries to produce the hormone oestrogen. Increasing levels of oestrogen feed back negatively, inhibiting further release of follicle-stimulating hormone. The level of the hormone returns to normal, its role of promoting the growth of egg follicles complete.

On pages 84–5 is the concept map for **homeostasis**. The numbers on the concept map refer to the checklist of points below. Study the concept map and its checklist carefully.

Checklist for homeostasis

1 ★ Each kidney consists of about one million tiny tubules called **nephrons**.

   ★ The nephron is the working unit of the kidney. It is the structure that brings about homeostatic control of the:
     • concentration of salts in the blood
     • water content of the body.

   The kidney tubules are also responsible for the excretion of urea and other wastes from the body.

2 ★ Hair is made of the protein keratin.

   ★ **Goose pimples** are bumps on the skin formed when empty hair follicles contract in response to cold.

Fact file

★ Liver metabolism releases a lot of heat energy, which is distributed all over the body by the blood. Humans (and other mammals and birds) have a high metabolic rate, which releases a large amount of heat. This is why mammals and birds are **warm blooded**.

Copy and complete this Mind Map to help your revision of co-ordination in humans and plants.

5.9 Health and disease

preview

At the end of this section you will:
• be able to distinguish between different categories of disease
• know about the defence mechanisms of the body
• understand the harmful effects of smoking
• understand the effects of drug abuse and solvent abuse on the body.

What is disease?

There are several categories of disease.

Infectious diseases are caused by a range of organisms:

• **bacteria**, for example cholera, typhoid fever, tuberculosis, syphilis, gonorrhoea
• **viruses**, for example AIDS, 'flu, poliomyelitis, German measles
• **fungi**, for example thrush, athlete's foot, ringworm
• **protists**, for example malaria, sleeping sickness.

Non-infectious diseases develop because the body is not working properly:

• **cancer** – the uncontrolled division of cells leads to the development of a cancerous growth (**tumour**)
• **degenerative illnesses** – organs and tissues work less well with wear and tear, for example, joints become arthritic and sight and hearing deteriorate with age
• **allergies** – reactions to substances which are normally harmless, for example sensitivity to pollen and dust causes **hay fever**
• **deficiency** – a poor diet may deprive the body of vitamins and other essential substances, for example scurvy (deficiency of vitamin C), rickets (deficiency of vitamin D), kwashiorkor (deficiency of protein).

Genetic diseases result from genetic defects and may be inherited. There are around 4000 genetic diseases in humans. Genetic make-up also influences our vulnerability to other diseases such as diabetes and heart disease.

- **Down's syndrome** is caused by an extra copy of chromosome 21.
- **Sickle-cell anaemia** is caused by a mutation of the gene (**allele**) controlling the synthesis of the blood pigment haemoglobin.

MUTATION
Page 47.

- **Cystic fibrosis** is caused by the mutation of an allele on chromosome 7. The allele controls the production of a polypeptide important for the transport of chloride ions (Cl^-) across the cell membrane.

Alleles are pairs of genes which control a particular characteristic – see page 96.

POLYPEPTIDE
Page 44.

- **Haemophilia** is caused by the mutation of an allele on the X chromosome, as described below.

The allele on the X chromosome normally controls production of **factor VIII**, a substance required for the blood to clot. The defective allele is recessive. The Y chromosome does not carry a dominant allele to mask the effect of the defective recessive allele on the X chromosome. Therefore a man with the defective allele produces no factor VIII, and suffers from haemophilia. For a woman to suffer from haemophilia, she would have to receive the recessive allele from both her father and her mother – a rare occurrence. A woman who has the defective allele on *one* of the X chromosomes is called a **carrier**. She does not suffer from haemophilia because the normal allele on the other X chromosome is dominant.

Muscular dystrophy is another genetic disease linked to the X chromosome.

Fighting disease

The body's natural defences against disease are shown below. **Physical** barriers and **chemical** barriers keep us healthy for most of our lives.

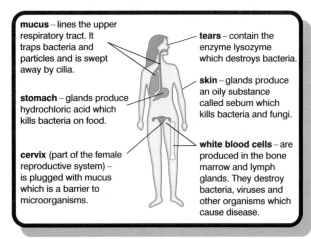

mucus – lines the upper respiratory tract. It traps bacteria and particles and is swept away by cilia.

stomach – glands produce hydrochloric acid which kills bacteria on food.

cervix (part of the female reproductive system) – is plugged with mucus which is a barrier to microorganisms.

tears – contain the enzyme lysozyme which destroys bacteria.

skin – glands produce an oily substance called sebum which kills bacteria and fungi.

white blood cells – are produced in the bone marrow and lymph glands. They destroy bacteria, viruses and other organisms which cause disease.

The body's natural defences against disease

White blood cells

Bacteria, viruses and other microorganisms may infect the blood and tissues of the body and cause disease. Two types of white blood cell, **lymphocytes** and **phagocytes**, protect the body. They work quickly to destroy bacteria, viruses or other cells or substances which the body does not recognise as its own. Such materials 'foreign' to the body are called **antigens**.

There are two types of lymphocyte.

★ **B-lymphocytes** produce **antibodies** which are proteins that attack antigens.

★ **T-lymphocytes** do not produce antibodies. Instead they bind with an antigen and destroy it.

Phagocytes in the blood engulf and destroy antigens. Some phagocytes pass through the walls of blood vessels and migrate through tissues to attack antigens that have entered the body through cuts or scratches. Their action causes an **inflammatory response** – swelling, redness and heat as the phagocytes destroy the invading antigens at the site of the infection. The diagram overleaf shows B-lymphocytes and phagocytes at work in the blood.

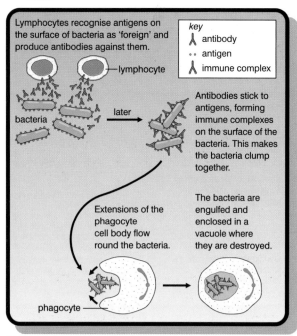

Lymphocytes recognise antigens on the surface of bacteria as 'foreign' and produce antibodies against them.

key
- antibody
- antigen
- immune complex

lymphocyte

bacteria → later →

Antibodies stick to antigens, forming immune complexes on the surface of the bacteria. This makes the bacteria clump together.

Extensions of the phagocyte cell body flow round the bacteria.

The bacteria are engulfed and enclosed in a vacuole where they are destroyed.

phagocyte

B-lymphocytes produce antibodies which damage bacteria 'foreign' to the body (antigens). Phagocytes engulf the bacteria.

Diseases of the upper respiratory tract and lungs

Despite its filtering and cleaning mechanisms, the upper respiratory tract may become infected by disease-causing microorganisms. Infection of the

- throat (pharynx) is called **pharyngitis**
- voicebox (larynx) is called **laryngitis**
- windpipe (trachea) is called **tracheitis**
- bronchi and bronchioles is called **bronchitis**.

RESPIRATORY TRACT Page 68.

Pneumonia is an infection of the lungs caused by a particular type of bacterium. In pneumonia,

- Fluid collects in the lungs.

As a result, the surface area available for the absorption of oxygen is reduced.

As a result, the patient becomes breathless.

Pleurisy is an infection of the pleural membranes caused by a particular type of bacterium. In pleurisy,

- Infection makes the membranes rough.

As a result, there is pain when the membranes rub together.

Antibiotic drugs are used to treat pneumonia and pleurisy.

Smoking

Smoking cigarettes is a major cause of lung cancer and heart disease. Cigarette smoke is acidic and contains various substances harmful to health.

★ **Nicotine** is a powerful drug which increases the heart rate and blood pressure.

★ **Carbon monoxide** is a poisonous gas which combines 300 times more readily with haemoglobin than oxygen does.

As a result, the level of oxygen in the blood is reduced.

★ **Tar** is a mixture of many compounds, some of which cause cancer (are **carcinogens**).

Some substances in cigarette smoke irritate the membrane lining the upper respiratory tract.

As a result, extra mucus (phlegm) forms in the trachea and bronchi.

As a result, the person may develop 'smoker's cough' in an attempt to remove the excess phlegm.

Other substances in cigarette smoke stop the cilia from beating.

As a result, particles and microorganisms enter the lungs.

As a result, the risk of infection is increased.

Emphysema is caused by repeated coughing, which destroys the walls of the alveoli.

As a result, the surface area available for the absorption of oxygen is reduced.

As a result, the person becomes breathless.

Lung cancer is caused by the carcinogens in tar. Abnormal cell division in lung tissue leads to the development of tumours (growths) which may be difficult to cure. Cancer cells may break away from the tumours and circulate in the blood to start **secondary** growths elsewhere in the body.

The smoking habit

Smoking cigarettes was fashionable in the early 1900s, and many people became smokers. Scientists soon suspected a link between smoking cigarettes and lung cancer.

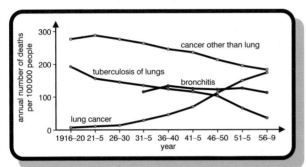

Deaths from lung cancer increased sharply in England and Wales from 1916 to 1960, which was the period when more and more people were smoking cigarettes. Other forms of lung disease were declining.

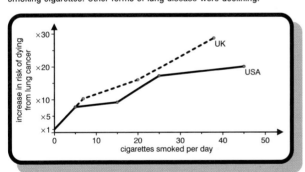

Studies have shown that the more cigarettes smoked, the greater is the risk of dying from lung cancer.

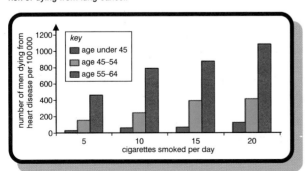

Studies have shown that the more cigarettes smoked, the greater is the risk of dying from heart disease.

Today there are fewer smokers than non-smokers in the United Kingdom. However, of the people who do smoke, there are many young people (especially girls). SMOKING IS A MUG'S GAME – DO NOT START!

REMEMBER – IF YOU DO SMOKE YOU CAN GIVE IT UP. Advice and help are available.

Drugs

Drugs are used to help in the fight against disease. For example,

★ **Antibiotics** are used to attack the different types of bacteria that cause disease.

★ **Analgesics** are drugs that reduce pain (painkillers).

Some drugs are highly **addictive** and may be **abused**. This means they are used for non-medical purposes.

Alcohol

Ethanol (the alcohol in beers, wine and spirits) depresses the activity of the nervous system. Small amounts affect the **cortex** of the brain which controls judgement. Large quantities affect the **motor cortex** which controls movement. Even more impairs memory. Drinking increasing amounts of alcohol affects other areas of the brain until it reaches brain centres that keep us alive. Death may follow.

Solvents

BRAIN
Page 74.

Glues, paints, nail varnish and cleaning fluids (dry cleaners) contain volatile solvents such as esters and ethanol. These are liquids in which other substances dissolve, and which readily produce a vapour at room temperature. Breathing them in gives a warm sense of well-being, but also produces dangerous disorientation. Long-term solvent abuse can damage the brain, kidneys and liver.

5

round-up

How much have you improved?
Work out your improvement index on page 111.

1 Simple tests identify the nutrients in different foods. Match the nutrient in column **A** with the test result that identifies the nutrient in column **B**.

A nutrients	B test results
starch	forms a milky emulsion when mixed with warm dilute ethanol
glucose	produces a violet/purple colour when mixed with dilute sodium hydroxide and a few drops of copper sulphate solution
fat	produces a blue/black colour when mixed with a few drops of iodine solution
protein	produces an orange colour when heated with Benedict's solution

[4]

2 Match each enzyme in column **A** with its role in digestion in column **B**.

A enzymes	B roles
amylase	digests maltose to glucose
pepsin	digests fat to fatty acids and glycerol
lipase	digests starch to maltose
maltase	digests protein to polypeptides

[4]

3 Complete the following paragraph using the words below. Each word may be used once, more than once or not at all.

thin exhalation fat oxygen inhalation moist carbon dioxide exchange alveoli surface area

The uptake of _____ and removal of _____ occur in the _____ of the lungs. These provide a large _____ for efficient gas _____ . They are _____-walled, have an excellent blood supply, are _____ and kept well supplied with air by breathing. _____ takes air into the lungs; _____ removes air from the lungs. [9]

4 Distinguish between the following pairs of terms.
  a) oxygenated and deoxygenated blood [4]
  b) antibody and antigen [5]
  c) HIV and AIDS [3]
  d) haemoglobin and haemophilia [5]
  e) thrombus and thrombosis [3]

5 The different parts of a motor nerve cell are listed in column **A**. Match each part with its description in column **B**.

A parts of a cell	B descriptions
axon	minute electrical disturbance
dendrite	boosts the transmission of nerve impulses
sheath	transmits nerve impulses from the cell body
nerve impulse	carries nerve impulses to the cell body

[4]

6 Explain the differences between the following pairs of terms.
  a) blind spot and fovea
  b) pupil and iris
  c) cornea and retina [6]

7 How do endocrine glands differ from other glands in the body? [2]

8 Briefly explain how antidiuretic hormone (ADH) keeps the water content of the body steady. [2]

9 Briefly explain
  a) why raised body hair helps us keep warm [3]
  b) why sweating helps us keep cool. [2]

10 Identify the cause of each disease in the list by writing either **B** (for bacterium) or **V** (for virus) next to each one.
  cholera AIDS syphilis 'flu pneumonia [5]

11 Identify the substances in cigarette smoke which are harmful to health. Briefly explain why they are harmful. [6]

Well done if you've improved. Don't worry if you haven't. Take a break and try again.

Inheritance and evolution

6.1 Reproduction

preview

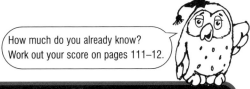

How much do you already know?
Work out your score on pages 111–12.

Test yourself

1 The diagram shows the
reproductive system of
a man. Name parts A–E.

[5]

2 Match each structure in column **A** with its correct
description in column **B**.

A structures	B descriptions
corm	a horizontal stem running above ground
runner	a short, swollen underground stem
tuber	a large underground bud
bulb	a swelling at the end of a rhizome

[4]

3 In humans, the gene for brown eyes (**B**) is dominant to
the gene for blue eyes (**b**).
   a) Using the symbols **B** and **b**, state the genotypes of the
   children that could be born from a marriage between a
   heterozygous father and a blue-eyed mother. [2]
   b) State whether the children are brown eyed or blue
   eyed. [2]

4 Distinguish between the following.
   a) restriction enzyme and ligase (splicing enzyme) [7]
   b) biotechnology and genetic engineering [5]
   c) batch culture and continuous culture [7]

5 Why are acquired characteristics not inherited? [3]

6 List the different sources of variation in living things. [6]

7 Why does sexual reproduction produce much more
genetic variation than asexual reproduction? [5]

8 Distinguish between the following terms.
   a) ancestors and descendants [1]
   b) adaptation and extinction [2]
   c) evolution and natural selection [3]

9 How are fossils formed? [4]

preview

At the end of this section you will:
- **know that reproduction gives rise to offspring**
- **understand that sexual reproduction gives
  rise to variation in offspring and that asexual
  reproduction gives rise to identical offspring**
- **be able to identify the components of the
  human reproductive system**
- **know how sexual reproduction occurs in
  humans and in flowering plants.**

Sexual or asexual?

Reproduction passes genetic
material on from parents to
their offspring. There are
two types of reproduction.

GENES AND
GENETICS
Pages 45 and 96.

In **sexual reproduction**, *two* parents (male and
female) produce sex cells called **gametes**.
Gametes are formed by **meiosis**. The male
gametes are **sperm**. The female gametes are **eggs**.
The sperm and egg fuse – this is called
fertilisation. The fertilised egg cell is called a
zygote. The zygote divides repeatedly, producing a
ball of cells called an **embryo** which develops into
the new individual. The offspring formed by
sexual reproduction inherit genes from each
parent, and are genetically *different* from one
another and from their parents. In other words,
they show **variation**.

Dear Student

   IMPORTANT ANNOUNCEMENT
Topic 3.3 about meiosis and mitosis is
REALLY REALLY important to your under-
standing of sexual and asexual reproduction.

   Luv Owl

In **asexual reproduction**, *one* parent divides by **mitosis** to produce daughter cells which form new individuals. These offspring are genetically *identical* to one another and to their parent because DNA replicates exact copies of itself during mitosis.

Sexual reproduction in humans and flowering plants

How much do you recall about the structure of the reproductive organs in flowering plants and humans? Remember that **flowers** are shoots which are specialised for reproduction. The **genitalia** are the visible parts of the human reproductive system. On the opposite page is the Mind Map for reproduction. The numbers on the Mind Map refer to the checklist below.

CHECK
LIST

Checklist for reproduction

1 ★ The testes hang down between the legs.

As a result, the testes are protected from injury.

★ The position of the testes keeps them about 3 °C lower than body temperature.

As a result, sperm develop properly in the slightly cooler conditions.

★ A woman's genitalia cover and protect the opening to the rest of the reproductive system inside her body.

2 ★ A fertilised egg is called a **zygote**. It develops into a new individual. The sequence reads:

MENSTRUAL
CYCLE
Page 83.

	mitosis produces a ball of cells	implantation buries the embryo in the wall of the uterus	
zygote ➡	**embryo** ➡	**fetus**	
– the fertilised egg	– passes down the oviduct to the uterus	– the tissues and organs of the body develop. The fetus is attached to the mother by the **placenta** and **umbilical cord.**	
adolescent ⬅	**child** ⬅	**baby** ⬅	
grows	grows	grows	**birth** after 9 months' development (**gestation** period)
adult			

The development of the zygote

★ In humans, pregnancy usually results in the birth of only one baby. However, sometimes **twins** are born.

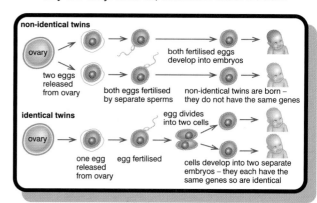

Producing twins

3 ★ **Contraception** aims to prevent pregnancy by
  • preventing sperm from reaching the egg, or
  • preventing eggs from being produced, or
  • preventing the fertilised egg from developing in the uterus.

4 ★ In flowering plants, sexual reproduction involves **pollination**, **fertilisation** and the formation of **fruits** and **seeds**. The sequence reads:

Pollination is the transfer of pollen from the anther to the stigma. * **Cross-pollination** is the transfer of pollen between anthers and stigma(s) of different plants. * **Self-pollination** is the transfer of pollen between the anthers and stigma(s) on the same plant.	**Fertilisation** is the fusion of a male sex nucleus with the female egg nucleus. The male sex nucleus passes down the **pollen tube** which grows from a pollen grain.	**Seed** is formed from the fertilised egg. It contains the embryo plant with its food store. The **fruit** (usually formed from the wall of the ovary) surrounds and protects the seed.

★ Flowers are adapted for pollination.
  • **Insect-pollinated** flowers are brightly coloured and produce nectar and scent to attract insect visitors.
  • **Wind-pollinated** flowers are often a dull colour and are adapted to distribute large quantities of pollen far and wide.

★ Fruits and seeds are adapted for distribution by either animals or wind.
  • **Spines** and **hooks** attach the fruit to passing animals.
  • Animals are attracted to feed on **brightly coloured** fruits. The seeds are protected from the digestive juices in the animal's intestine, and eventually pass out in the animal's faeces.
  • **Parachutes** and **wings** increase the surface area of fruits, helping them travel in the wind.

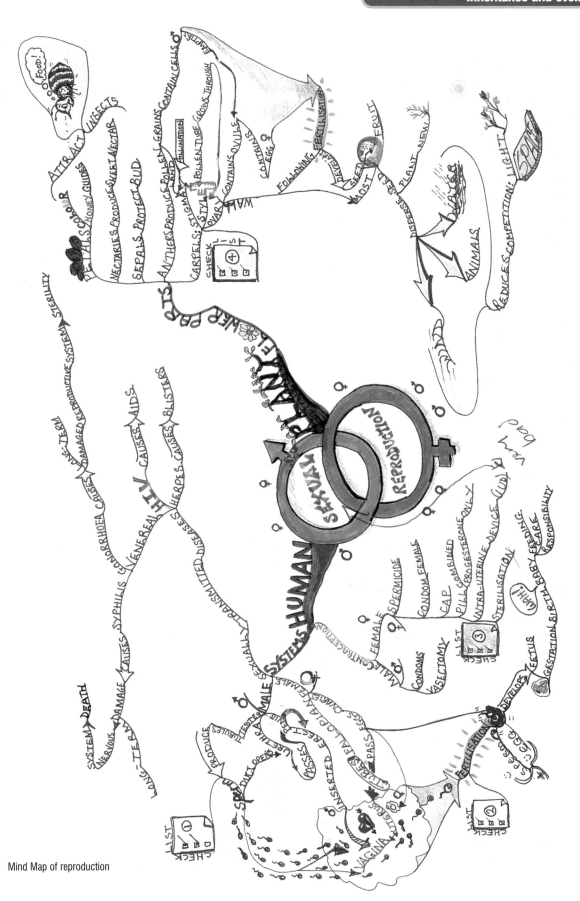

Mind Map of reproduction

6.2 Asexual reproduction in plants

preview

At the end of this section you will:

- **be able to identify the organs of asexual reproduction in flowering plants**
- **know that cuttings, graftings and micropropagation are used by farmers and gardeners to produce many identical plants**
- **understand that asexual reproduction preserves desirable characteristics and so guarantees plant quality.**

Remember that asexual reproduction gives rise to **genetically identical** individuals, because DNA replicates during mitosis. This process passes on exact copies of the parent's genetic material to the daughter cells.

```
                    exact copy
                    of parent's genetic
          mitosis   material is inherited   develop

parent  ➡  replication  ➡  daughter   ➡  offspring
                            cells
```

Remember

★ Genetically identical individuals are called **clones** (see page 37).

Vegetative reproduction

Different parts of flowering plants can reproduce asexually. They are called the **vegetative parts** and are formed from the **root**, **leaf** or **stem**.

Asexual reproduction in flowering plants is sometimes called **vegetative reproduction**. Since the new plants come from a single parent, they are genetically the same and are therefore **clones**.

The vegetative parts of plants store food. The stored food is used for the development of the new plant(s). We sometimes eat these food storage organs as vegetables, for example, potatoes.

The concept map for **asexual reproduction in plants** is shown opposite. It is your revision guide, so study it carefully.

Artificial vegetative reproduction

Gardeners and farmers need to produce fresh stocks of plants that have desirable characteristics such as disease resistance, colour of fruit or shape of flower. The diagram below shows how they use vegetative propagation.

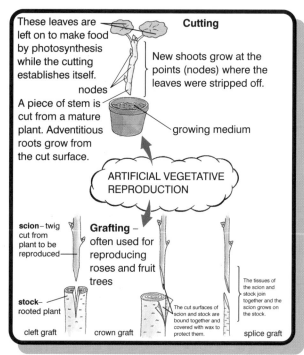

Exploiting vegetative reproduction

Micropropagation is used to grow plants from small pieces, using a technique called **tissue culture**.

★ Small fragments of plant tissue are grown in a liquid or gel that contains all the necessary ingredients.

★ Conditions are sterile.

   As a result, the new plants are free of disease.

★ The temperature is carefully controlled.

All the plants grown from pieces of one parent plant will be genetically identical. They are clones. The advantages are that the plants

- are healthy
- are the same
- retain the desirable characteristics of the parent plant.

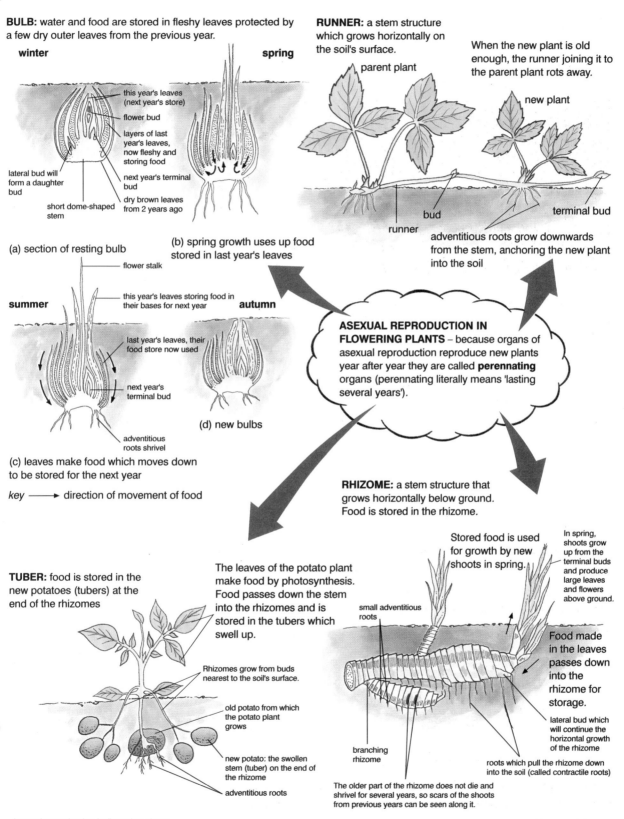

BULB: water and food are stored in fleshy leaves protected by a few dry outer leaves from the previous year.

winter   spring

this year's leaves (next year's store)
flower bud
layers of last year's leaves, now fleshy and storing food
next year's terminal bud
dry brown leaves from 2 years ago
lateral bud will form a daughter bud
short dome-shaped stem

(a) section of resting bulb

(b) spring growth uses up food stored in last year's leaves

flower stalk

summer   autumn

this year's leaves storing food in their bases for next year
last year's leaves, their food store now used
next year's terminal bud
adventitious roots shrivel

(d) new bulbs

(c) leaves make food which moves down to be stored for the next year

key ——→ direction of movement of food

RUNNER: a stem structure which grows horizontally on the soil's surface.

parent plant

When the new plant is old enough, the runner joining it to the parent plant rots away.

new plant

bud   terminal bud
runner
adventitious roots grow downwards from the stem, anchoring the new plant into the soil

ASEXUAL REPRODUCTION IN FLOWERING PLANTS – because organs of asexual reproduction reproduce new plants year after year they are called **perennating** organs (perennating literally means 'lasting several years').

RHIZOME: a stem structure that grows horizontally below ground. Food is stored in the rhizome.

Stored food is used for growth by new shoots in spring.

In spring, shoots grow up from the terminal buds and produce large leaves and flowers above ground.

TUBER: food is stored in the new potatoes (tubers) at the end of the rhizomes

The leaves of the potato plant make food by photosynthesis. Food passes down the stem into the rhizomes and is stored in the tubers which swell up.

small adventitious roots

Food made in the leaves passes down into the rhizome for storage.

Rhizomes grow from buds nearest to the soil's surface.

old potato from which the potato plant grows

new potato: the swollen stem (tuber) on the end of the rhizome

adventitious roots

branching rhizome

lateral bud which will continue the horizontal growth of the rhizome

roots which pull the rhizome down into the soil (called contractile roots)

The older part of the rhizome does not die and shrivel for several years, so scars of the shoots from previous years can be seen along it.

Asexual reproduction in flowering plants

95

6.3 Monohybrid inheritance

preview

At the end of this section you will:

- understand genetic terms
- be able to work out the expected outcome of a monohybrid cross
- understand the inheritance of gender
- understand sex-linked inheritance.

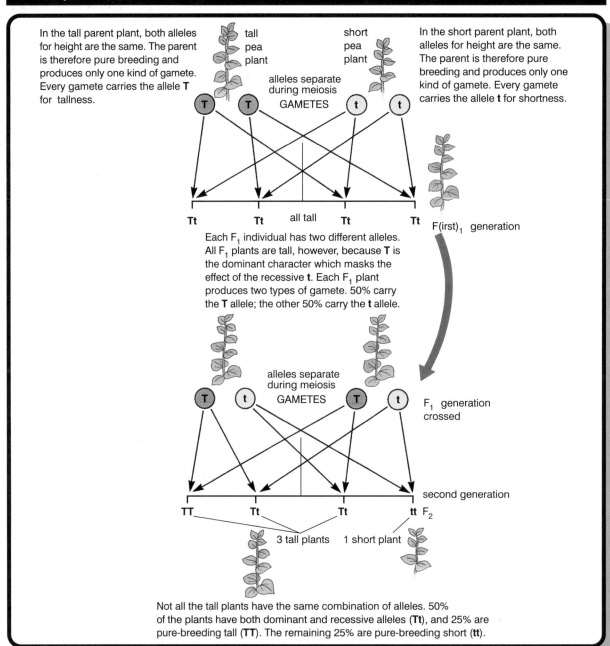

In the tall parent plant, both alleles for height are the same. The parent is therefore pure breeding and produces only one kind of gamete. Every gamete carries the allele **T** for tallness.

tall pea plant

short pea plant

In the short parent plant, both alleles for height are the same. The parent is therefore pure breeding and produces only one kind of gamete. Every gamete carries the allele **t** for shortness.

alleles separate during meiosis
GAMETES

(T) (T) (t) (t)

Tt   Tt   all tall   Tt   Tt   F(irst)$_1$ generation

Each F$_1$ individual has two different alleles. All F$_1$ plants are tall, however, because **T** is the dominant character which masks the effect of the recessive **t**. Each F$_1$ plant produces two types of gamete. 50% carry the **T** allele; the other 50% carry the **t** allele.

alleles separate during meiosis
GAMETES

(T) (t) (T) (t)   F$_1$ generation crossed

second generation

TT   Tt   Tt   tt F$_2$

3 tall plants   1 short plant

Not all the tall plants have the same combination of alleles. 50% of the plants have both dominant and recessive alleles (**Tt**), and 25% are pure-breeding tall (**TT**). The remaining 25% are pure-breeding short (**tt**).

How alleles controlling a characteristic (height) pass from one generation to the next

Fact file

Gregor Mendel was a monk who lived in the Augustinian monastery at the town of Brünn (now Brno in the Czech Republic). He observed the inheritance of different characteristics in the garden pea, and reported the results of his experiments in 1865. The work established the basis of modern genetics.

The vocabulary of genetics

★ **monohybrid inheritance** – the processes by which a single characteristic is passed from parents to offspring, for example flower colour or eye colour

★ **pure breeding** – characteristics that breed true, appearing unchanged generation after generation

★ **parental generation** (symbol **P**) – individuals that are pure breeding for a characteristic

★ **first filial generation** (symbol F_1) – the offspring produced by a parental generation

★ **second filial generation** (symbol F_2) – the offspring produced by crossing members of the first filial generation

★ **gene** – a length of DNA which codes for the whole of one protein

GENES Page 45.

★ **allele** – one of a pair of genes that control a particular characteristic

★ **homozygote** – an individual with identical alleles controlling a particular characteristic. Individuals that are pure breeding for a particular characteristic are **homozygous** for that characteristic

★ **heterozygote** – an individual with different alleles controlling a particular characteristic

★ **expressed** – a gene is expressed when a protein is produced from the activity of the gene

★ **dominant** - any characteristic that appears in the F_1 offspring of a cross between pure-breeding parents with contrasting characteristics, such as tallness and shortness in pea plants, *or* any characteristic expressed by an allele in preference to the form of the characteristic controlled by the allele's partner

★ **recessive** – any characteristic present in the parental generation that misses the F_1 generation but reappears in the F_2 generation, *or* any characteristic of an allele that is not expressed because the form of the characteristic of the allele's partner is expressed in preference, *or* any characteristic of an allele that is only expressed in the absence of the allele's dominant partner

★ **genotype** – the genetic make-up (all of the genes) of an individual

★ **phenotype** – the outward appearance of an individual; the result of those genes of the genotype which are actively expressing characteristics.

Some rules of genetics

★ Paired genes controlling a particular characteristic are called alleles.

★ Letters are used to symbolise alleles.

★ A capital letter is used to symbolise the dominant member of a pair of alleles.

★ A small letter is used to symbolise the recessive member of a pair of alleles.

★ The letter used to symbolise the recessive allele is the same letter as that for the dominant allele.

A monohybrid cross

T is used to symbolise the allele that produces tallness in pea plants, and **t** is used to symbolise the allele that produces shortness. The diagram on the left sets out the results of crosses between tall and short pea plants. Other contrasting characteristics of the pea plant such as seed shape (round or wrinkled), flower colour (purple or white) and pod shape (smooth or wrinkled) are inherited in a similar way.

Inheritance of sex

The photograph shows the chromosomes that determine the sex of a person. The larger chromosome is the **X** chromosome; the smaller chromosome is the **Y** chromosome. The body cells of a woman carry two X chromosomes; those of a man carry an X chromosome and a Y chromosome.

Human sex chromosomes

The diagram below shows how a person's sex is inherited. Notice that

- a baby's sex depends on whether the egg is fertilised by a sperm carrying an X chromosome or one carrying a Y chromosome
- the birth of (almost) equal numbers of girls and boys is governed by the production of equal numbers of X and Y sperms at meiosis.

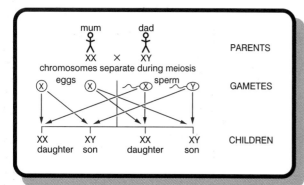

Inheritance of sex in humans

Sex-linked inheritance

Characteristics controlled by alleles situated on the sex chromosomes are said to be **sex-linked** characteristics. The disease **haemophilia** is an example. The diagram shows what happens.

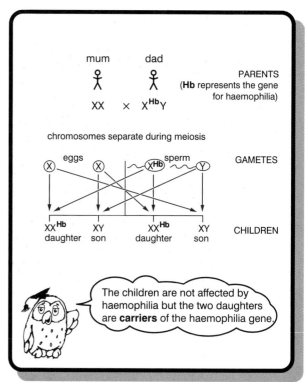

The outcome when a man affected by haemophilia becomes a father

The outcome when a woman who is a carrier of the haemophilia allele becomes a mother

6.4 Biotechnology

preview

At the end of this section you will:

- **know that the processes of biotechnology have a long history in the production of bread and alcoholic drinks**
- **understand that the techniques of genetic engineering manipulate genes to human advantage**
- **realise that genetic engineering has transformed biotechnology into a rapidly expanding industry which provides food, medicines and a range of industrial chemicals.**

Fact file

★ The word **biotechnology** describes the way we use plant cells, animal cells and microorganisms to produce substances that are useful to us.

Using biotechnology

The history of biotechnology demonstrates the importance of some of the processes of biotechnology.

The traditional: for thousands of years humans have exploited different organisms to make food, using

- **yeast** to make wine, beer and bread
- **moulds** to make cheese
- **bacteria** to make yogurt and vinegar.

The diagram below traces the processes in the production of wine and bread.

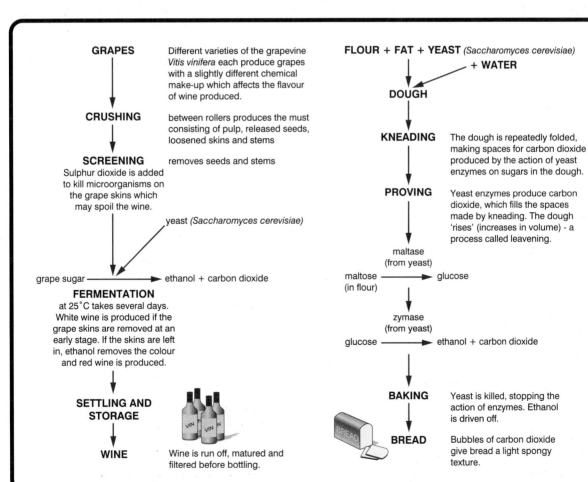

Making wine and bread

Yeast cells use **anaerobic respiration** to convert glucose into **ethanol** ('alcohol' in wines and beers) and **carbon dioxide** (the gas that makes bread rise). The reaction is called **fermentation**. Biotechnology exploits a range of fermentation reactions to produce different substances.

The new: in the 1970s scientists developed the techniques of **genetic engineering**, which introduced the modern era of biotechnology. New methods of manipulating genes became possible because of the discovery of different enzymes in bacteria.

ANAEROBIC RESPIRATION Page 67.

★ **Restriction enzymes** cut DNA into pieces, making it possible to isolate specific genes.

★ **Ligase** (splicing enzyme) allows desirable genes to be inserted into the genetic material of host cells.

Using genetic engineering we can create organisms with specific genetic characteristics, such that they produce substances that we need and want. The microorganisms are cultured in a solution containing all the substances they require for rapid growth and multiplication inside huge containers called **fermenters**. In this way, medicines, foods and industrial chemicals can be made on an industrial scale. The diagram below shows how genetically engineered insulin is made.

INSULIN Page 83.

Remember that the products of biotechnology come from the action of **genes** producing useful substances.

GENES Page 45.

Fact file

★ **Batch culture** produces batches of product in a fermenter. The fermenter is then emptied of the product and the nutrient solution. The fermenter is sterilised with super-heated steam ready for the next batch.

★ **Continuous culture** produces substances as an ongoing process. The product is drawn off the fermenter and nutrients are replaced as they are used.

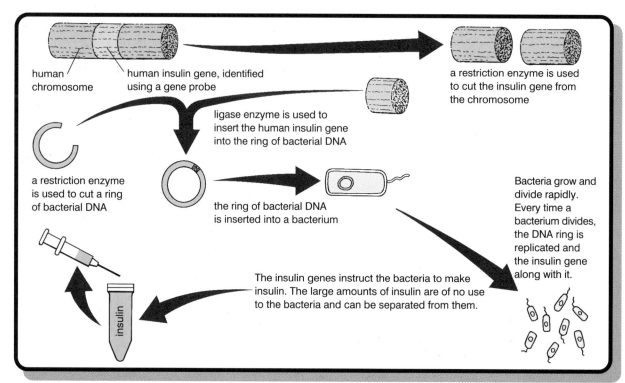

human chromosome

human insulin gene, identified using a gene probe

a restriction enzyme is used to cut the insulin gene from the chromosome

ligase enzyme is used to insert the human insulin gene into the ring of bacterial DNA

a restriction enzyme is used to cut a ring of bacterial DNA

the ring of bacterial DNA is inserted into a bacterium

Bacteria grow and divide rapidly. Every time a bacterium divides, the DNA ring is replicated and the insulin gene along with it.

The insulin genes instruct the bacteria to make insulin. The large amounts of insulin are of no use to the bacteria and can be separated from them.

insulin

Making genetically engineered insulin

6.5 Variation

preview

At the end of this section you will:
- understand the difference between continuous variation and discontinuous variation
- be able to identify the sources of variation
- know that variation is either inherited or acquired.

Genetic and environmental variation

Look closely at your family, friends and classmates. Notice the differently coloured hair and eyes, and the differently shaped faces. We all show **variations** in the different characteristics that make up our physical appearance (**phenotype**).

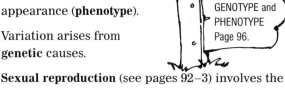

GENOTYPE and PHENOTYPE Page 96.

Variation arises from **genetic** causes.

Sexual reproduction (see pages 92–3) involves the fusion of the nucleus of a **sperm** with the nucleus of the **egg**. The fertilisation recombines the genetic material from each parent in new ways within the **zygote**.

Mutations arise as a result of mistakes in the **replication** of DNA (see page 46). Occasionally the wrong base adds to the growing strand of DNA, making the new DNA slightly different from the original. **Ionising radiation** and some **chemicals** increase the probability of gene mutation.

★ Ionising radiation strips electrons from matter exposed to it (ionises the atoms). Emissions from radioactive substances are ionising radiations. They may cause mutations by damaging DNA directly, or by generating highly active components of molecules called **free radicals** which cause the damage indirectly.

★ Chemicals such as the **carcinogens** (substances that cause cancer) in tobacco may lead to mutations of the genes that normally inhibit cell division.

As a result, cell division runs out of control and a cancer develops.

★ **Crossing over** during **meiosis** exchanges a segment of one chromosome (and the genes it carries) with the corresponding segment of its homologous chromosome.

As a result, the sex cells produced by meiosis have a different combination of genes from the parent cell.

Variations that arise from genetic causes are inherited from parents by their offspring, who pass them on to their offspring, and so on from generation to generation. Inherited variation is the raw material on which **natural selection** acts, resulting in **evolution**.

NATURAL SELECTION and EVOLUTION Pages 102–5.

Variation also arises from **environmental** causes. Here, 'environmental' means all the external influences affecting an organism, for example:

★ **Nutrients** in the food we eat and minerals that plants absorb in solution through the roots. In many countries, children are now taller and heavier, age for age, than they were 50 years ago because of improved diet and standards of living.

★ **Drugs**, which may have a serious effect on appearance. **Thalidomide** was given to pregnant women in the 1960s to prevent them feeling sick and help them sleep. The drug can affect the development of the fetus and some women who were prescribed thalidomide gave birth to seriously deformed children.

★ **Temperature** affects the rate of enzyme-controlled chemical reactions. For example, warmth increases the rate of photosynthesis and improves the rate of growth of plants kept under glass.

★ **Physical training** uses muscles more than normal, increasing their size and power. Weightlifters develop bulging muscles as they train for their sport.

Variations that arise from environmental causes are *not* inherited, because the sex cells are not affected. Instead the characteristics are said to be **acquired**. The fact that the weightlifter has developed bulging muscles does not mean that his or her children will have bulging muscles – unless they take up weightlifting as well! Because variations as a result of acquired characteristics are not inherited, they do not affect evolution.

Continuous and discontinuous variation

The variations shown by some characteristics are spread over a range of measurements. All intermediate forms of a characteristic are possible between one extreme and the other. We say that the characteristic shows **continuous variation**. The height of a population is an example of continuous variation, as shown.

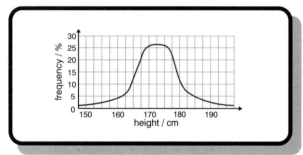

Variation in the height of the adult human population – an example of continuous variation

Other characteristics do not show a continuous trend in variation from one extreme to another. They show categories of the characteristic without any intermediate forms. The ability to roll the tongue is an example – you can either do it or you can't. There are no half-rollers! We say that the characteristic shows **discontinuous variation**.

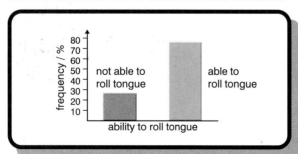

Ability to roll the tongue – an example of discontinuous variation

6.6 Evolution

preview

At the end of this section you will:

- **know that the British naturalist Charles Darwin was the first person to explain how species can evolve**
- **understand Darwin's evidence showing that evolution occurs, and that natural selection is the mechanism of evolution**
- **be able to interpret examples of evolution in action**
- **know that fossils give a record of organisms that have become extinct.**

Fact file – Darwin

★ Charles Darwin (1809–82) was a keen British naturalist who abandoned medicine at Edinburgh and studied theology at Cambridge. His world voyage on HMS *Beagle* (1831–6) provided much of the evidence that

- organisms **evolve** and that
- **natural selection** is the mechanism of evolution.

It was another 20 years before he published these proposals in his book *The Origin of Species*.

The process of evolution

Present-day living things are descended from ancestors that have changed through thousands of generations. The process of change is called **evolution**. The concept map for evolution is shown opposite. It shows that other people's ideas influenced Darwin's thinking on how species can evolve. The numbers on the concept map refer to the checklist of points on page 104. The concept map and its checklist are your revision guide to evolution.

Evidence
- The fossils that Darwin collected on expeditions inland showed him that organisms today are not the same as organisms that lived a long time ago. In other words, organisms change through time – they evolve.
- There is an enormous variety of living things.

Evidence
- Lyell's work showed that the geology of the Earth changed through long periods of time.
- Darwin reasoned that if the geology of Earth had changed then so too could organisms.

Darwin travelled around the coast of South America on HMS *Beagle*.

CHECK **1** LIST

Charles Darwin (1809–82)

Charles Lyell
Darwin and Lyell became friends on Darwin's return to England from the voyage in the *Beagle*. Lyell believed that the Earth was very old.

CHECK **2** LIST

THE COMPONENTS OF EVOLUTION

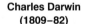

variation + natural selection $\xrightarrow{\text{time}}$ evolution

Evidence
- Darwin reasoned that since the number of individuals in a population does not increase indefinitely, then limiting factors must check the increase in numbers.

Evidence
- Artificial selection helped confirm natural selection in Darwin's mind as the mechanism of evolution.

CHECK **4** LIST

Reverend Thomas Malthus
Malthus suggested that the growth in numbers of a population outstrips resources.

CHECK **3** LIST

The variety of pigeons bred by 'fanciers' over hundreds of years originated from a 'wild' type common ancestor.

How Darwin arrived at a theory of evolution through natural selection (checklist overleaf)

Checklist for evolution

1 A survey of the South American coast was among the tasks undertaken by the crew of HMS *Beagle* during its world voyage. At that time Darwin took over as the ship's naturalist. He

- collected **fossils** and specimens of plants and animals on expeditions inland
- noticed that one type of organism gave way to another as the *Beagle* sailed around the coast of South America
- observed that the animals along the Pacific coast of South America were different from those along the Atlantic coast
- compared the wildlife of the Galapagos Islands with the wildlife of the South American mainland, noting the differences between similar species.

The variety of species that Darwin discovered on his expeditions in South America and the Galapagos Islands convinced him that species change through time; that is, they **evolve**.

2 The famous geologist Charles Lyell (1797–1875) believed that

- Earth's rocks are very old
- natural forces produce continuous geological change during the course of Earth's history
- fossils can be used to date rocks
- the fossil record was laid down over hundreds of millions of years.

Darwin read Lyell's books.

As a result, Darwin reasoned that if rocks have changed slowly over long periods of time, living things might have a similar history.

3 In 1798 the Reverend Thomas Malthus wrote *An Essay on the Principle of Population*. He stated that a population would increase in number indefinitely unless kept in check by shortages of resources such as food and living space. Darwin read the essay in 1838 and reasoned that in nature a 'struggle for existence' must occur. In modern language we say that organisms **compete** for resources in limited supply.

COMPETITION
Pages 22–3.

4 For centuries we have selected animals and plants for their desirable characteristics, and bred from them. This is called **artificial selection**. For example, dogs have been bred for shape, size and coat colour, resulting in a wide variety of breeds. Darwin investigated the work of breeders of animals and plants, and added to his experience by breeding pigeons. He reasoned that if artificial selection produced change in domestic animals and plants, then natural selection should have the same effect on wildlife.

Fact file – age of the Earth

★ Evidence suggests that Earth was formed about 4500 million years ago and that very simple forms of life first appeared around 4000 million years ago.

The checklist above sets out the different components which were the key to Darwin's understanding of how species evolve.

Variation: Darwin's work during the voyage of HMS *Beagle* and his experience of selectively breeding pigeons provided evidence for the large amount of variation in the characteristics of different species (checklist **1** and **4**).

Natural selection: Malthus' work contributed to Darwin's idea of a 'struggle for existence' (competition for resources). The result is the natural selection of those organisms best suited (**adapted**) to survive (checklist **3**).

Time: Lyell's work showed Darwin that the Earth is very old, giving time for the evolution of species to occur (checklist **2**).

How species evolve – the modern argument summarised

1 Because individuals vary genetically, individuals are slightly different from one another.

2 This variation in a population of individuals is the raw material on which natural selection works, resulting in evolution.

3 Individuals with genes that express characteristics which adapt the individuals to obtain scarce resources are more likely to survive than other less well adapted individuals.

4 The best adapted individuals are more likely to survive and reproduce, and so their offspring will inherit the genes for those favourable characteristics.

5   In this way organisms accumulate genes for favourable characteristics and change through time; that is, they evolve over many generations.

6   If the environment in which individuals are living changes, then genes for different characteristics might favour survival. Individuals with these characteristics will survive to reproduce and so evolution continues from generation to generation.

> It took Darwin nearly 30 years to develop a theory of evolution through natural selection. The ideas were a revolution in scientific thinking.

Evolution in action

Evolution is still happening. Maintaining the balance between the pale and the dark forms of the peppered moth *Biston betularia* is an example. The diagram below shows what happens.

The fossil record

Fossils are the remains of dead organisms, or impressions made by them. Fossils are usually preserved in sedimentary rocks which are formed layer on layer by the deposition of mud, sand and silt over millions of years. Providing the layers are undisturbed, then the more recent the layer, the nearer it is to the Earth's surface.

As a result, the fossils in each rock layer are a record of life on Earth at the time when the layer was formed.

As a result, a sequence of layers each with its fossils traces the history of life on Earth.

Extinction

Species may die out (become **extinct**) because of the harmful effects of human activities on the environment. Natural extinction also happens over longer periods of time. It makes room for new species to evolve and replace the previous ones. Naturally occurring extinctions are caused by

*   competition between species
*   changes in the environment.

The mass extinction of whole groups of organisms have occurred at intervals throughout the history of life on Earth. Extinction of the dinosaurs and many other species of reptile about 70 million years ago is a well known example. Their extinction made way for mammals and birds to fill the vacant spaces in the environment.

> That's why you and I are here!

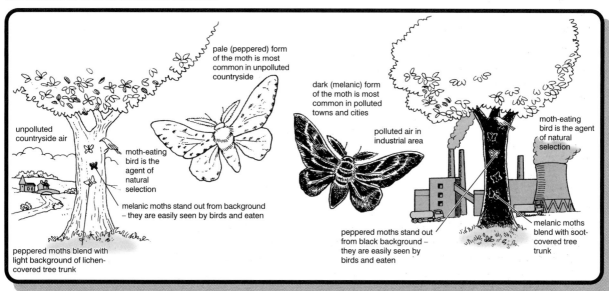

Different forms of *Biston betularia* adapt the moth to survive in different environments

6

round-up

How much have you improved?
Work out your improvement index on page 112.

1 Match each structure in column **A** with its correct
description in column **B**.

A structures	B descriptions
seed	structure to which pollen grains attach
ovule	produces a sugar solution
fruit	contains the egg nucleus
stigma	a fertilised ovule
nectary	develops from the ovary after fertilisation [5]

2 What are the advantages to growers of reproducing
crops asexually? [3]

3 Name the food stored in the organs of asexual
reproduction of plants. [1]

4 Briefly explain why the production of clones depends
on the process of mitosis. [5]

5 Match each term in column **A** with its correct
description in column **B**.

A terms	B descriptions
allele	the processes by which a single characteristic passes from parents to offspring
pure breeding	offspring of the offspring of the parental generation
second filial generation	characteristics that appear unchanged from generation to generation
monohybrid inheritance	one of a pair of genes that control a particular characteristic [4]

6 The diagram shows a glass container called a
demijohn, in which wine is produced from the
fermentation of grape juice by yeast.

- trap
- water
- demijohn
- nutrient solution and yeast

a) The trap is filled with water. What is the purpose of
the trap? [2]

b) Name the gas bubbling through the water in the
trap. [1]

c) Why is the grape juice called a nutrient solution? [1]

d) Name the substance in the grape juice fermented
by the yeast. [1]

7 In a population of 300 goldfish, variations in two
characteristics were measured and the results displayed
as charts. Chart A shows variation in the length of the
fish; chart B shows variation in their colour.

a) Which chart shows
   (i) continuous variation
   (ii) discontinuous variation?
   (iii) Briefly give reasons for your answers. [6]
b) Using chart B, calculate the percentage of
   yellow goldfish in the population. [1]
c) Albino goldfish are relatively rare. Give a
   possible genetic explanation for the occurrence
   of albino goldfish. [1]

8 a) Look at the diagram on page 105. Briefly explain
   why the population densities of pale peppered
   moths and dark peppered moths are different in the
   countryside from in industrial areas. [8]
   b) Why is the moth-eating bird called an agent
   of natural selection? [2]

9 Briefly explain why genes for characteristics that
favour the survival of individuals tend to accumulate
from generation to generation. [4]

10 Outline the contributions of the ideas of Charles Lyell
and Thomas Malthus to Darwin's development of a
theory of evolution through natural selection. [5]

Answers

1 Test yourself (page 10)

Introducing biology

1 a) It would increase (✓).   **b)** It would decrease (✓).

2 a)

	b)	c)
Movement	✓	✗
Respiration	✓	✗
Sensitivity	✓	✗
Growth	✓	✗
Reproduction	✓	✗
Excretion	✓	✗
Nutrition	✓	✗

[✓ × 10]

d) No – plants do not move from place to place (✓).

3 Annual: a plant that grows from seed to maturity and produces new seeds all within one growing season (✓). It then dies (✓). Perennial: a plant that continues to grow and produce seeds for many years (✓).

4 a) To identify different living things by name (✓).
b) These characteristics vary too much (✓) even between members of the same group of organisms (✓) to be reliable indicators for identification (✓).

5 Soil: is damp (✓); shields organisms from ultraviolet light (✓); maintains a relatively stable temperature compared with air (✓); contains food (✓).

Your score: **7** out of 24

1 Round-up (page 15)

Introducing biology

1 a) It would boil away (✓).
b) It would freeze and form ice (✓).

2 a) Oxygen (✓)
b) Carbon dioxide (✓)

3 a) Respiration releases energy from food (✓). Gaseous exchange takes in oxygen needed for respiration (✓) and removes carbon dioxide produced by respiration (✓).
b) Excretion removes the waste substances produced by metabolism (✓). Defecation removes the undigested remains of food (✓).

4 The answer should include the idea that although cars move (✓), need fuel (= nutrition) (✓), burn fuel (= respiration) (✓) and produce waste gases (= excretion) (✓) they do not grow (✓) or reproduce (✓) and are not sensitive (✓). Cars therefore do not show all the characteristics associated with living things (✓).

5

A characteristics		B descriptions
Movement	(✓)	Changing position
Respiration	(✓)	Releasing energy from food
Sensitivity	(✓)	Responding to stimuli
Growth	(✓)	Increasing in size
Reproduction	(✓)	Producing new individuals
Excretion	(✓)	Removing waste substances produced by cells
Nutrition	(✓)	Making or obtaining food

6

A animals		B descriptions
Insect	(✓)	Six legs
Worm	(✓)	No legs
Spider	(✓)	Eight legs
Bird	(✓)	Two legs

7 The unfamiliar specimen is compared with the descriptions in the key (✓).
The descriptions are followed through (✓) until the description that matches the specimen is found (✓).
The matching description identifies the specimen (✓).

8 The system gives each living organism a name in two parts (✓). The first is the name of the genus (✓); the second is the species name (✓). The genus and species names identify the organism (✓).

9 Paired statements (✓).

Your score: **21** out of 37

Your improvement index: $\dfrac{\boxed{7}/24}{\boxed{21}/37} \times 100\% = \boxed{}\%$

2 Test yourself (page 16)

Organisms in the environment

1

A terms		B descriptions
Biosphere	(✓)	All the ecosystems of the world
Community	(✓)	All the organisms that live in a particular ecosystem
Habitat	(✓)	The place where a group of organisms lives
Population	(✓)	A group of individuals of the same species

2 a) Most animals eat more than one type of plant or other animal (✓). A food web shows the range of different foods eaten (✓).
b) Plants produce food by photosynthesis (✓). Animals consume this food directly when they eat plants (✓) or indirectly when they eat other animals (✓) which depend on plant food (✓).

3 a) The pyramid of biomass takes into account differences in size (✓) of producers and consumers (✓).

b) The energy pyramid shows the amount of food being produced (✓) and consumed (✓) in a given time (✓).

4 Improvements in food production (✓); more jobs (✓); new drugs (accept improvement in medicines/medical care) (✓); improvement in public health (✓).

5 Benefits: more food (✓), reliably produced (✓). Costs: loss of wildlife (✓), loss of habitats (✓), pollution from agrochemicals (✓). (Accept other sensible alternatives.)

Your score: ☐ 7 out of 24

2 Round-up (page 31)

Organisms in the environment

1 Physical *or* abiotic (✓), environment (✓), living *or* biotic (✓), community (✓), habitats (✓), niches (✓).

2 a) The non-living part of an ecosystem (✓).

b) The amount of light affects the rate of photosynthesis (✓) and therefore the amount of plant growth under the canopy layer (✓). This in turn affects the animals that depend on plants for food and shelter (✓) and so on along the food chain (✓).

3 a) 3 (✓)

b) Water weed (✓)

c) Water weed makes food by photosynthesis (✓).

d) Tadpoles (✓)

e) Tadpoles eat water weed (accept plants) (✓).

f) Minnows (✓) and perch (✓).

g) Minnow and perch eat tadpoles (accept meat) (✓).

4 Light is reflected from the leaf surface (✓). Light passes through the leaf (✓). Only red and blue light is absorbed by chlorophyll (✓).

5 When the different organisms in the community show an approximation (are roughly the same) in size (✓).

6 a) Saw wrack (✓).

b) Dog whelks (✓).

c) The biomass of dog whelks would decrease (✓). The biomass of saw wrack would increase (✓).

7 a) Intraspecific competition – competition between individuals of the same species (✓). Interspecific competition – competition between individuals of different species (✓).

b) Adaptation – an organism is adapted (suited) to survive (✓). Survival – an organism survives (lives) because of its adaptations (✓).

c) Camouflage – coloration that conceals organisms (✓). Warning coloration – colours that deter predators from attacking prey (✓).

8 a) When prey is scarce predator numbers fall (✓). When prey numbers build up predator numbers follow because there is more prey food (✓). Predator breeds and reproduces more slowly than prey (✓).

b) The population numbers of each species are stable (✓). (Allow: population numbers of each species fluctuated around a mean (average) number for that species.)

c) Numbers would increase (✓).

d) Numbers would decline (✓) to the former level (✓).

e) Numbers would decline (✓) because of lack of food (✓). (Allow sensible alternative suggestions, e.g. increased mortality due to disease or parasites.)

9

A terms		B descriptions
Fertiliser	(✓)	Supplies plants with nutrients
Herbicide	(✓)	Kills plants
Irrigation	(✓)	Supplies plants with water
Monoculture	(✓)	A crop grown over a large area
Weed	(✓)	An unwanted plant

Your score: ☐ out of 47

Your improvement index: $\dfrac{☐/47}{☐/24} \times 100\% = ☐\%$

3 Test yourself (page 32)

Cell activity

1

A structures		B functions
Mitochondrion	(✓)	Where energy is released from the oxidation of glucose
Cell membrane	(✓)	Partially permeable to substances in solution
Chloroplast	(✓)	Where light energy is captured
Cell wall	(✓)	Fully permeable to substances in solution
Nucleus	(✓)	Contains the chromosomes

2 Because molecules of the substance are moving against a concentration gradient (✓).

3 a) A plasmolysed cell is one from which water has passed out of the vacuole, out of the cytoplasm, out of the cell membrane and cell wall into the solution outside the cell (accept water has passed out of the cell) (✓). As a result the cytoplasm pulls away from the cell wall (accept cell content disrupted) (✓) and the cell becomes limp (✓). A turgid cell is one which contains as much water as it can hold (✓).

b) A fully permeable membrane allows most substances to pass through it (✓). A partially permeable membrane allows some substances to pass through it (✓) and stops other substances (✓).

4 A group of genetically identical cells (or organisms) (✓).

5 During replication each chromosome (and its DNA) (✓) makes an exact copy of itself (✓).

6 a) Cells die (✓). New cells (✓) which are replicas of the old cells are produced by mitosis (✓).

b) The daughter cells have the same number of chromosomes as the parent cell (✓). The chromosomes in the daughter cells are identical to those in the parent cells (✓).

7 Haploid cells receive half the diploid number of chromosomes (✓) from their parent cell (✓).
Diploid cells receive the full number of chromosomes (✓) from their parent cell (✓).

8 Cells (✓), cells (✓), tissues (✓), an organ (✓), organs (✓), an organ (✓).

9 Cellulose in plant cell walls (✓); chitin in insect exoskeletons (✓).

10 The molecules of unsaturated fats have double bonds between some carbon atoms (✓). Saturated fats have only single bonds between carbon atoms (✓).

11 A nucleotide consists of the sugar ribose (✓) or deoxyribose (✓), one of five different bases (✓) and a phosphate group (✓).

Your score: ☐ out of 39

3 Round-up (page 47)
Cell activity

1 a) Nucleus (✓), cell membrane (✓), mitochondria (✓), cytoplasm (✓).
b) Cell wall (✓), large vacuole (✓), chloroplasts (✓).

2 Water is taken into the cells (✓) by osmosis (✓). The cells become turgid (✓). The wilted plant (✓) will become upright again (✓) as its cells become turgid following watering.

3 Down (✓), faster (✓), against (✓), energy (✓), partially (✓), osmosis (✓).

4 Damaged tissues can be replaced by new cells that are identical to the parent cells (✓).

5 Similarities: replication of each chromosome into chromatids (✓); lining up of the chromosomes on the equator of the cell (✓); separation of the chromatids (✓); chromatids form the new chromosomes in daughter cells (✓); destruction and reformation of the nuclear membrane during the process of cell division (✓).
Differences: chromosomes form homologous pairs in meiosis but not in mitosis (✓); there are two divisions during meiosis but only one division during mitosis (✓); meiosis results in four daughter cells, mitosis in two daughter cells (✓).

6 Cells (✓), tissues (✓), organs (✓), organ systems (✓), organism (✓).

7

A substances		B functions
Fat	(✓)	Insulates the body
Cellulose	(✓)	A component of the plant cell wall
DNA	(✓)	Carries the genetic code
Polypeptide	(✓)	Made of about 40 amino acids
Glycogen	(✓)	A food substance stored in the liver
Protein	(✓)	Enzymes are made of this substance

8 a) 4 (✓) **b)** 4 (✓)

Your score: ☐ out of 40

Your improvement index: $\dfrac{\boxed{}/40}{\boxed{}/39} \times 100\% = \boxed{}\%$

4 Test yourself (page 48)
Green plants as organisms

1 a) Carbon dioxide (✓) and water (✓).
b) Oxygen (✓).

2

A substances		B functions
Nitrogen	(✓)	Used to make protein
Phosphorus	(✓)	Used to make cell membranes
Magnesium	(✓)	Used to make chlorophyll

3 Increase (✓), osmotic (✓), osmosis (✓), xylem (✓), active transport (✓), xylem (✓), evaporation (✓), stomata (✓).

4

A tropisms		B descriptions
Phototropism	(✓)	Growth movement in response to light
Geotropism	(✓)	Growth movement in response to gravity
Hydrotropism	(✓)	Growth movement in response to water
Thigmotropism	(✓)	Growth movement in response to touch

Your score: ☐ out of 18

4 Round-up (page 57)
Green plants as organisms

1 Palisade cells (✓), spongy mesophyll cells (✓), guard cells (✓).

2 The cells of the upper surface of the leaf do not contain chloroplasts (✓). Most light therefore reaches the palisade cells (✓) which are packed with chloroplasts (✓). Photosynthesis occurs at a maximum rate (✓).

3 Temperature (✓), light intensity (✓), supplies of carbon dioxide (✓) and water (✓). A modern greenhouse provides warmth (✓), lighting (✓), a source of carbon dioxide (✓) and water from sprinkler systems (✓).

4 Sugar (✓), sugar (✓), phloem (✓), sugar (✓), phloem (✓), active transport (✓), water (✓), phloem (✓), pressure (✓), translocation (✓), sugar (✓), pressure (✓), phloem (✓).

5 Warm (✓), windy (✓), low humidity (✓) and bright sunlight (✓).

6 The stomata close (✓). If the plant continues to lose more water than it gains then its cells lose turgor (✓) and it wilts (✓).

7

Xylem		Phloem
Dead tissue (cells)	(✓)	Living tissue (cells)
Tissue (cells) waterproofed with lignin	(✓)	Tissue (cells) not waterproofed with lignin
Transports water and minerals	(✓)	Transports sugar and other substances
Transport of materials is one way	(✓)	Transport of materials is two ways
Xylem tissue does not have companion cells	(✓)	Phloem tissue has companion cells

8 Plant hormone (✓), tip (✓), weedkiller (✓), unfertilised (✓), seedless (✓), ripens (✓).

9
   a) Hypothesis: a substance produced in the shoot tip of a growing seedling (✓) controls the response of the shoot to light (✓).
   b) A: the shoot will remain upright and not bend towards the source of light (✓).
   Explanation: the piece of metal prevents the substance that controls the response of the shoot to light and which is produced in the shoot tip (✓) from diffusing to the region behind the shoot tip where it has its effect (✓).
   B: the shoot will bend towards the source of light (✓).
   Explanation: the substance that controls the response of the shoot to light and which is produced in the shoot tip (✓) is able to diffuse to the region behind the shoot tip where it has its effect (✓).

Your score: [ ] out of 54

Your improvement index: $\dfrac{[\ ]/54}{[\ ]/18} \times 100\% = [\ ]\%$

5 Test yourself   (page 58)

Humans as organisms

1
   a) Carbohydrates (✓), fats (✓), proteins (✓).
   b) Protein (✓)
   c) Fat (✓)
   d) Minerals (✓) and vitamins (✓).

2

A terms		B descriptions
Ingestion	(✓)	Food is taken into the mouth
Digestion	(✓)	Food is broken down
Absorption	(✓)	Digested food passes into the body
Egestion	(✓)	The removal of undigested food through the anus

3
   a) There are two bronchi, one branching to each lung (✓). Each bronchus branches many times into small tubes called bronchioles (✓).
   b) A person has two lungs (✓). Within each lung, bronchioles subdivide into even smaller tubes which end in clusters of small sacs called alveoli (✓).

   c) During aerobic respiration, cells use oxygen to oxidise digested food substances (accept glucose) (✓), releasing energy (✓). During anaerobic respiration, cells break down digested food substances (accept glucose) without oxygen (✓). Less energy is released during anaerobic respiration than during aerobic respiration (✓).
   d) Breathing takes in (inhales) (✓) and expels (exhales) (✓) air. Gaseous exchange occurs across the surfaces of the alveoli (✓).

4 The right ventricle pumps blood into the pulmonary artery (✓) on its way to the lungs (✓); the left ventricle pumps blood into the aorta (✓) which takes it around the rest of the body (✓).

5

A components		B descriptions
Plasma	(✓)	Contains dissolved food substances
Red blood cells	(✓)	Contain haemoglobin
White blood cells	(✓)	Produce antibodies
Platelets	(✓)	Promote the formation of blood clots

6 Receptor (✓), sensory neurone (✓), relay neurone (✓), motor neurone (✓), effector.

7
   a) The eardrum vibrates (✓) in response to sound waves (✓).
   b) The bones pass vibrations through the middle ear (✓) and also amplify them (✓).
   c) The pinna funnels sound waves down the ear canal (✓) to the eardrum (✓).
   d) The hair cells are stimulated by the vibrations of the basilar membrane (✓). They fire off nerve impulses to the brain along the auditory nerve (✓).

8 Hormones are chemical substances (✓) which circulate in the blood (✓).

9 Insulin decreases the level of glucose in the blood (✓). Glucagon increases the level of glucose in the blood (✓).

10 Glomerulus (✓), Bowman's capsule (✓), tubule (✓), collecting duct (✓), ureter (✓), bladder (✓), urethra (✓).

11

A body structures		B roles
Tear gland	(✓)	Produces the enzyme lysozyme which destroys bacteria
Glands in the stomach wall	(✓)	Produce hydrochloric acid which kills bacteria
Skin	(✓)	Produces sebum which kills bacteria and fungi
Cilia lining the upper respiratory tract	(✓)	Sweep away mucus containing trapped microorganisms and particles
Blood	(✓)	White cells produce antibodies which destroy antigens

Your score: [ ] out of 58

5 Round-up (page 90)

Humans as organisms

1

A nutrients		B test results
Starch	(✓)	Produces a blue/black colour when mixed with a few drops of iodine solution
Glucose	(✓)	Produces an orange colour when heated with Benedict's solution
Fat	(✓)	Forms a milky emulsion when mixed with warm dilute ethanol
Protein	(✓)	Produces a violet/purple colour when mixed with dilute sodium hydroxide and a few drops of copper sulphate solution

2

A enzymes		B roles
Amylase	(✓)	Digests starch to maltose
Pepsin	(✓)	Digests protein to polypeptides
Lipase	(✓)	Digests fat to fatty acids and glycerol
Maltase	(✓)	Digests maltose to glucose

3 Oxygen (✓), carbon dioxide (✓), alveoli (✓), surface area (✓), exchange (✓), thin (✓), moist (✓), inhalation (✓), exhalation (✓).

4
a) Oxygenated blood contains a lot of oxyhaemoglobin (✓). It is bright red (✓). Deoxygenated blood contains little oxyhaemoglobin (✓). It is deep red-purple (✓).

b) Antibodies are proteins (✓) produced by lymphocytes (accept white blood cells) (✓) in response to antigens (✓) which are materials 'foreign' to (accept not recognised by) the body (✓). Antibodies destroy antigens (✓).

c) HIV is the abbreviation for human immunodeficiency virus (✓) which causes the diseases (✓) that characterise AIDS (✓).

d) Haemoglobin is the protein (✓) in red blood cells (✓) that absorbs oxygen (✓). Haemophilia is a genetic disease (✓) characterised by the slow clotting time of blood (✓).

e) A thrombus is a clot (✓) that causes a thrombosis (blockage) (✓) in a blood vessel (✓).

5

A parts of cell		B descriptions
Axon	(✓)	Transmits nerve impulses from the cell body
Dendrite	(✓)	Carries nerve impulses to the cell body
Sheath	(✓)	Boosts the transmission of nerve impulses
Nerve impulse	(✓)	Minute electrical disturbances

6
a) The blind spot is the region of the retina insensitive to light (✓). The fovea is the most sensitive region of the retina, where cone cells are most dense (✓).

b) The pupil is the central hole formed by the iris (✓). The iris is the coloured ring of muscle that controls the amount of light entering the eye (✓).

c) The cornea bends light (✓) and helps to focus light onto the retina (✓).

7 Endocrine glands are ductless glands (✓) which release hormones directly into the blood (✓).

8 Antidiuretic hormone promotes reabsorbtion of water into the body (✓) by making the collecting duct of the nephron more permeable to water (✓).

9
a) Raised hairs trap a layer of air (✓) which insulates the body in cold weather (✓). Air is a poor conductor of heat (✓).

b) Sweat cools the body because it carries heat energy away from the body (✓) as it evaporates (✓).

10 Cholera (B) (✓), AIDS (V) (✓), syphilis (B) (✓), 'flu (V) (✓), pneumonia (B) (✓).

11 Nicotine is a poison which increases the heart rate (✓) and blood pressure (✓).
Carbon monoxide combines with haemoglobin (✓) more readily than oxygen (✓).
Tar is a mixture of substances (✓), some of which cause cancer (accept are carcinogens) (✓).

Your score: ☐ out of 67

Your improvement index: $\dfrac{\boxed{}/67}{\boxed{}/58} \times 100\% = \boxed{}\%$

6 Test yourself (page 91)

Inheritance and evolution

1 A sperm duct (✓), B urethra (✓), C scrotal sac (accept scrotum) (✓), D = testis (✓), E = penis (✓).

2

A structures		B descriptions
Corm	(✓)	A short, swollen underground stem
Runner	(✓)	A horizontal stem running above ground
Tuber	(✓)	A swelling at the end of a rhizome
Bulb	(✓)	A large underground bud

3
a) **Bb** (✓) or **bb** (✓).

b) 50% of the children would be brown eyed (✓); 50% blue eyed (✓).

4
a) Restriction enzyme cleaves (cuts up) lengths of DNA into different fragments (✓) depending on the restriction enzyme used (✓). A particular DNA fragment corresponds to a desired gene (✓). (Accept sensible alternative explanation.) Ligase splices the desired gene from among the fragments of DNA produced by restriction enzyme (✓) into a plasmid vector (✓) which is a loop of bacterial DNA (✓) into which the desired gene is inserted (✓).

b) Biotechnology uses microorganisms (✓) on a large scale for the production of useful substances (✓).
Genetic engineering manipulates genes (✓) to create organisms (✓) with specific genetic characteristics for producing a range of useful substances (✓).

c) Batch culture produces batches of substances in a fermenter (✓). The fermenter is then emptied of product and nutrient solution (✓) and sterilised (✓) in preparation for the next batch (✓).
Continuous culture produces substances over an extended period (✓). Product is drawn off and nutrients replaced as they are used (✓) during an ongoing process (✓).

5 Acquired characteristics are those produced in the individual as a result of the influence (effects) of the environment (✓). These characteristics are not the result of genetic influence (✓) and are therefore not inherited (✓).

6 Genetic recombination (✓) as a result of sexual reproduction (✓), mutation (✓), crossing over (✓) during meiosis (✓) and the effects of the environment (✓).

Well done if you mentioned crossing over!

7 During sexual reproduction, genetic material inherited from both parents (✓) recombines in the fertilised egg (✓) producing combinations of genetic material in the offspring different from the combination in each of the parents (✓). During asexual reproduction, offspring inherit identical genetic material from one parent (✓). Mutation is the only source of variation (✓).

8 **a)** Ancestors are organisms that give rise to offspring, who are their descendants (✓).

b) Adaptation – an organism with a structure and way of life that best suits it to survive is said to be adapted (✓). Extinction occurs when a species dies out (✓).

c) Evolution – the change that occurs through many generations of descendants from different ancestors (✓). Natural selection – the process whereby favourable variations survive (✓) so that descendants evolve from ancestors (✓). (Allow: the mechanism of evolution (✓) through the survival of favourable variations (✓).)

9 Fossil formation occurs under the following conditions:
- the replacement of decayed organic material with a permanent alternative (✓)
- the burying of an organism in hardening mud or cooling volcanic ash (✓) followed by the formation of a cast (allow: material that takes on the shape of the original organism) (✓)
- rapid freezing of the organism following its death (✓).

Your score: ☐ out of 56

6 Round-up (page 106)

Inheritance and evolution

1
A structures		B descriptions
Seed	(✓)	A fertilised ovule
Ovule	(✓)	Contains the egg nucleus
Fruit	(✓)	Develops from the ovary after fertilisation
Stigma	(✓)	Structure to which pollen grains attach
Nectary	(✓)	Produces a sugar solution

2 Plants are healthy (✓), the same (accept uniform) (✓), and retain desirable characteristics (✓).

3 Starch (✓)

4 During mitosis, the DNA of the parent cell replicates (✓) so that daughter cells receive exact copies of the parent cell's genetic material (✓). Daughter cells divide and develop into new individuals which inherit the exact characteristics of the parent (✓). Offspring of the parent are also genetically identical to one another (✓) and are a clone (✓).

5
A terms		B descriptions
Allele	(✓)	One of a pair of genes that control a particular characteristic
Pure breeding	(✓)	Characteristics that appear unchanged from generation to generation
Second filial generation	(✓)	Offspring of the offspring of the parental generation
Monohybrid inheritance	(✓)	The processes by which a single characteristic passes from parents to offspring

6 **a)** The trap allows gas to escape (✓) and prevents unwanted airborne microorganisms from contaminating the mixture (✓).

b) Carbon dioxide (✓)

c) The grape juice provides the substances yeast cells need to grow and multiply (✓)

d) Sugar (accept glucose) (✓).

7 **a)** **(i)** A (✓)
(ii) B (✓)
(iii) Chart A shows intermediate lengths of fish (✓) over a range of measurements (✓). Chart B shows categories of colour (✓) without any intermediate forms (✓).

b) 90% (✓)

c) Albino fish occur as a result of a mutation of the alleles controlling colour (✓).

8 **a)** In unpolluted countryside, pale peppered moths blend with the light background of (are camouflaged on) the lichen-covered tree trunk (✓). Fewer are eaten by moth-eating birds (suffer less predation) (✓) than dark peppered moths (✓) which are more conspicuous (✓). In polluted industrial areas, dark peppered moths are less conspicuous against the soot-covered tree trunks (✓). Fewer are eaten by moth-eating birds (suffer less predation) (✓) than pale peppered moths (✓) which are more conspicuous (✓).

b) The bird eats the moths which are conspicuous (✓) and therefore not adapted to blend with their surroundings (✓).

9 Individuals with genes for characteristics that favour survival are more likely to reproduce (✓). Their offspring inherit the favourable genes (✓) and in turn are more likely to survive and reproduce (✓) so handing on the favourable genes to the next generation, and so on (✓).

10 Charles Lyell stated that the Earth was very old (✓). This suggested to Darwin that there was sufficient time for the process of evolution to occur (✓). Malthus suggested that limited resources regulated population numbers (✓) which would otherwise increase indefinitely (✓). Darwin concluded that there must be a struggle for existence (competition for limited resources) (✓).

Your score: ☐ out of 50

Your improvement index: $\dfrac{\boxed{}/50}{\boxed{}/56} \times 100\% = \boxed{}\%$

Materials and their properties

Matter and the kinetic theory

preview

At the end of this topic you will be able to:

- describe the states of matter and changes of state
- apply the kinetic theory of matter to solids, liquids, gases, changes of state, dissolving, diffusion and Brownian motion.

How much do you already know? Work out your score on page 202.

Test yourself

1 Name the three chief states of matter. [3]

2 What can you tell about the purity of a solid from its melting point? [2]

3 What is the difference between evaporation and boiling? [2]

4 How can you tell when a liquid is boiling? [1]

5 Why do vegetables cook faster in a pressure cooker? [2]

6 Why does it take a long time to boil potatoes on a high mountain? [2]

7 What is **a)** the resemblance **b)** the difference between a plastic material and an elastic material? [3]

8 Why are crystals shiny? [3]

9 What happens to the heat energy that is supplied to a solid to make it melt? [2]

10 One litre of water forms 1333 litres of steam. Explain the big difference in volume. [2]

11 Explain why a spoonful of salt can flavour a whole pan of soup. [3]

1.1 States of matter

Everything in the Universe is composed of matter. Matter exists in three chief states: the solid, liquid and gaseous states. Their characteristics are shown in the table.

	volume	shape	effect of rise in temperature
solid	fixed	definite	expands slightly
liquid	fixed	flows – changes shape to fit the shape of the container	expands
gas	changes to fit the container	changes to fit the container	expands greatly (gases have much lower densities than solids and liquids)

Characteristics of the solid, liquid and gaseous states

1.2 Change of state

Matter can change from one state into another, as shown in the diagram.

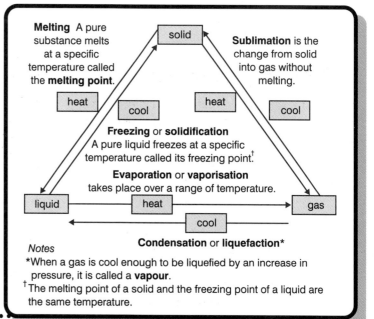

Melting A pure substance melts at a specific temperature called the **melting point**.

Sublimation is the change from solid into gas without melting.

Freezing or **solidification**
A pure liquid freezes at a specific temperature called its freezing point.[†]

Evaporation or **vaporisation** takes place over a range of temperature.

Condensation or **liquefaction***

Notes

*When a gas is cool enough to be liquefied by an increase in pressure, it is called a **vapour**.

[†] The melting point of a solid and the freezing point of a liquid are the same temperature.

1.3 Some properties of materials

★ **Density:** density = $\dfrac{\text{mass}}{\text{volume}}$.

★ **Melting point:** while a pure solid melts, the temperature remains constant at the melting point of the solid.

★ **Boiling point:** while a pure liquid boils, the temperature remains constant at the boiling point of the liquid.

★ **Conductivity** (thermal and electrical): the ability to conduct heat and electricity is a characteristic of metals and alloys.

★ **Solubility:** a solution consists of a **solute** dissolved in a **solvent**. A concentrated solution contains a high proportion of solute; a dilute solution contains a low proportion of solute. A saturated solution contains as much solute as it is possible to dissolve at the stated temperature.

Solubility is the mass of solute that will dissolve in 100 g of solvent at the stated temperature.

Two ways of expressing concentration are:

concentration = $\dfrac{\text{mass of solute}}{\text{volume of solution}}$

concentration = $\dfrac{\text{amount (moles) of solute}}{\text{volume of solution}}$

(see page 191)

1.4 Composite materials

A **composite material** is a mixture of two or more materials which combines their properties. Here are some examples.

• Reinforced concrete combines the compressive (crushing) strength of concrete with the tensile (stretching) strength of the reinforcing steel rods.
• Glass-fibre-reinforced plastic combines plasticity with the strength of fibres, which prevent cracking.
• Plasterboard combines plaster, a brittle material, with paper fibres that prevent cracking.

1.5 The kinetic theory

According to the **kinetic theory of matter**, all forms of matter are made up of small particles which are in constant motion. The theory explains the states of matter and changes of state.

In a solid, the particles are close together and attract one another strongly. They are arranged in a regular three-dimensional structure. The particles can vibrate, but they cannot move out of their positions in the structure.

The arrangement of particles in a solid

When the solid is heated, the particles vibrate more energetically. If they gain enough energy, they may break away from the structure and become free to move independently. When this happens, the solid has melted.

In a liquid, the particles are further apart than in a solid. They are free to move about. This is why a liquid flows easily and has no fixed shape. There are forces of attraction between particles. When a liquid is heated, some particles gain enough energy to break away from the other particles and become a gas.

The arrangement of particles in a liquid

Most of a gas is space, through which the particles move at high speed. There are only very small forces of attraction between the particles. When a mass of liquid vaporises, it forms a very much larger volume of gas because the particles are so much further apart in a gas.

The arrangement of particles in a gas

Collisions between the gas particles and the container create pressure on the container.

Crystals

A crystal is a piece of matter with a regular shape and smooth surfaces which reflect light. Viewed through an electron microscope, crystals can be seen to consist of a regular arrangement of particles. The regular arrangement of particles gives the crystal its regular shape.

A beam of X-rays passed through a crystal onto a photographic plate produces a regular pattern of dots called an **X-ray diffraction photograph**. From the pattern of dots, a crystallographer can work out the arrangement of particles in the crystal.

1.6 What does the kinetic theory explain?

Dissolving of a solid

When a solid dissolves, particles of solid separate from the crystal and spread out through the solvent to form a solution.

Diffusion of a gas

When a gas is released into a container, particles of gas move through the container until the gas has spread evenly through all the space available.

Evaporation or vaporisation

Attractive forces exist between the particles in a liquid. Some particles with more energy than the average break away from the attraction of other particles and escape into the vapour phase. The average energy of the particles that remain is lower than before – the liquid has cooled.

Brownian motion

The botanist William Brown used his microscope a century ago to observe grains of pollen suspended in water. He saw that the grains were in constant motion. The explanation is that water molecules collide with a pollen grain and give it a push. The direction of the push changes as different numbers of molecules strike the pollen grain from different sides.

round-up

How much have you improved? Work out your improvement index on page 202.

1 The graph shows temperature against time as a liquid is heated. What is happening at A and B? [3]

2 The graph below shows temperature of a solid against time as it is heated. What is happening at C, D and E? Is the solid a pure substance? [7]

3 Medical instruments are sterilised in an autoclave, which heats them in steam formed from water boiled under pressure. Why is this more effective than heating them in a pan of boiling water? [2]

4 Why do gases have a much lower density than solids and liquids? [1]

5 Why does compression reduce the volume of a gas more than that of a solid or a liquid? [2]

6 Give an example of the expansion of a gas with rising temperature. [1]

7 Give an example of the increase of gas pressure with rising temperature. [1]

8 Angela is wearing 'L'esprit de la chemie'. Explain why her friends can still smell her perfume after she leaves the room. [3]

9 Aftershave lotions contain a liquid which vaporises readily at room temperature. When the lotion is dabbed on the skin, it produces a cooling effect. Explain what causes this cooling effect. [2]

Elements, compounds and equations

preview

At the end of this topic you will be able to:

- list the differences between metallic and non-metallic elements
- describe the structures of some elements
- distinguish between an element, a compound and a mixture
- write an equation for a chemical reaction.

How much do you already know? Work out your score on page 202.

Test yourself

1 Explain what is meant by an element. [3]

2 What chemical properties of zinc classify it as a metallic element? [7]

3 Explain why diamond is hard while graphite is soft. [4]

4 Name two methods that can be used to split a compound into elements. [2]

5 How many atoms are there in $2Al(OH)_3$? [1]

6 Balance the equation and insert state symbols. [8]

$$Na \quad + \quad H_2O \quad \rightarrow \quad NaOH \quad + \quad H_2$$

2.1 Metallic and non-metallic elements

Elements are pure substances that cannot be split up into simpler substances. Some elements exist as **allotropes** – forms of the same element which have different crystalline structures. Allotropes of carbon are shown on page 119. Elements are classified as metallic and non-metallic, as shown in the table overleaf.

2.2 Structures of elements

Individual molecules

Some elements consist of small individual molecules with negligible forces of attraction between them, e.g. oxygen O_2 and chlorine Cl_2.

Molecular structures

Some elements consist of molecules held in a crystal structure by weak intermolecular forces. Solid iodine is a structure composed of I_2 molecules; iodine vapour consists of individual I_2 molecules.

Giant molecules

Some elements consist of giant molecules or macromolecules, which are composed of millions of atoms bonded together in a three-dimensional structure, e.g. the allotropes of carbon – diamond, graphite and fullerenes – shown on page 119.

2.3 Compounds

A **compound** is a pure substance that consists of two or more elements which are chemically combined in fixed proportions by mass. Some compounds can be **synthesised** from their elements, e.g. calcium burns in oxygen to form calcium oxide; hot copper combines with chlorine to form copper chloride.

It may be possible to split up a compound into its elements

- by **thermal decomposition**, e.g. silver oxide splits up into silver and oxygen when heated
- by **electrolysis**, e.g. water is electrolysed to hydrogen and oxygen.

metallic elements	non-metallic elements
physical properties	*physical properties*
solids except for mercury	solids and gases, except for bromine (which is a liquid)
dense, hard	Most of the solid elements are softer than metals (diamond is exceptional).
A smooth metallic surface is shiny; many metals tarnish in air.	Most non-metallic elements are dull (diamond is exceptional).
The shape can be changed without breaking by the application of force – either compression, as in hammering, or tension, as in stretching, e.g. drawing out into a wire.	Many non-metallic elements are brittle – they break when a force is applied.
conduct heat (although highly polished surfaces reflect heat)	are poor thermal conductors
are good electrical conductors	are poor electrical conductors, except for graphite; some, e.g. silicon, are semiconductors
are sonorous – make a pleasing sound when struck	are not sonorous
The properties of metals derive from the metallic bond – see pages 179–80.	
chemical properties	*chemical properties*
electropositive – able to donate electrons	electronegative – able to accept electrons
many displace hydrogen from dilute acids to form salts	do not react with acids, except for oxidising acids, e.g. concentrated sulphuric acid
The metal is the cation (positive ion) in the salts, e.g. Na^+, Ca^{2+}; some metals also form oxoanions, e.g. ZnO_2^{2-}, AlO_3^-.	form anions (negative ions), e.g. S^{2-}, and oxoanions, e.g. SO_4^{2-}
form basic oxides and hydroxides, e.g. Na_2O, $NaOH$, CaO, $Ca(OH)_2$	form acidic oxides, e.g. CO_2, SO_2, or neutral oxides, e.g. CO, NO
The chlorides are ionic solids, e.g. $MgCl_2$, $AlCl_3$.	The chlorides are covalent volatile liquids, e.g. SCl_2, PCl_3.
Hydrides are formed only by the metals in Groups 1 and 2, and these hydrides are unstable, e.g. NaH.	form stable hydrides, e.g. HBr, H_2S

Characteristics of metallic and non-metallic elements

A compound differs from a mixture of elements as shown in the table on the opposite page.

2.4 Symbols

Every element has its own **symbol**. The symbol is a letter or two letters which stand for one atom of the element, e.g. aluminium Al, iron Fe. See the table on page 127.

2.5 Formulas

Every compound has a **formula**. This is composed of the symbols of the elements present along with numbers which give the ratio in which the atoms are present.

A molecule of sulphuric acid (see below) contains 2 hydrogen atoms, 1 sulphur atom and 4 oxygen atoms, giving the formula H_2SO_4.

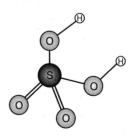

H_2SO_4 – a single molecule

carbon atom
Chemical bond between
two carbon atoms. Every
carbon atom is bonded
to four others.

a the structure of diamond

carbon atom
Bond between two carbon
atoms. A flat layer of
bonded atoms is formed.

There are weak forces of
attraction between layers.

A second layer of bonded
carbon atoms. Within the
layer, every carbon atom
is bonded to three others.

b the structure of graphite

In C_{60} the 60 carbon atoms
are bonded together in 20
hexagons and 12 pentagons
which fit together like the surface
of a football.

c the structure of C_{60}, one of the fullerenes discovered in 1985

The allotropes of carbon

mixtures	compounds
No chemical change takes place when a mixture is made.	When a compound is made, a chemical reaction takes place, and heat is often taken in or given out.
A mixture has the same properties as its components.	A compound has a new set of properties; it does not behave in the same way as the components.
A mixture can be separated into its parts by methods such as distillation (see pages 121–3).	A compound can be split into its elements or into simpler compounds only by a chemical reaction.
A mixture can contain its components in any proportions.	A compound contains its elements in fixed proportions by mass, e.g. magnesium oxide always contains 60% by mass of magnesium.

Differences between mixtures and compounds

Silicon(IV) oxide, shown here, consists of
macromolecules which contain twice as many
oxygen atoms as silicon atoms, giving the
formula SiO_2.

The formula of ammonium sulphate is $(NH_4)_2SO_4$.
The '2' multiplies the symbols in brackets: there
are 2 nitrogen, 8 hydrogen, 1 sulphur and
4 oxygen atoms.

Writing $2Al_2O_3$ means that the numbers below the
line each multiply the symbols in front of them,
and the 2 on the line multiplies everything that
comes after it, giving a total of 4 aluminium and
6 oxygen atoms.

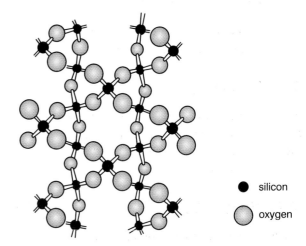

silicon
oxygen

SiO_2 – a macromolecule

2.6 Equations

To write an equation for a chemical reaction:

1 Write a word equation for the reaction.

2 Put in the symbols for the elements and the formulas for the compounds.

3 Put in the **state symbols** (s) for solid, (l) for liquid, (g) for gas, (aq) for in aqueous solution (in water).

4 **Balance** the equation. This means making the number of atoms of each element on the left-hand side (LHS) equal the number on the right-hand side (RHS). Do this by writing a 2, 3 or other numeral in front of a symbol or a formula to multiply that symbol or formula. **Never try to balance an equation by altering a formula**.

Example

1 calcium + water → hydrogen + calcium hydroxide solution

2 $Ca + H_2O \rightarrow H_2 + Ca(OH)_2$

3 $Ca(s) + H_2O(l) \rightarrow H_2(g) + Ca(OH)_2(aq)$

4 There are 2 hydrogen atoms on the LHS and 4 hydrogen atoms on the RHS. There is 1 oxygen atom on the LHS and 2 oxygen atoms on the RHS. Multiply H_2O by 2:

$Ca(s) + 2H_2O(l) \rightarrow H_2(g) + Ca(OH)_2(aq)$

The equation is now balanced.

Ionic equations

In **ionic equations**, only the ions that take part in the reaction are shown. Here are some examples.

★ **Neutralisation**

acid + alkali → salt + water
$H^+(aq) + OH^-(aq) \rightarrow H_2O(l)$

★ **Displacement**

zinc + copper(II) sulphate solution → zinc sulphate solution + copper
$Zn(s) + Cu^{2+}(aq) \rightarrow Zn^{2+}(aq) + Cu(s)$

★ **Precipitation**

barium chloride + sodium sulphate → barium sulphate + sodium chloride
solution   solution   precipitate   solution
$Ba^{2+}(aq) + SO_4^{2-}(aq) \rightarrow BaSO_4(s)$

round-up

How much have you improved?
Work out your improvement index on pages 202–3

1 The element Q forms ions Q^{2+}. Is Q metallic or non-metallic?   [1]

2 The element R forms an acidic oxide RO_2. Is R metallic or non-metallic?   [1]

3 The element E forms a crystalline chloride ECl_2. Is E metallic or non-metallic?   [1]

4 The element G forms a stable hydride HG. Is G metallic or non-metallic?   [1]

5 Contrast four physical properties for sulphur and copper (a non-metallic element and a metallic element).   [4]

6 How would you distinguish between a mixture of powdered sulphur and iron filings and a compound of iron and sulphur?   [4]

7 How many atoms are present in $3(NH_4)_2SO_4$?   [1]

8 Balance the equation and insert state symbols: [4]

$CaCO_3 + HCl \rightarrow CaCl_2 + CO_2 + H_2O$

9 Write an ionic equation for the reaction: [3]

iron(II)   +   sodium   →   iron(II)   +   sodium
sulphate   hydroxide   hydroxide   sulphate

Well done if you've improved. Don't worry if you haven't. Take a break and try again.

Separating substances

preview

At the end of this topic you will be able to:

- **describe methods for separating the components of mixtures.**

How much do you already know? Work out your score on page 203.

Test yourself

1 Suggest methods for separating
  a) sand and gravel from a mixture of both [1]
  b) blood cells from plasma [1]
  c) salts A and B, where both are soluble in hot water but only B is soluble in cold water [4]
  d) vinegar and olive oil [1]
  e) small diamonds from a mixture of diamonds and salt crystals [2]
  f) ethanol and water. [1]

3.1 Mixtures from the Earth

All the materials we use must come from the Earth's crust and atmosphere. Few of the raw materials we use are found in a pure state in the Earth's crust, and we have to separate the substances we want from a mixture of substances. The table shows some separation methods.

3.2 Soluble solid from insoluble solid

To separate a soluble solid from a mixture with an insoluble solid, add a solvent, e.g. water, and stir to dissolve the soluble solid. Filter as shown in the diagram. The insoluble solid is left on the filter paper. Evaporate the filtrate to obtain the soluble solid.

A faster method of filtration is filtration under reduced pressure.

filter paper

filter funnel

The solid remains in the filter as the **residue**.

support

The liquid filters through: it is called the **filtrate**.

a normal filtration

A Buchner funnel has a perforated plate, which is covered by a circle of filter paper.

A pump connected to the side-arm flask speeds up the flow of liquid through the funnel.

b filtration under reduced pressure

Filtration

mixture	type	method
solid + solid	solid mixture	Utilise a difference in properties, e.g. solubility or magnetic properties.
	in a solution	Use chromatography.
solid + liquid	mixture	Filter or centrifuge.
	solution	Crystallise to obtain the solid; distil to obtain the liquid.
liquid + liquid	miscible (form one layer)	Use fractional distillation.
	immiscible (form two layers)	Use a separating funnel.

Methods of separating pure substances from mixtures

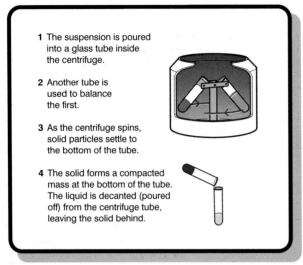

1 The suspension is poured into a glass tube inside the centrifuge.

2 Another tube is used to balance the first.

3 As the centrifuge spins, solid particles settle to the bottom of the tube.

4 The solid forms a compacted mass at the bottom of the tube. The liquid is decanted (poured off) from the centrifuge tube, leaving the solid behind.

Centrifuging a suspension

Filtration cannot separate particles which are so small that they pass through the pores in filter paper. An example is bacteria, which form a **suspension** in water. When a suspension of bacteria in liquid is spun at high speed, bacteria settle to the bottom. This method of separation is called **centrifuging** or **centrifugation**.

3.3 Soluble solids by chromatography

The following diagram shows chromatography on a solution of the pigments in green leaves. The solvent, ethanol, carries the pigments through a strip of **chromatography paper**. The pigments separate because they travel at different speeds.

tank with lid enables separation to take place in an atmosphere of solvent vapour

The level of solvent in the tank is below the spot.

The pigments have been extracted with ethanol. Drops of solution have been applied to the paper. Ethanol evaporates to leave a spot of pigment.

the solvent front after the solvent has travelled up the paper

stapled chromatography paper

The chromatogram shows separate spots of the two pigments chlorophyll and xanthophyll.

Chromatography on an extract from green leaves

3.4 Immiscible liquids

The mixture of immiscible liquids, e.g. oil and water, is poured into a **separating funnel**. The mixture settles into two layers. The tap is opened to allow the bottom layer to run into a receiver. Then the tap is closed and the receiver is changed. The top layer is run into the second receiver.

3.5 Solvent from solute

To separate the solvent and solute in a solution, heat the solution in the **distillation** apparatus shown here. The solvent distils over and condenses into the receiver, leaving the solute behind in the distillation flask.

thermometer records boiling point of liquid

Liebig condenser

water out

distillation flask

anti-bumping granules assist smooth boiling

cold water in

receiver

distillate

heat

A laboratory distillation apparatus

3.6 Miscible liquids

Heat the mixture in the **fractional distillation** apparatus shown here. The lower boiling point liquid, e.g. ethanol, b.p. 78 °C, distils over first. Then the temperature rises as the liquid with the higher boiling point, e.g. water, b.p. 100 °C, distils over.

Fractional distillation can be run continuously (non-stop). Continuous fractional distillation is used to separate crude petroleum oil into a number of useful fuels (see pages 195–6).

The fractionating column has a large surface area. Vaporisation followed by condensation of the vapour takes place many times on the surface of the fractionating column. The liquid with the lowest boiling point reaches the top of the column first and distils over.

Thermometer– the temperature remains constant at the boiling point of each liquid as it distils separately.

water out

Liebig condenser

distillation flask

cold water in

anti-bumping granules

Receiver– a fresh receiver is used to catch each distillate.

heat

Apparatus for fractional distillation

round-up

How much have you improved? Work out your improvement index on page 203.

1 Suggest a method of separating steel drink cans from a collection of empty steel cans and aluminium cans. [2]

2 A mixture contains the salts C and D. Neither is soluble in water. C is soluble in ethanol. Suggest a method you could use to separate C and D. Mention any safety precautions. [5]

3 How are gasoline and diesel oil separated from crude oil? Explain why the method works. [3]

4 The manufacturer Colorit has a patent on three pigments A, B and C. The firm suspects that a rival firm which has brought out the pigments P1 and P2 is using Colorit's pigments. The works analytical chemist runs a chromatogram on all five pigments. The results of her analysis are shown in the diagram. What conclusions can you draw? [2]

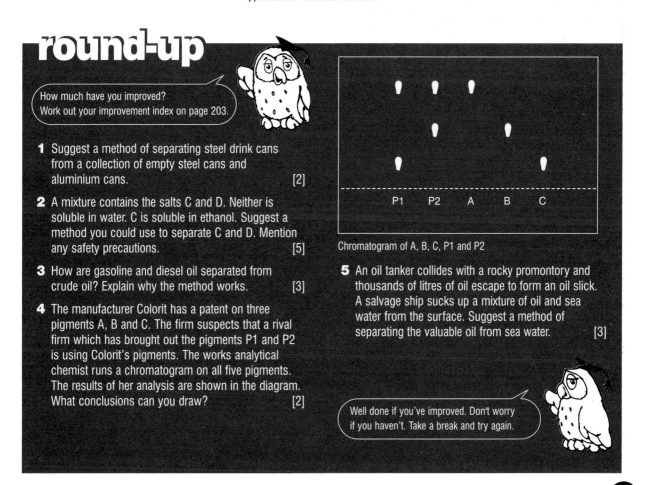

Chromatogram of A, B, C, P1 and P2

5 An oil tanker collides with a rocky promontory and thousands of litres of oil escape to form an oil slick. A salvage ship sucks up a mixture of oil and sea water from the surface. Suggest a method of separating the valuable oil from sea water. [3]

Well done if you've improved. Don't worry if you haven't. Take a break and try again.

The structure of the atom

4

preview

At the end of this topic you will:

- know the names of the particles of which atoms are composed
- know how particles are arranged in the atom
- understand the terms atomic number, mass number, relative atomic mass, relative molecular mass and isotope.

How much do you already know?
Work out your score on page 203.

Test yourself

1 An atom is made of charged particles called protons and electrons. Why is an atom uncharged? [2]

2 An atom of potassium has mass number 39 and atomic number 19. What is **a)** the number of electrons and **b)** the number of neutrons? [2]

3 Why do the isotopes of an element have the same chemical reactions? [2]

4 What is meant by **a)** the atomic number and **b)** the mass number of an element? [3]

5 Write the symbol, with mass number and atomic number, for each of the following isotopes:
   a) phosphorus with atomic number 15 and mass number 31 [2]
   b) potassium with atomic number 19 and mass number 39. [2]

6 An atom of carbon has 6 electrons. Say how the electrons are divided between shells. [2]

4.1 Protons, neutrons and electrons

The concept map opposite gives a summary of the nature of the sub-atomic particles, their masses and charges and some ways of expressing the masses of atoms.

4.2 Focus on the atom

The diagram below shows how protons, neutrons and electrons are arranged in the atom.

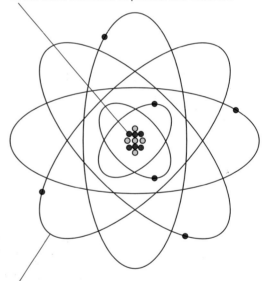

The nucleus occupies a tiny volume in the centre of the atom. It consists of protons and neutrons.

The electrons occupy the space surrounding the nucleus. They repel the electrons of neighbouring atoms. The electrons are in constant motion, moving round the nucleus in circular paths called orbitals.

The arrangement of particles in the atom

The electrons moving in orbitals further away from the nucleus have more energy than those close to the nucleus. A group of orbitals of similar energy is called a **shell** (see diagram on page 126). In the outermost shell of any atom, the maximum number of electrons is eight.

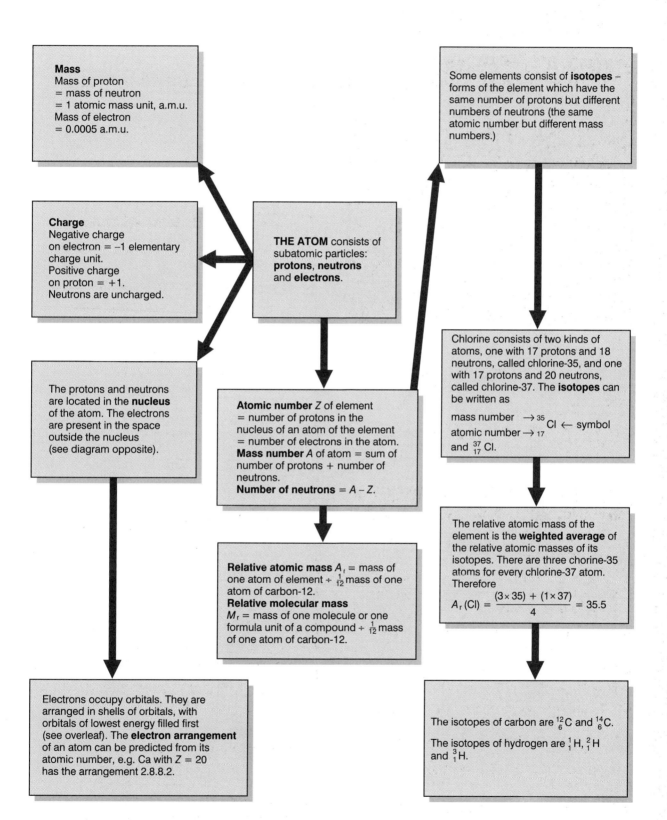

Mass
Mass of proton
= mass of neutron
= 1 atomic mass unit, a.m.u.
Mass of electron
= 0.0005 a.m.u.

Some elements consist of **isotopes** –
forms of the element which have the
same number of protons but different
numbers of neutrons (the same
atomic number but different mass
numbers.)

Charge
Negative charge
on electron = –1 elementary
charge unit.
Positive charge
on proton = +1.
Neutrons are uncharged.

THE ATOM consists of
subatomic particles:
protons, **neutrons**
and **electrons**.

The protons and neutrons
are located in the **nucleus**
of the atom. The electrons
are present in the space
outside the nucleus
(see diagram opposite).

Atomic number Z of element
= number of protons in the
nucleus of an atom of the element
= number of electrons in the atom.
Mass number A of atom = sum of
number of protons + number of
neutrons.
Number of neutrons = $A - Z$.

Chlorine consists of two kinds of
atoms, one with 17 protons and 18
neutrons, called chlorine-35, and one
with 17 protons and 20 neutrons,
called chlorine-37. The **isotopes** can
be written as

mass number $\rightarrow$ $^{35}_{17}$Cl $\leftarrow$ symbol
atomic number $\rightarrow$
and $^{37}_{17}$Cl.

Relative atomic mass A_r = mass of
one atom of element $\div \frac{1}{12}$ mass of one
atom of carbon-12.
Relative molecular mass
M_r = mass of one molecule or one
formula unit of a compound $\div \frac{1}{12}$ mass
of one atom of carbon-12.

The relative atomic mass of the
element is the **weighted average** of
the relative atomic masses of its
isotopes. There are three chorine-35
atoms for every chlorine-37 atom.
Therefore
$$A_r\,(\text{Cl}) = \frac{(3\times 35) + (1\times 37)}{4} = 35.5$$

Electrons occupy orbitals. They are
arranged in shells of orbitals, with
orbitals of lowest energy filled first
(see overleaf). The **electron arrangement**
of an atom can be predicted from its
atomic number, e.g. Ca with Z = 20
has the arrangement 2.8.8.2.

The isotopes of carbon are $^{12}_{6}$C and $^{14}_{6}$C.
The isotopes of hydrogen are $^{1}_{1}$H, $^{2}_{1}$H
and $^{3}_{1}$H.

Concept map: the nature of the atom

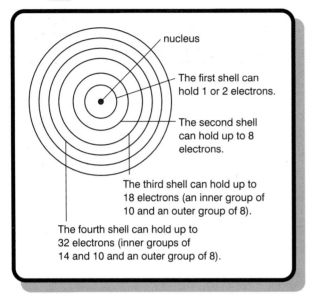

Shells of electrons

energy levels. The arrangements of electrons in an atom of carbon (atomic number 6) and an atom of magnesium (atomic number 12) are shown here.

The arrangement of electrons in the carbon atom (2.4)

The arrangement of electrons in the magnesium atom (2.8.2)

If you know the atomic number of an element, you can work out the arrangement of electrons.
The lower energy levels are filled before the higher

The table opposite gives the electron arrangements of the first 20 elements.

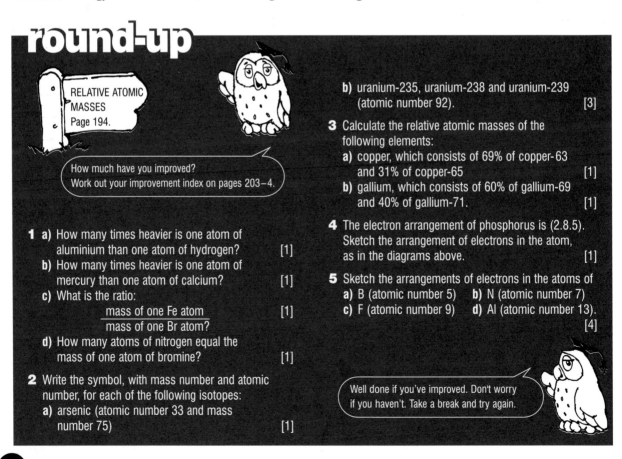

round-up

RELATIVE ATOMIC
MASSES
Page 194.

How much have you improved?
Work out your improvement index on pages 203–4.

1 a) How many times heavier is one atom of
aluminium than one atom of hydrogen? [1]
b) How many times heavier is one atom of
mercury than one atom of calcium? [1]
c) What is the ratio:

$$\frac{\text{mass of one Fe atom}}{\text{mass of one Br atom?}}$$ [1]

d) How many atoms of nitrogen equal the
mass of one atom of bromine? [1]

2 Write the symbol, with mass number and atomic
number, for each of the following isotopes:
a) arsenic (atomic number 33 and mass
number 75) [1]

b) uranium-235, uranium-238 and uranium-239
(atomic number 92). [3]

3 Calculate the relative atomic masses of the
following elements:
a) copper, which consists of 69% of copper-63
and 31% of copper-65 [1]
b) gallium, which consists of 60% of gallium-69
and 40% of gallium-71. [1]

4 The electron arrangement of phosphorus is (2.8.5).
Sketch the arrangement of electrons in the atom,
as in the diagrams above. [1]

5 Sketch the arrangements of electrons in the atoms of
a) B (atomic number 5)   **b)** N (atomic number 7)
c) F (atomic number 9)   **d)** Al (atomic number 13). [4]

Well done if you've improved. Don't worry
if you haven't. Take a break and try again.

element	symbol	atomic number	number of electrons in				electron arrangement
			1st level	2nd level	3rd level	4th level	
hydrogen	H	1	1				1
helium	He	2	2				2
lithium	Li	3	2	1			2.1
beryllium	Be	4	2	2			2.2
boron	B	5	2	3			2.3
carbon	C	6	2	4			2.4
nitrogen	N	7	2	5			2.5
oxygen	O	8	2	6			2.6
fluorine	F	9	2	7			2.7
neon	Ne	10	2	8			2.8
sodium	Na	11	2	8	1		2.8.1
magnesium	Mg	12	2	8	2		2.8.2
aluminium	Al	13	2	8	3		2.8.3
silicon	Si	14	2	8	4		2.8.4
phosphorus	P	15	2	8	5		2.8.5
sulphur	S	16	2	8	6		2.8.6
chlorine	Cl	17	2	8	7		2.8.7
argon	Ar	18	2	8	8		2.8.8
potassium	K	19	2	8	8	1	2.8.8.1
calcium	Ca	20	2	8	8	2	2.8.8.2

Electron arrangements of the first 20 elements

Electrolysis

5

preview

At the end of this topic you will be able to:

- **explain what happens when compounds are electrolysed**
- **predict which ions will be discharged in electrolysis**
- **give examples of the use of electrolysis in industry.**

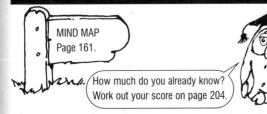

MIND MAP
Page 161.

How much do you already know?
Work out your score on page 204.

Test yourself

1 Which of the following solids conduct electricity?
A zinc   **B** sulphur   **C** bronze
D crystalline copper(II) sulphate   [2]

2 Which of the following liquids conduct electricity?
A a solution of dilute sulphuric acid
B a solution of sodium sulphate
C ethanol
D a solution of ethanoic acid   [3]

3 What do the following terms mean?
a) an electrolyte   **b)** an electrode   [4, 1]

4 a) Explain the terms cation and anion, and give two examples of each.   [6]
b) Explain why ions move towards electrodes.   [2]
c) Explain why solid copper(II) chloride does not conduct electricity, but an aqueous solution of copper(II) chloride does.   [2]

5 Sodium is obtained by the electrolysis of molten sodium chloride. Why is it important that the sodium chloride electrolysed to give sodium is anhydrous?   [1]

6 Some parts of a car body are painted to protect against rusting, and others are chromium-plated. What advantage does chromium-plating have over painting?   [1]

7 What is the advantage of gold-plated jewellery over
a) gold jewellery **b)** brass jewellery?   [2]

8 Aluminium is obtained by the electrolysis of aluminium oxide.
a) Why is aluminium oxide dissolved in molten cryolite before electrolysis?   [1]
b) Write the equations for the electrode processes.   [5]
c) Suggest why this method of extracting aluminium is expensive.   [1]

5.1 Conducting electricity

When substances conduct electricity changes happen at the electrodes. For example, a solution of copper chloride gives a deposit of copper at the negative electrode and a stream of chlorine at the positive electrode. The explanation is that copper chloride consists of positively charged particles of copper, called copper ions, and negatively charged particles of chlorine, called chloride ions. Experiments show that the copper ion carries two units of positive charge, Cu^{2+}, whereas the chloride ion carries one unit of negative charge, Cl^-. Copper chloride contains two chloride ions for every copper ion so that the charges balance, and the formula is $CuCl_2$.

In solid copper chloride, the ions are not free to move because they are held in a three-dimensional crystal structure, and the solid does not conduct electricity. When the salt is dissolved in water, the ions become free to move, the solution conducts electricity and electrolysis occurs.

There is another way of giving the ions freedom to move – to melt the solid. The electrolysis of molten sodium chloride is used for the extraction of sodium.

5.2 Ions

ATOMIC
STRUCTURE
Page 124.

How is an ion formed from an atom? Atoms are uncharged. The number of protons in an atom is the same as the number of electrons. If an atom either gains or loses electrons, it will become electrically charged. Metal atoms and hydrogen atoms form positive ions (**cations**) by losing one or more electrons. Atoms of non-metallic elements form negative ions (**anions**) by gaining one or more electrons.

sodium atom Na $\rightarrow$ electron e^- + sodium ion Na^+
(11 protons,   (11 protons,
11 electrons,   10 electrons,
charge = 0)   charge = +1)

chlorine atom Cl + electron e^- $\rightarrow$ chloride ion Cl^-
(17 protons,   (17 protons,
17 electrons,   18 electrons,
charge = 0)   charge = −1)

The table below gives the symbols and formulas of some ions.

cations	anions
hydrogen ion H^+	bromide ion Br^-
sodium ion Na^+	chloride ion Cl^-
copper(II) ion Cu^{2+}	iodide ion I^-
lead(II) ion Pb^{2+}	hydroxide ion OH^-
aluminium ion Al^{3+}	nitrate ion NO_3^-
	sulphate ion SO_4^{2-}

5.3 At the electrodes

Copper(II) chloride solution

The diagram below shows what happens at the electrodes when copper(II) chloride is electrolysed.

Sodium chloride solution

The products of electrolysis are hydrogen and chlorine. Why is sodium not formed when sodium

Electrons flow through the external circuit from the positive electrode to the negative electrode.

copper(II) chloride solution

Chloride ions are attracted to the positive electrode. The positive charge enables the electrode to take electrons from chloride ions, discharging them to form chlorine atoms. Chlorine atoms then combine to form molecules. The electrode process is

chloride ion $\rightarrow$ chlorine atom + electron

$$Cl^-(aq) \rightarrow Cl(g) + e^-$$

followed by

$$2Cl(g) \rightarrow Cl_2(g)$$

Copper ions are attracted to the negative electrode. The negative charge on the electrode is due to the presence of electrons, and copper ions take electrons and are discharged to become copper atoms. The electrode process is

copper(II) ion + 2 electrons $\rightarrow$ copper atom

$$Cu^{2+}(aq) + 2e^- \rightarrow Cu(s)$$

The electrolysis of copper(II) chloride with carbon electrodes chloride solution is electrolysed? The water present in the solution is ionised to a very small extent:

water $\rightleftharpoons$ hydrogen ions + hydroxide ions

$$H_2O(l) \rightleftharpoons H^+(aq) + OH^-(aq)$$

The hydrogen ions are attracted to the cathode (negative electrode). It is easier for the cathode to discharge a hydrogen ion than a sodium ion, and hydrogen is formed.

electrode process $\quad H^+(aq) + e^- \rightarrow H(g)$

followed by $\quad\quad 2H(g) \rightarrow H_2(g)$

Although the concentration of hydrogen ions in water is small, when these hydrogen ions are discharged more water molecules ionise to replace them, and the discharge of hydrogen ions continues. As more water molecules ionise, the concentration of hydroxide ions increases and the solution of sodium chloride gradually turns into a solution of sodium hydroxide.

The electrolysis of sodium chloride solution is used commercially to obtain the important products sodium hydroxide, hydrogen and chlorine.

Copper(II) sulphate solution

The products of electrolysis are copper and oxygen. How is oxygen formed when an aqueous solution of copper(II) sulphate is electrolysed? Again, the dissociation of water molecules must be considered. Hydroxide ions formed by the ionisation of water molecules are present at the anode. It is easier for the anode to remove electrons from hydroxide ions than from sulphate ions. Consequently hydroxide ions are discharged, and the OH groups which are formed rearrange to give oxygen and water.

electrode process $\quad OH^-(aq) \rightarrow OH(aq) + e^-$

followed by $\quad\quad 4OH(aq) \rightarrow O_2(g) + 2H_2O(l)$

The hydroxide ions that are discharged are replaced by the ionisation of more water molecules. Hydrogen ions are also formed by the dissociation of water, and the solution gradually turns into a solution of sulphuric acid.

5.4 Which ions are discharged?

Anions

★ Sulphate ions and nitrate ions are very difficult to discharge. In solutions of these ions, hydroxide ions are discharged to form oxygen.

Cations

★ The ions of very reactive metals, e.g. sodium and potassium, are difficult to discharge. In solutions of these ions, hydrogen ions are discharged instead.

★ The ions of less reactive metals, e.g. copper and lead, are easier to discharge. In a solution that contains a mixture of metal ions, the ions are discharged in order of the reactivity of the metals. Ions of the least reactive metals are discharged first. For example, in a solution containing Cu^{2+} ions and Zn^{2+} ions, Cu^{2+} ions are discharged while Zn^{2+} ions remain in solution.

5.5 Electrodes taking part

Sometimes electrodes are changed by the cell reaction. For example, when copper(II) sulphate is electrolysed with copper electrodes, the products differ from those just described. At the cathode, copper is deposited as before. The copper anode, the positive electrode, needs to gain electrons. Instead of gaining electrons by discharging SO_4^{2-} ions or OH^- ions, it gains electrons by ionising Cu atoms:

$$Cu(s) \rightarrow Cu^{2+}(aq) + 2e^-$$

The result of electrolysis is that copper is dissolved from the anode and an equal amount of copper is deposited on the cathode.

The table on the next page shows the products of electrolysis of some electrolytes.

5.6 Applications of electrolysis

Extraction of metals from their ores

★ **Sodium** is obtained from sodium chloride in the mineral rock salt. When molten anhydrous sodium chloride is electrolysed, the products are sodium and chlorine.

electrolyte	products of electrolysis and electrode processes	
	cathode (negative electrode)	anode (positive electrode)
molten sodium chloride	sodium $Na^+(l) + e^- \rightarrow Na(l)$	chlorine $Cl^-(l) \rightarrow Cl(g) + e^-$ $2Cl(g) \rightarrow Cl_2(g)$
sodium chloride solution	hydrogen $H^+(aq) + e^- \rightarrow H(g)$ $2H(g) \rightarrow H_2(g)$	chlorine $Cl^-(aq) \rightarrow Cl(g) + e^-$ $2Cl(g) \rightarrow Cl_2(g)$
copper(II) sulphate solution	copper $Cu^{2+}(aq) + 2e^- \rightarrow Cu(s)$	oxygen $OH^-(aq) \rightarrow OH(aq) + e^-$ $4OH(aq) \rightarrow O_2(g) + 2H_2O(l)$
copper(II) sulphate solution, with copper electrodes	copper is discharged $Cu^{2+}(aq) + 2e^- \rightarrow Cu(s)$	copper dissolves $Cu(s) \rightarrow Cu^{2+}(aq) + 2e^-$
dilute sulphuric acid	hydrogen $H^+(aq) + e^- \rightarrow H(g)$ $2H(g) \rightarrow H_2(g)$	oxygen $OH^-(aq) \rightarrow OH(aq) + e^-$ $4OH(aq) \rightarrow O_2(g) + 2H_2O(l)$

★ **Potassium**, **calcium** and **magnesium** are also obtained by electrolysis of molten anhydrous chlorides. The cost of electricity makes this method of extracting metals expensive.

★ **Aluminium** is mined as the ore bauxite, $Al_2O_3.2H_2O$. Purified anhydrous aluminium oxide is obtained from the ore. Before the oxide can be electrolysed, it must be melted. The high melting point of aluminium oxide, 2050°C, makes this difficult so it is dissolved in molten cryolite, Na_3AlF_6, at 1000°C before electrolysis. See diagram below.

Electrolysis of molten aluminium oxide

Purification of copper

The electrolysis of copper(II) sulphate with copper electrodes (see page 130) is used in the purification of copper. The diagram opposite shows the setup.

Electroplating

Electrolysis is used to coat a metal with a thin even film of another metal, as shown in the diagram below.

1 A cheaper metal may be coated with a more beautiful and more expensive metal, e.g. silver or gold.

2 To prevent steel from rusting, it is electroplated with nickel and chromium which give the steel a bright surface that is not corroded in air.

3 Food cans are made of iron plated with a layer of tin. Tin is not corroded by food juices.

4 A layer of zinc is applied to iron in the manufacture of galvanised iron. Electroplating is one of the methods employed.

Electrolytic purification of copper

Electroplating

round-up

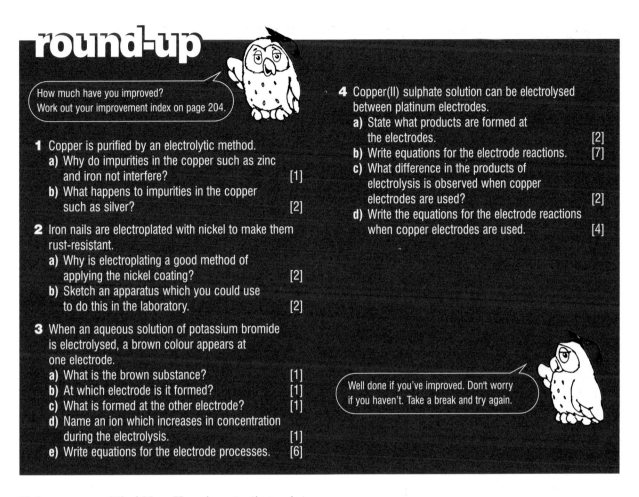

How much have you improved?
Work out your improvement index on page 204.

1 Copper is purified by an electrolytic method.
  a) Why do impurities in the copper such as zinc and iron not interfere? [1]
  b) What happens to impurities in the copper such as silver? [2]

2 Iron nails are electroplated with nickel to make them rust-resistant.
  a) Why is electroplating a good method of applying the nickel coating? [2]
  b) Sketch an apparatus which you could use to do this in the laboratory. [2]

3 When an aqueous solution of potassium bromide is electrolysed, a brown colour appears at one electrode.
  a) What is the brown substance? [1]
  b) At which electrode is it formed? [1]
  c) What is formed at the other electrode? [1]
  d) Name an ion which increases in concentration during the electrolysis. [1]
  e) Write equations for the electrode processes. [6]

4 Copper(II) sulphate solution can be electrolysed between platinum electrodes.
  a) State what products are formed at the electrodes. [2]
  b) Write equations for the electrode reactions. [7]
  c) What difference in the products of electrolysis is observed when copper electrodes are used? [2]
  d) Write the equations for the electrode reactions when copper electrodes are used. [4]

Well done if you've improved. Don't worry if you haven't. Take a break and try again.

Make your own Mind Map. Here is a starting point:

The chemical bond

preview

At the end of this topic you will:

- **understand how atoms combine by forming ionic bonds and covalent bonds**
- **understand how ionic compounds and covalent compounds differ in properties and structure.**

How much do you already know?
Work out your score on pages 204–5.

Test yourself

1 Write words in the spaces to complete the sentences.

When an ionic compound is formed, some atoms lose electrons to become _____ ions while other atoms gain electrons to become _____ ions. Ions are held together by _____ attraction in a three-dimensional structure called a _____ . [4]

2 The element E has the electron arrangement E(2.8.2). The element Q has the electron arrangement Q(2.8.7). Explain what happens to atoms of E and Q when they combine to form an ionic compound, and give the formula of the compound. [3]

3 The element T has the electron arrangement T(2.7). Sketch the arrangement of electrons in an atom of T and in the molecule T_2. [2]

4 Name the following compounds:
a) $MgBr_2$ b) $FeCl_2$ c) $FeCl_3$ d) Na_2O e) $BaSO_4$. [5]

5 State the formulas of the following compounds:
a) potassium bromide b) calcium carbonate
c) lead(II) oxide   d) lead(II) sulphate
e) silver chloride. [5]

6.1 Bond formation

When chemical reactions take place, it is the electrons in the outer shell that are involved in the formation of bonds. The resistance of the noble gases to chemical change is believed to be due to the stability of the full outer shell of eight electrons (two for helium). When atoms react, they gain, lose or share electrons to attain an outer shell of eight electrons. Metallic elements frequently combine with non-metallic elements to form compounds.

6.2 Ionic bonding

> ### Example 1

Sodium burns in chlorine to form sodium chloride. This is what happens to the electrons:

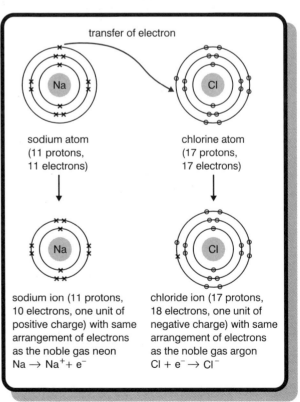

transfer of electron

sodium atom (11 protons, 11 electrons)

chlorine atom (17 protons, 17 electrons)

sodium ion (11 protons, 10 electrons, one unit of positive charge) with same arrangement of electrons as the noble gas neon
$Na \rightarrow Na^+ + e^-$

chloride ion (17 protons, 18 electrons, one unit of negative charge) with same arrangement of electrons as the noble gas argon
$Cl + e^- \rightarrow Cl^-$

The formation of sodium chloride

There is an electrostatic force of attraction between oppositely charged ions. This force is called an **ionic bond** or **electrovalent bond**. The ions Na^+ and Cl^- are part of a **giant ionic structure** (a crystal). The ions cannot move out of their positions in the structure, and the crystal cannot conduct electricity. When the solid is melted or dissolved, the ions become free to move and conduct electricity (see page 128).

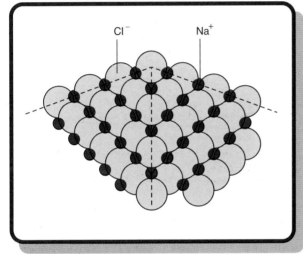

The structure of sodium chloride

Example 2

Magnesium + fluorine → magnesium fluoride

One magnesium atom gives away two electrons to become the ion Mg^{2+} (12p, 10e$^-$).
$Mg \rightarrow Mg^{2+} + 2e^-$

Each of the two fluorine atoms gains one electron to become a fluoride ion F^- (9p, 10e$^-$).
$F + e^- \rightarrow F^-$

The formation of magnesium fluoride

The formula of magnesium fluoride is $Mg^{2+}2F^-$ or MgF_2.

Example 3

Magnesium + oxygen → magnesium oxide

A magnesium atom gives away two electrons to form a Mg^{2+} ion.
$Mg \rightarrow Mg^{2+} + 2e^-$

An oxygen atom gains two electrons to become an oxide ion O^{2-}.
$O + 2e^- \rightarrow O^{2-}$

The formation of magnesium oxide

The formula of magnesium oxide is $Mg^{2+}O^{2-}$ or MgO.

6.3 Covalent bonding

When two non-metallic elements combine, both want to gain electrons; neither wants to form positive ions. They combine by sharing electrons. A shared pair of electrons is a **covalent bond**. If two pairs of electrons are shared, the bond is a **double bond**.

Example 1

Hydrogen + fluorine → hydrogen fluoride, HF

The hydrogen atom shares its electron with the fluorine atom. H has a full shell of two electrons, the same arrangement as helium.

The fluorine atom shares one of its electrons with the hydrogen atom. F has a full shell of eight electrons, the same arrangement as neon.

The formation of hydrogen fluoride

The shared pair of electrons is attracted to the hydrogen nucleus and to the fluorine nucleus, and bonds the two nuclei together.

Example 2

Hydrogen + oxygen → water, H_2O

Two hydrogen atoms each share an electron with an oxygen atom. Each hydrogen atom has an outer shell of two electrons, and the oxygen atom has an outer shell of eight electrons.

The formation of water

Example 3

Nitrogen + hydrogen → ammonia, NH_3

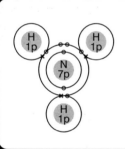
One nitrogen atom shares three electrons, one with each of three hydrogen atoms. The nitrogen atom has eight electrons in its outer shell (like neon), and each hydrogen has two electrons in its outer shell (like helium).

The formation of ammonia

Example 4

Carbon + hydrogen → methane, CH_4

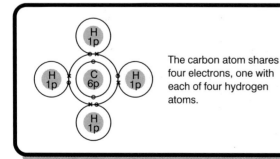
The carbon atom shares four electrons, one with each of four hydrogen atoms.

The formation of methane

Example 5

Carbon + oxygen → carbon dioxide, CO_2

The carbon atom shares four electrons, two with each of two oxygen atoms. Each oxygen atom shares two electrons with the carbon atom. Two pairs of electrons are shared between the carbon atom and each oxygen atom. Each C $=$ O bond is called a double bond.

The formation of carbon dioxide

6.4 Ionic and covalent substances

The concept map opposite summarises the types of bonds formed by different substances.

6.5 The formula of an ionic compound

Ionic compounds consist of positive and negative ions. A sample of the compound is uncharged because the positive and negative charges balance exactly. In a sample of calcium chloride, $CaCl_2$, the number of chloride ions, Cl^-, is exactly twice the number of calcium ions, Ca^{2+}, so the formula is $Ca^{2+}2Cl^-$ or $CaCl_2$.

Worked example

Compound:	*sodium sulphate*
Ions present are:	Na^+ and SO_4^{2-}
To balance the charges:	two Na^+ are needed to balance one SO_4^{2-}
The ions needed are:	$2Na^+$ and SO_4^{2-}
The formula is:	Na_2SO_4

IONIC AND COVALENT SUBSTANCES

Ionic bonding
Ionic compounds are formed when a metallic element combines with a non-metallic element. An **ionic bond** is formed by **transfer of electrons** from one atom to another to form ions.

Covalent bonding
Atoms of non-metallic elements combine with other non-metallic elements by **sharing pairs of electrons** in their outer shells. A shared pair of electrons is a **covalent bond**.

There are three **types of covalent substances**.

1 Many covalent substances are composed of small individual molecules with only very small forces of attraction between molecules, e.g. the gases HCl, SO_2, CO_2, CH_4.

2 Some covalent substances consist of small molecules with weak forces of attraction between molecules, e.g. the volatile liquid ethanol, C_2H_5OH, and solid carbon dioxide.

3 Some covalent substances consist of giant molecules, e.g. quartz (silicon(IV) oxide). These substances have high melting and boiling points.

Atoms of **metallic elements** form positive ions (cations). Elements in Groups 1, 2 and 3 of the periodic table form ions with charges +1, +2 and +3, e.g. Na^+, Mg^{2+}, Al^{3+}. Atoms of **non-metallic elements** form negative ions (anions). Elements in Groups 6 and 7 of the periodic table form ions with charges –2 and –1, e.g. O^{2-} and Cl^-.

The maximum number of covalent bonds that an atom can form is equal to the number of electrons in the outer shell. An atom may not use all its outer electrons in bond formation.

Ionic compounds are **electrolytes** – they conduct electricity when molten or in solution and are split up (**electrolysed**) in the process. Covalent compounds are **non-electrolytes**

The strong electrostatic attraction between ions of opposite charge is an **ionic bond**. An ionic compound is composed of a giant regular structure of ions (see diagram of sodium chloride structure on page 135). This regular structure makes ionic compounds **crystalline**. The strong forces of attraction between ions make it difficult to separate the ions, and ionic compounds therefore have **high melting and boiling points**.

Organic solvents, e.g. ethanol and propanone, have covalent bonds. They dissolve covalent compounds but not ionic compounds.

Concept map: ionic and covalent substances

Compound:	iron(II) sulphate
Ions present are:	Fe^{2+} and SO_4^{2-}
To balance the charges:	one Fe^{2+} balances one SO_4^{2-}
The ions needed are:	Fe^{2+} and SO_4^{2-}
The formula is:	$FeSO_4$
Compound:	iron(III) sulphate
Ions present are:	Fe^{3+} and SO_4^{2-}
To balance the charges:	two Fe^{3+} balance three SO_4^{2-}
The ions needed are:	$2Fe^{3+}$ and $3SO_4^{2-}$
The formula is:	$Fe_2(SO_4)_3$

Note

The sulphates of iron are named iron(II) sulphate and iron(III) sulphate. The Roman numerals II and III show which type of ion, Fe^{2+} or Fe^{3+}, is present.

The symbols and charges of some ions

Hints & Tips

If you know the symbols and charges of these ions, you can work out the formulas of their compounds.

H^+ Na^+ K^+ Ag^+ NH_4^+	OH^- NO_3^- HCO_3^- Cl^- Br^- I^-
Ca^{2+} Cu^{2+} Zn^{2+} Pb^{2+} Mg^{2+} Fe^{2+} Ba^{2+}	SO_4^{2-} SO_3^{2-} CO_3^{2-} O^{2-} S^{2-}
Al^{3+} Fe^{3+}	

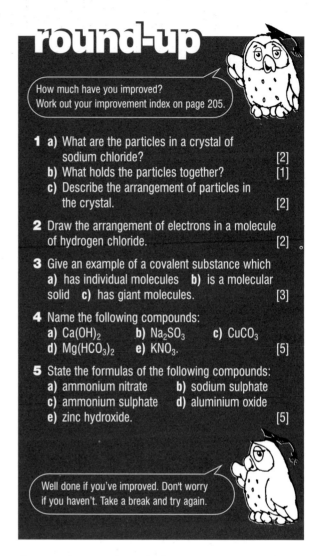

round-up

How much have you improved? Work out your improvement index on page 205.

1 a) What are the particles in a crystal of sodium chloride? [2]
   b) What holds the particles together? [1]
   c) Describe the arrangement of particles in the crystal. [2]

2 Draw the arrangement of electrons in a molecule of hydrogen chloride. [2]

3 Give an example of a covalent substance which **a)** has individual molecules **b)** is a molecular solid **c)** has giant molecules. [3]

4 Name the following compounds:
   a) $Ca(OH)_2$ **b)** Na_2SO_3 **c)** $CuCO_3$
   d) $Mg(HCO_3)_2$ **e)** KNO_3. [5]

5 State the formulas of the following compounds:
   a) ammonium nitrate **b)** sodium sulphate
   c) ammonium sulphate **d)** aluminium oxide
   e) zinc hydroxide. [5]

Well done if you've improved. Don't worry if you haven't. Take a break and try again.

Can you summarise this topic in a Mind Map? Copy and complete:

The periodic table

preview

At the end of this topic you will:

- **understand the structure of the periodic table**
- **know the nature of the elements in Groups 0, 1, 2, 7 and the transition elements.**

How much do you already know? Work out your score on page 205.

Test yourself

1 a) What are the noble gases? [2]
  b) In which group of the periodic table are they? [1]
  c) What do the noble gases have in common regarding
    (i) their electron arrangements and
    (ii) their chemical reactions? [2]

2 X is a metallic element. It reacts slowly with water to give a strongly alkaline solution. In which group of the periodic table would you place X? [1]

3 Y is a non-metallic element. It reacts vigorously with sodium to give a salt of formula NaY. In which group of the periodic table would you place Y? [1]

4 Z is a metallic element which reacts rapidly with water to give a flammable gas and an alkaline solution. In which group of the periodic table would you place Z? [1]

5 a) Name the halogens. [4]
  b) In which group of the periodic table are they? [1]
  c) Does the chemical reactivity of the halogens increase or decrease with atomic number? [1]
  d) Give the formulas of the products of the reactions of
    (i) sodium **(ii)** iron with each of the halogens. [8]

6 a) What is a transition metal? [1]
  b) Name two transition metals. [1]

7.1 Classifying elements

Topic 2 dealt with the classification of elements as metallic and non-metallic elements. A major advance was made by John Newlands in 1866 and Dmitri Mendeleev in 1871 when they originated the periodic table. The modern periodic table is based on arranging the elements in order of increasing atomic number. A vertical row of elements is called a **group** and a horizontal row is called a **period**.

The following patterns can be seen in the arrangement of the elements in the periodic table.

1   The reactive metals are at the left-hand side of the table, less reactive metallic elements in the middle block and non-metallic elements at the right-hand side.

2   The differences between the metals in Group 1, those in Group 2 and the transition metals are summarised in the table at the top of page 141.

3   Silicon and germanium are on the borderline between metals and non-metals. These elements are semiconductors, intermediate between metals, which are electrical conductors, and non-metals, which are non-conductors of electricity. Semiconductors are vital to the computer industry.

4   Group 7 is a set of very reactive non-metallic elements called the **halogens**. They react with metals to form salts; see the table on page 141.

5   When Mendeleev drew up his periodic table in 1871, only 55 elements were known. He left gaps in the table and predicted that new elements would be discovered which would fit the gaps. When the noble gases were discovered, one by one, their atomic numbers placed them in between Groups 1 and 7, and a new Group 0 had to be created for them.

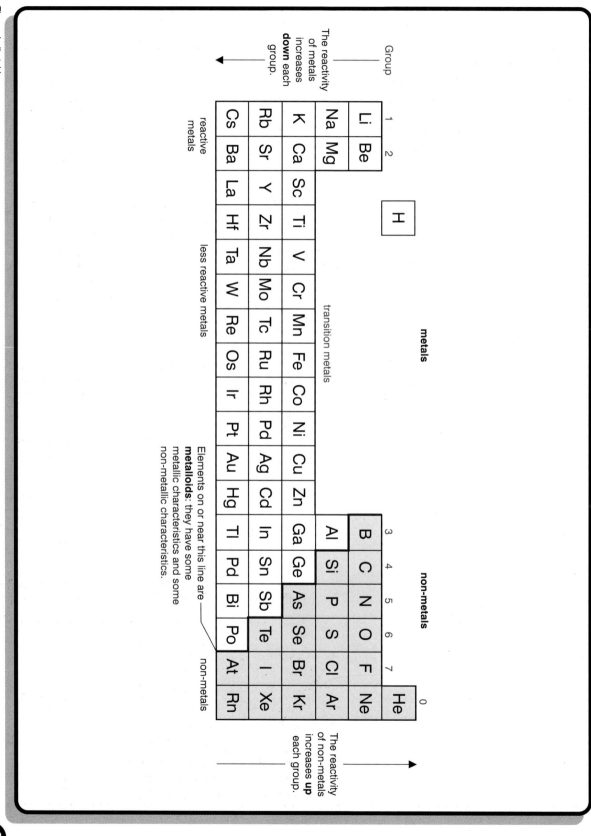

Group

The reactivity of metals increases **down** each group.

1	2
Li	Be
Na	Mg
K	Ca
Rb	Sr
Cs	Ba

reactive metals

H

transition metals

less reactive metals

metals

Sc	Ti	V	Cr	Mn	Fe	Co	Ni	Cu	Zn
Y	Zr	Nb	Mo	Tc	Ru	Rh	Pd	Ag	Cd
La	Hf	Ta	W	Re	Os	Ir	Pt	Au	Hg

non-metals

3	4	5	6	7	0
					He
B	C	N	O	F	Ne
Al	Si	P	S	Cl	Ar
Ga	Ge	As	Se	Br	Kr
In	Sn	Sb	Te	I	Xe
Tl	Pd	Bi	Po	At	Rn

non-metals

Elements on or near this line are **metalloids**: they have some metallic characteristics and some non-metallic characteristics.

The reactivity of non-metals increases **up** each group.

metal	reaction with air	reaction with water	reaction with dilute hydrochloric acid	trend	
Group 1 the alkali metals					
lithium sodium potassium rubidium caesium	Burn vigorously to form the strongly basic oxide M_2O which dissolves in water to give the strong alkali MOH.	React vigorously to form hydrogen and a solution of the strong alkali MOH.	The reaction is dangerously violent.	The vigour of all these reactions increases down the group.	
Group 2 the alkaline earths					
beryllium magnesium calcium strontium barium	Burn to form the strongly basic oxides MO, which are sparingly soluble or insoluble.	Reacts very slowly. Burns in steam. React readily to form hydrogen and the alkali $M(OH)_2$.	React readily to give hydrogen and a salt, e.g. MCl_2.	The vigour of all these reactions increases down the group. Group 2 elements are less reactive than Group 1.	
Transition metals					
iron zinc copper	When heated, form oxides without burning. The oxides and hydroxides are weaker bases than those of Groups 1 and 2 and are insoluble.	Iron rusts slowly. Iron and zinc react with steam to form hydrogen and the oxide. Copper does not react.	Iron and zinc react to give hydrogen and a salt. Copper does not react.	Transition metals are less reactive than Groups 1 and 2. In general, their compounds are coloured; they are used as catalysts.	

Some reactions of metals

Note

M stands for the symbol of a metallic element. Dilute sulphuric acid reacts with metals in the same way as dilute hydrochloric acid. Dilute nitric acid is an oxidising agent and attacks metals, e.g. copper, which are not sufficiently reactive to react with other dilute acids.

OXIDISING AGENT Page 153.

halogen	state at room temperature	reaction with sodium	reaction with iron	trend	
fluorine	gas	explosive	explosive		
chlorine	gas	Heated sodium burns in chlorine to form sodium chloride.	Reacts vigorously with hot iron to form iron(III) chloride.	The vigour of these reactions decreases down the group.	
bromine	liquid	Reacts less vigorously to form sodium bromide.	Reacts less vigorously to form iron(III) bromide.		
iodine	solid	Reacts less vigorously than bromine to form sodium iodide.	Reacts less vigorously than bromine to form iron(II) iodide.		

Some reactions of the halogens

7

7.2 A repeating pattern

You can see that the arrangement opposite has the following features:

★ The elements are listed in order of increasing atomic number.

★ Elements which have the same number of electrons in the outermost shell fall into the same **group** (vertical column) of the periodic table.

★ The noble gases are in Group 0. For the rest of the elements, the group number is the number of electrons in the outermost shell.

★ The first **period** (horizontal row) contains only hydrogen and helium. The second period contains the elements lithium to neon. The third period contains the elements sodium to argon.

									Group 0
Period 1	H (1)								He (2)

	Group 1	Group 2	Group 3	Group 4	Group 5	Group 6	Group 7	
Period 2	Li (2.1)	Be (2.2)	B (2.3)	C (2.4)	N (2.5)	O (2.6)	F (2.7)	Ne (2.8)
Period 3	Na (2.8.1)	Mg (2.8.2)	Al (2.8.3)	Si (2.8.4)	P (2.8.5)	S (2.8.6)	Cl (2.8.7)	Ar (2.8.8)
Period 4	K (2.8.8.1)	Ca (2.8.8.2)						

A section of the periodic table

round-up

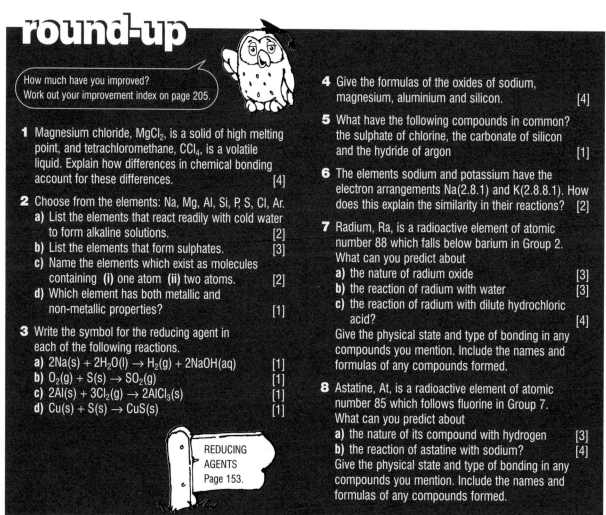

How much have you improved?
Work out your improvement index on page 205.

1 Magnesium chloride, $MgCl_2$, is a solid of high melting point, and tetrachloromethane, CCl_4, is a volatile liquid. Explain how differences in chemical bonding account for these differences. [4]

2 Choose from the elements: Na, Mg, Al, Si, P, S, Cl, Ar.
   a) List the elements that react readily with cold water to form alkaline solutions. [2]
   b) List the elements that form sulphates. [3]
   c) Name the elements which exist as molecules containing **(i)** one atom **(ii)** two atoms. [2]
   d) Which element has both metallic and non-metallic properties? [1]

3 Write the symbol for the reducing agent in each of the following reactions.
   a) $2Na(s) + 2H_2O(l) \rightarrow H_2(g) + 2NaOH(aq)$ [1]
   b) $O_2(g) + S(s) \rightarrow SO_2(g)$ [1]
   c) $2Al(s) + 3Cl_2(g) \rightarrow 2AlCl_3(s)$ [1]
   d) $Cu(s) + S(s) \rightarrow CuS(s)$ [1]

REDUCING AGENTS Page 153.

4 Give the formulas of the oxides of sodium, magnesium, aluminium and silicon. [4]

5 What have the following compounds in common? the sulphate of chlorine, the carbonate of silicon and the hydride of argon [1]

6 The elements sodium and potassium have the electron arrangements Na(2.8.1) and K(2.8.8.1). How does this explain the similarity in their reactions? [2]

7 Radium, Ra, is a radioactive element of atomic number 88 which falls below barium in Group 2. What can you predict about
   a) the nature of radium oxide [3]
   b) the reaction of radium with water [3]
   c) the reaction of radium with dilute hydrochloric acid? [4]
   Give the physical state and type of bonding in any compounds you mention. Include the names and formulas of any compounds formed.

8 Astatine, At, is a radioactive element of atomic number 85 which follows fluorine in Group 7. What can you predict about
   a) the nature of its compound with hydrogen [3]
   b) the reaction of astatine with sodium? [4]
   Give the physical state and type of bonding in any compounds you mention. Include the names and formulas of any compounds formed.

Acids, bases and salts

preview

At the end of this topic you will:

- **be able to define the terms 'acid', 'base' and 'alkali'**
- **know the typical reactions of acids and bases**
- **know how to prepare salts and know the uses of some important salts.**

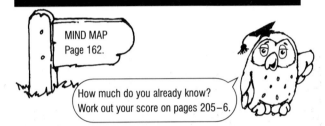

MIND MAP
Page 162.

How much do you already know?
Work out your score on pages 205–6.

Test yourself

1 Say whether the substances listed are strongly acidic (SA), weakly acidic (WA), strongly basic (SB), weakly basic (WB) or neutral (N).
  a) battery acid, pH 0   [1]
  b) rainwater, pH 6.5   [1]
  c) blood, pH 7.4   [1]
  d) sea water, pH 8.5   [1]
  e) cabbage juice, pH 5.0   [1]
  f) saliva, pH 7.0   [1]
  g) washing soda, pH 11.5   [1]

2 You are given two bottles labelled 'acid 1' and 'acid 2'. One is a weak acid and the other is a strong acid. Describe two tests you could do to find out which is which.   [3]

3 Name
  a) a strong acid present in your stomach   [1]
  b) a base present in indigestion tablets   [1]
  c) a weak acid present in fruits   [1]
  d) a weak base used as a domestic cleaning fluid.   [1]

4 Kleenit is an oven spray for cleaning greasy ovens. It contains a concentrated solution of sodium hydroxide.
  a) Why does sodium hydroxide remove grease?   [1]
  b) Why does sodium hydroxide work better than ammonia?   [1]
  c) What two safety precautions should you take when using Kleenit?   [2]
  d) Why does Moppit, a fluid used for cleaning floors, contain ammonia rather than sodium hydroxide?   [1]
  e) Why do soap manufacturers use sodium hydroxide, not ammonia?   [1]

8.1 Acids

Where are acids found?

The following are strong acids:

- Hydrochloric acid occurs in the stomach, where it aids digestion.
- Nitric acid is used in the production of fertilisers and explosives.
- Sulphuric acid is used car batteries and in the production of fertilisers.

The following are weak acids:

- Carbonic acid is used in fizzy drinks.
- Citric acid occurs in lemons and other citrus fruits.
- Ethanoic acid occurs in vinegar.
- Lactic acid is present in sour milk.

What do acids do?

Acids are compounds that release hydrogen ions when dissolved in water. The hydrogen ions are responsible for the typical reactions of acids. Strong acids are completely ionised; for example, hydrochloric acid solution consists of the ions H^+ and Cl^- and water molecules. There are no molecules of HCl in the solution. Weak acids consist chiefly of molecules, but a small fraction of the molecules are ionised. Weak acids therefore have a low concentration of hydrogen ions in solution and react less readily than strong acids.

The concept map overleaf gives a summary of the properties of acids.

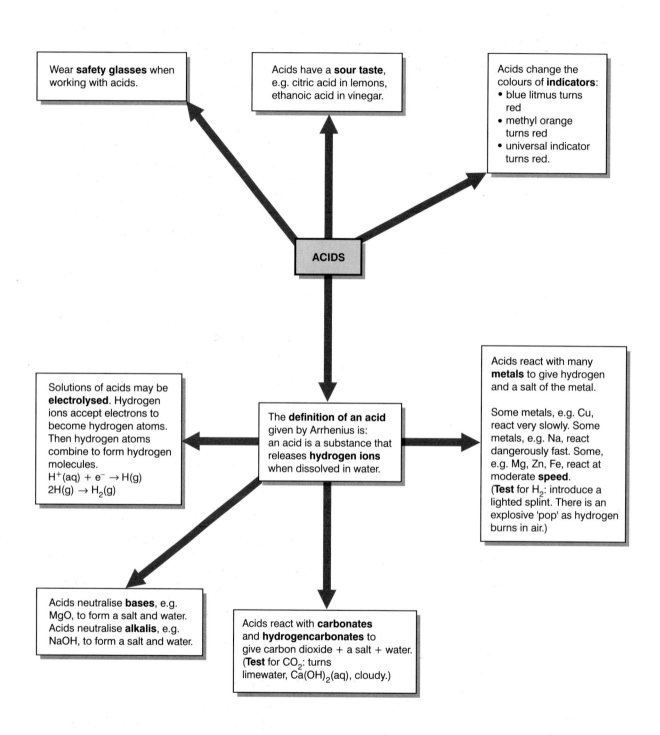

Wear **safety glasses** when working with acids.

Acids have a **sour taste**, e.g. citric acid in lemons, ethanoic acid in vinegar.

Acids change the colours of **indicators**:
• blue litmus turns red
• methyl orange turns red
• universal indicator turns red.

ACIDS

Solutions of acids may be **electrolysed**. Hydrogen ions accept electrons to become hydrogen atoms. Then hydrogen atoms combine to form hydrogen molecules.
$H^+(aq) + e^- \rightarrow H(g)$
$2H(g) \rightarrow H_2(g)$

The **definition of an acid** given by Arrhenius is: an acid is a substance that releases **hydrogen ions** when dissolved in water.

Acids react with many **metals** to give hydrogen and a salt of the metal.

Some metals, e.g. Cu, react very slowly. Some metals, e.g. Na, react dangerously fast. Some, e.g. Mg, Zn, Fe, react at moderate **speed**.
(**Test** for H_2: introduce a lighted splint. There is an explosive 'pop' as hydrogen burns in air.)

Acids neutralise **bases**, e.g. MgO, to form a salt and water.
Acids neutralise **alkalis**, e.g. NaOH, to form a salt and water.

Acids react with **carbonates** and **hydrogencarbonates** to give carbon dioxide + a salt + water.
(**Test** for CO_2: turns limewater, $Ca(OH)_2(aq)$, cloudy.)

Concept map: The properties of acids

Equations for some reactions in the concept map

With metals

zinc + sulphuric acid → hydrogen + zinc sulphate

$Zn(s) + H_2SO_4(aq) → H_2(g) + ZnSO_4(aq)$

or the ionic equation:

$Zn(s) + 2H^+(aq) → Zn^{2+}(aq) + H_2(g)$

With bases

magnesium oxide + sulphuric acid → magnesium sulphate + water

$MgO(s) + H_2SO_4(aq) → MgSO_4(aq) + H_2O(l)$

or the ionic equation:

$O^{2-}(s) + 2H^+(aq) → H_2O(l)$

calcium hydroxide + hydrochloric acid → calcium chloride + water

$Ca(OH)_2(s) + 2HCl(aq) → CaCl_2(aq) + 2H_2O(l)$

or the ionic equation:

$OH^-(aq) + H^+(aq) → H_2O(l)$

With carbonates

calcium carbonate + hydrochloric acid → carbon dioxide + calcium chloride + water

$CaCO_3(s) + 2HCl(aq) → CO_2(g) + CaCl_2(aq) + H_2O(l)$

or the ionic equation:

$CO_3^{2-}(s) + 2H^+(aq) → CO_2(g) + H_2O(l)$

With alkalis

ammonia + sulphuric acid → ammonium sulphate

$2NH_3(aq) + H_2SO_4(aq) → (NH_4)_2SO_4(aq)$

8.2 Bases

Where do you find bases?

The following are strong bases:

- Calcium hydroxide is used to treat soil which is too acidic.
- Calcium oxide is used in the manufacture of cement and concrete.
- Magnesium hydroxide is used in anti-acid indigestion tablets.

- Sodium hydroxide is used in soap manufacture and as a degreasing agent.
- The weak base ammonia is used in cleaning fluids, as a degreasing agent and in the manufacture of fertilisers.

What do bases do?

A **base** is a substance that reacts with an acid to form a salt and water as the only products. A soluble base is called an **alkali**. Sodium hydroxide, NaOH, is a strong base and a strong alkali. It is completely ionised in solution as Na^+ and OH^- ions. Ammonia is only slightly ionised and the concentration of hydroxide ions in the solution is small. Ammonia is therefore a weak base.

The concept map overleaf gives a summary of the properties of bases.

Equations for some reactions in the concept map

With acids

magnesium oxide + hydrochloric acid → magnesium chloride + water

$MgO(s) + 2HCl(aq) → MgCl_2(aq) + H_2O(l)$

or the ionic equation:

$O^{2-}(s) + 2H^+(aq) → H_2O(l)$

sodium hydroxide + hydrochloric acid → sodium chloride + water

$NaOH(aq) + HCl(aq) → NaCl(aq) + H_2O(l)$

sodium hydroxide + sulphuric acid → sodium sulphate + water

$2NaOH(aq) + H_2SO_4(aq) → Na_2SO_4(aq) + 2H_2O(l)$

or the ionic equation:

$OH^-(aq) + H^+(aq) → H_2O(l)$

With metal salts

sodium hydroxide + iron(II) sulphate → iron(II) hydroxide + sodium sulphate

$2NaOH(aq) + FeSO_4(aq) → Fe(OH)_2(s) + Na_2SO_4(aq)$

or the ionic equation:

$Fe^{2+}(aq) + 2OH^-(aq) → Fe(OH)_2(s)$

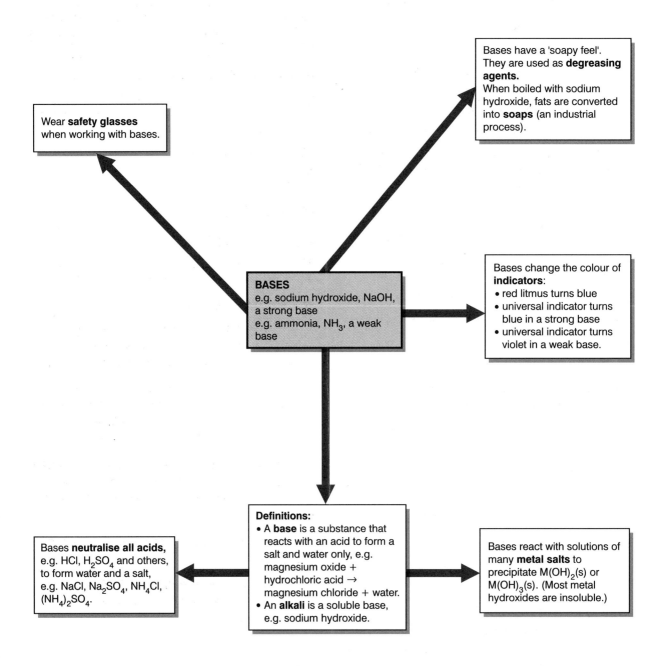

Wear **safety glasses** when working with bases.

Bases have a 'soapy feel'. They are used as **degreasing agents.**
When boiled with sodium hydroxide, fats are converted into **soaps** (an industrial process).

BASES
e.g. sodium hydroxide, NaOH, a strong base
e.g. ammonia, NH_3, a weak base

Bases change the colour of **indicators**:
• red litmus turns blue
• universal indicator turns blue in a strong base
• universal indicator turns violet in a weak base.

Definitions:
• A **base** is a substance that reacts with an acid to form a salt and water only, e.g. magnesium oxide + hydrochloric acid → magnesium chloride + water.
• An **alkali** is a soluble base, e.g. sodium hydroxide.

Bases **neutralise all acids,** e.g. HCl, H_2SO_4 and others, to form water and a salt, e.g. NaCl, Na_2SO_4, NH_4Cl, $(NH_4)_2SO_4$.

Bases react with solutions of many **metal salts** to precipitate $M(OH)_2(s)$ or $M(OH)_3(s)$. (Most metal hydroxides are insoluble.)

Concept map: The properties of bases

$$\text{sodium hydroxide} + \text{iron(III) sulphate} \rightarrow \text{iron(III) hydroxide} + \text{sodium sulphate}$$

$$6NaOH(aq) + Fe_2(SO_4)_3(aq) \rightarrow 2Fe(OH)_3(s) + 3Na_2SO_4(aq)$$

or the ionic equation:

$$Fe^{3+}(aq) + 3OH^-(aq) \rightarrow Fe(OH)_3(s)$$

8.3 Neutralisation

Neutralisation is the combination of hydrogen ions (from an acid) and hydroxide ions (from an alkali) or oxide ions (from an insoluble base) to form water. In the process a salt is formed. For example, with an alkali:

$$\text{hydrochloric acid} + \text{sodium hydroxide} \rightarrow \text{sodium chloride} + \text{water}$$

$$HCl(aq) + NaOH(aq) \rightarrow NaCl(aq) + H_2O(l)$$

acid + alkali → salt + water

The hydrogen ions and hydroxide ions combine to form water molecules.

$$H^+(aq) + OH^-(aq) \rightarrow H_2O(l)$$

Sodium ions and chloride ions remain in the solution, which becomes a solution of sodium chloride.

With a base:

$$\text{sulphuric acid} + \text{copper(II) oxide} \rightarrow \text{copper(II) sulphate} + \text{water}$$

$$H_2SO_4(aq) + CuO(s) \rightarrow CuSO_4(aq) + H_2O(l)$$

acid + base → salt + water

Hydrogen ions and oxide ions combine to form water:

$$2H^+(aq) + O^{2-}(s) \rightarrow H_2O(l)$$

Copper(II) ions and sulphate ions remain in the solution, which becomes a solution of copper(II) sulphate.

8.4 Indicators

indicator	acidic colour	neutral colour	alkaline colour
litmus	red	purple	blue
phenolphthalein	colourless	colourless	red
methyl orange	red	orange	yellow

Universal indicator can distinguish between strong and weak bases, as shown in the diagram below.

8.5 Salts

Common salt

The importance of common salt, sodium chloride, NaCl, is outlined in the concept map overleaf.

Some useful salts

★ **Sodium carbonate-10-water**, $Na_2CO_3.10H_2O$, 'washing soda', is used as a water softener, an ingredient of washing powders and bath salts.

★ **Sodium hydrogencarbonate**, $NaHCO_3$, 'baking soda', is added to self-raising flour. It decomposes at oven temperature to give carbon dioxide and steam, which make bread and cakes rise.

★ **Calcium sulphate-$\frac{1}{2}$-water**, $CaSO_4.\frac{1}{2}H_2O$, is plaster of Paris. When mixed with water it combines and sets to form a strong 'plaster cast'. It is also used for plastering walls.

★ **Silver bromide**, AgBr, is used in black-and-white photographic film.

★ **Iron(II) sulphate-7-water**, $FeSO_4.7H_2O$, is used in some kinds of 'iron tablets' which people take for anaemia.

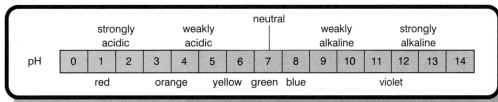

The colour of universal indicator in solutions of different pH

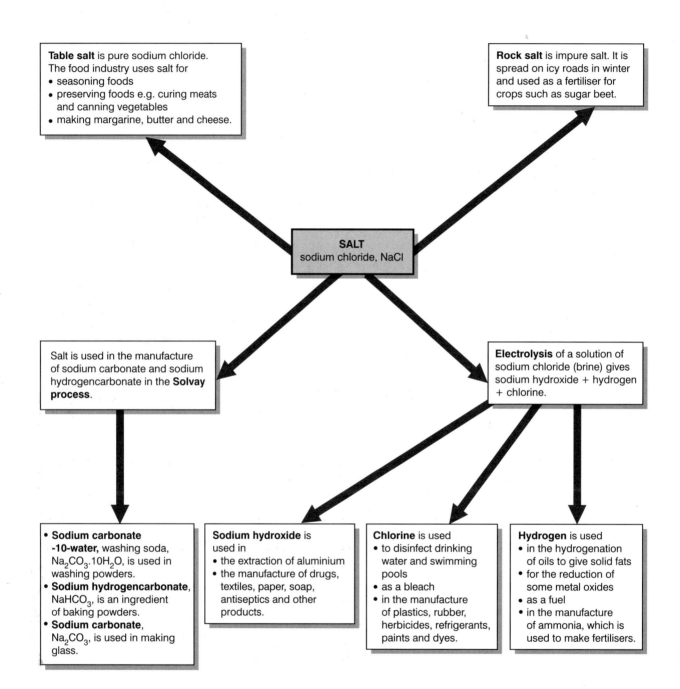

Table salt is pure sodium chloride.
The food industry uses salt for
- seasoning foods
- preserving foods e.g. curing meats
  and canning vegetables
- making margarine, butter and cheese.

Rock salt is impure salt. It is
spread on icy roads in winter
and used as a fertiliser for
crops such as sugar beet.

SALT
sodium chloride, NaCl

Salt is used in the manufacture
of sodium carbonate and sodium
hydrogencarbonate in the **Solvay
process**.

Electrolysis of a solution of
sodium chloride (brine) gives
sodium hydroxide + hydrogen
+ chlorine.

- **Sodium carbonate
  -10-water,** washing soda,
  $Na_2CO_3.10H_2O$, is used in
  washing powders.
- **Sodium hydrogencarbonate**,
  $NaHCO_3$, is an ingredient
  of baking powders.
- **Sodium carbonate**,
  Na_2CO_3, is used in making
  glass.

Sodium hydroxide is
used in
- the extraction of aluminium
- the manufacture of drugs,
  textiles, paper, soap,
  antiseptics and other
  products.

Chlorine is used
- to disinfect drinking
  water and swimming
  pools
- as a bleach
- in the manufacture
  of plastics, rubber,
  herbicides, refrigerants,
  paints and dyes.

Hydrogen is used
- in the hydrogenation
  of oils to give solid fats
- for the reduction of
  some metal oxides
- as a fuel
- in the manufacture
  of ammonia, which is
  used to make fertilisers.

Concept map: common salt

★ **Barium sulphate**, $BaSO_4$, is used in 'barium meals' because barium ions show up well on X-rays and reveal the position of a stomach ulcer (see page 265).

★ **Copper(II) sulphate**, $CuSO_4$, is used as a fungicide for spraying grapes, potatoes and other crops.

★ **Calcium fluoride**, CaF_2, is added to toothpastes. Tooth enamel reacts with fluorides to form a harder enamel which is better at resisting attack by mouth acids. Many water companies add a small amount of calcium fluoride to drinking water.

★ **NPK fertilisers** contain ammonium nitrate, NH_4NO_3, and ammonium sulphate, $(NH_4)_2SO_4$, as sources of nitrogen; calcium phosphate, $Ca_3(PO_4)_2$, as a source of phosphorus; and potassium chloride, KCl, as a source of potassium.

Making soluble salts

To make a soluble salt, an acid is neutralised by adding a metal, a solid base, a solid metal carbonate or a solution of an alkali.

★ **Method 1:** acid + metal → salt + hydrogen

★ **Method 2:** acid + metal oxide → salt + water

★ **Method 3:**

$$acid + \frac{metal}{carbonate} \rightarrow salt + water + \frac{carbon}{dioxide}$$

★ **Method 4:** acid + alkali → salt + water

Here are the practical details for methods **1**, **2** and **3**.

a) Carry out the neutralisation as shown in the table and diagram below.

b) Filter to remove the excess of solid, using a filter funnel and filter paper.

c) Evaporate the filtrate, preferably on a water bath.

d) As the solution cools, crystals of the salt form. Separate the crystals by filtration. Using a little distilled water, wash the crystals in the filter funnel. Leave the crystals to dry.

method 1 (acid + metal)	method 2 (acid + metal oxide)	method 3 (acid + metal carbonate)
Warm the acid, then switch off the Bunsen burner.	Warm the acid.	
Add an excess of the metal to the acid. When no more hydrogen is evolved, the reaction is complete.	Add an excess of the metal oxide to the acid. When the solution no longer turns blue litmus paper red, the reaction is complete.	Add an excess of the metal carbonate to the acid. When no more carbon dioxide is evolved, the reaction is complete.

Neutralisation details for methods **1** to **3**

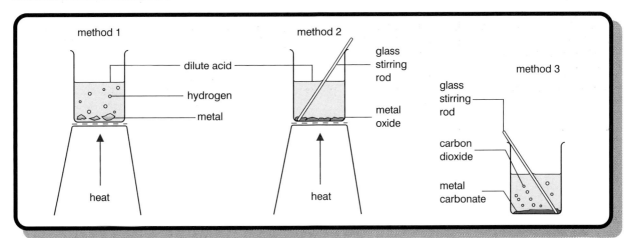

Adding an excess of a solid reactant to an acid

1 Add ammonia solution to dilute sulphuric acid, stirring constantly.

ammonia solution

dilute sulphuric acid

2 From time to time, use the glass rod to remove a drop of acid. Spot it onto a strip of indicator paper. When the indicator shows that the solution has become alkaline, stop adding ammonia.

3 Evaporate the solution until it begins to crystallise. Leave it to stand. Filter to obtain crystals of ammonium sulphate.

Laboratory preparation of ammonium sulphate

Here are the practical details for method **4** (acid + alkali). For example, the neutralisation of an acid by ammonia solution can be used to make ammonium salts. The diagram above shows the steps in the preparation of ammonium sulphate.

Making insoluble salts: precipitation

Insoluble salts are made by mixing two solutions. For example, barium sulphate is insoluble. A soluble barium salt and a soluble sulphate must be chosen to make barium sulphate. The precipitate is separated by filtering or centrifuging.

The equation for the reaction is:

barium chloride + sodium sulphate → barium sulphate + sodium chloride

$$BaCl_2(aq) + Na_2SO_4(aq) \rightarrow BaSO_4(s) + 2NaCl(aq)$$

or the ionic equation:

$$Ba^{2+}(aq) + SO_4^{2-}(aq) \rightarrow BaSO_4(s)$$

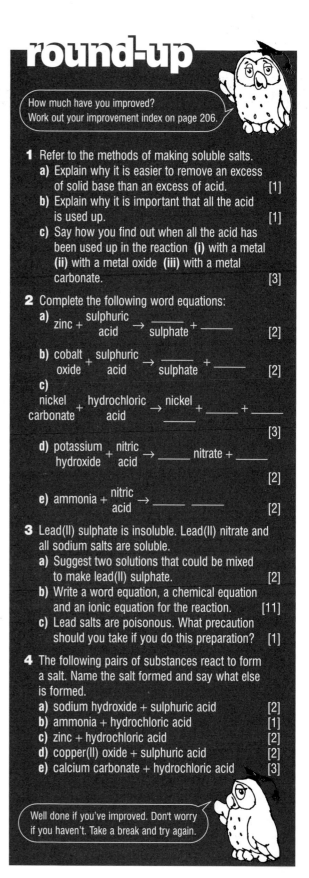

round-up

How much have you improved? Work out your improvement index on page 206.

1 Refer to the methods of making soluble salts.
  a) Explain why it is easier to remove an excess of solid base than an excess of acid. [1]
  b) Explain why it is important that all the acid is used up. [1]
  c) Say how you find out when all the acid has been used up in the reaction **(i)** with a metal **(ii)** with a metal oxide **(iii)** with a metal carbonate. [3]

2 Complete the following word equations:
  a) zinc + sulphuric acid → _____ sulphate + _____ [2]
  b) cobalt oxide + sulphuric acid → _____ sulphate + _____ [2]
  c) nickel carbonate + hydrochloric acid → nickel _____ + _____ + _____ [3]
  d) potassium hydroxide + nitric acid → _____ nitrate + _____ [2]
  e) ammonia + nitric acid → _____ _____ [2]

3 Lead(II) sulphate is insoluble. Lead(II) nitrate and all sodium salts are soluble.
  a) Suggest two solutions that could be mixed to make lead(II) sulphate. [2]
  b) Write a word equation, a chemical equation and an ionic equation for the reaction. [11]
  c) Lead salts are poisonous. What precaution should you take if you do this preparation? [1]

4 The following pairs of substances react to form a salt. Name the salt formed and say what else is formed.
  a) sodium hydroxide + sulphuric acid [2]
  b) ammonia + hydrochloric acid [1]
  c) zinc + hydrochloric acid [2]
  d) copper(II) oxide + sulphuric acid [2]
  e) calcium carbonate + hydrochloric acid [3]

Well done if you've improved. Don't worry if you haven't. Take a break and try again.

Air

preview

At the end of this topic you will:

- **know how Earth's atmosphere originated**
- **know the reactions and importance of oxygen**
- **understand oxidation–reduction reactions**
- **know the importance of the nitrogen cycle and the carbon cycle**
- **appreciate the effects of pollutants in the atmosphere.**

MIND MAP
Page 163.

How much do you already know?
Work out your score on page 206.

Test yourself

1 How did Earth's original atmosphere, formed billions of years ago, differ from today's atmosphere in its content of water vapour, carbon dioxide, oxygen and nitrogen? [4]

2 Give the percentage by volume in pure dry air of oxygen and nitrogen. [2]

3 Give two industrial uses for oxygen. [2]

4 What is the name for an oxidation reaction in which energy is released? [1]

5 Describe a test for oxygen. [1]

6 Suggest identities for the following elements. [4]
 A burns with a blue flame to give an acidic gas.
 B burns with a yellow flame to give a basic solid.
 C burns with a bright white flame to give a basic solid.
 D burns with a red glow to give an invisible gas.

7 Complete the sentence.

Oxidation is the _____ of oxygen or the _____ of hydrogen or the _____ of electrons. [3]

8 Name two processes which turn atmospheric nitrogen into compounds. [2]

9 Name two processes which take carbon dioxide out of the atmosphere. [2]

10 How would you test an invisible gas to find out if it is carbon dioxide? [2]

11 Name four atmospheric pollutants and state one source of each. [8]

9.1 How the atmosphere evolved

A mixture of gases was released from the interior of Earth about 4.6 billion years ago. The mixture was probably similar to the gases released from volcanoes today: water vapour 64% by mass, carbon dioxide 24%, sulphur dioxide 10%, nitrogen 1.5%. Water vapour condensed to make oceans. Carbon dioxide dissolved in the oceans, where it was used by the first living things in a process which developed into photosynthesis:

$$\text{carbon dioxide} + \text{water} + \text{sunlight} \rightarrow \text{organic matter} + \text{oxygen}$$

$$CO_2 + H_2O \rightarrow (CH_2O) + O_2$$

The oxygen formed in photosynthesis would have poisoned primitive plants. It was not released into the air, but was converted into iron oxides.

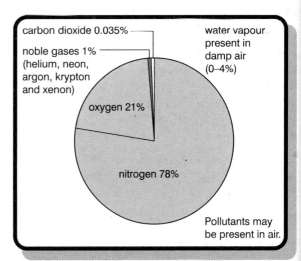

carbon dioxide 0.035%

water vapour present in damp air (0–4%)

noble gases 1% (helium, neon, argon, krypton and xenon)

oxygen 21%

nitrogen 78%

Pollutants may be present in air.

The composition of pure, dry air in percentage by volume

9

Eventually bacteria living in the ocean developed the ability to use oxygen in respiration. Oxygen began to accumulate in the atmosphere, and the ozone layer formed. This shields Earth from receiving too much radiation from the Sun, and makes Earth an environment in which things can live. About 450 million years ago land plants emerged, followed by land animals 400 million years ago. The composition of the atmosphere has remained the same for about 300 million years.

Separating gases from air

Oxygen, nitrogen and argon are obtained by fractional distillation of liquid air. Liquid air at –190°C is fed into an insulated fractionation column. Nitrogen (boiling point –196°C) vaporises at the top of the column, argon (boiling point –186°C) vaporises from the middle of the column, and oxygen (boiling point –183°C) is left at the bottom of the column.

9.2 Oxygen

Plants and animals need oxygen for respiration. Aquatic plants and animals depend on the oxygen dissolved in water. Pollutants such as excess decaying organic matter use up dissolved oxygen and put aquatic animals and plants at risk.

Uses of pure oxygen

★ Aeroplanes which fly at high altitude, and all space flights, carry oxygen.

★ Deep-sea divers carry cylinders which contain a mixture of oxygen and helium.

★ An oxyacetylene torch (which burns ethyne, C_2H_2, in oxygen) has a very hot flame, about 4000°C, and is used for welding and cutting metals.

★ Cast iron contains carbon, which is burnt off in a stream of oxygen to make steel.

★ Oxygen is pumped into polluted rivers and lakes.

Reactions of oxygen

Oxygen is colourless, odourless and slightly soluble in water. Many elements react with oxygen to form oxides as shown in the table below.

★ Combination with oxygen is called **oxidation**.

★ Oxidation in which energy is given out is called **combustion**.

★ Combustion accompanied by a flame is called **burning**.

★ Substances which undergo combustion to give out a lot of energy are called **fuels**.

★ Many substances burn in oxygen, and all substances burn more rapidly in oxygen than in air.

★ **Test for oxygen:**
a glowing wooden splint lowered into oxygen starts to burn brightly.

The concept map opposite shows the properties of oxides.

FACTS

element	observation	product	action of product on water
calcium (metal)	burns with a red flame	calcium oxide (white solid)	dissolves to give a strongly alkaline solution
copper (metal)	turns black without burning	copper(II) oxide (black solid)	insoluble
iron (metal)	burns with yellow sparks	iron oxide, Fe_3O_4	insoluble
magnesium (metal)	burns with a white flame	magnesium oxide (white solid)	dissolves slightly to give an alkaline solution
sodium (metal)	burns with a yellow flame	sodium oxide	dissolves readily to give a strongly alkaline solution
carbon (non-metal)	glows red	carbon dioxide (invisible gas)	dissolves slightly to give a weakly acidic solution
sulphur (non-metal)	burns with a blue flame	sulphur dioxide (fuming gas)	dissolves readily to give a strongly acidic solution

Reactions of oxygen with some elements

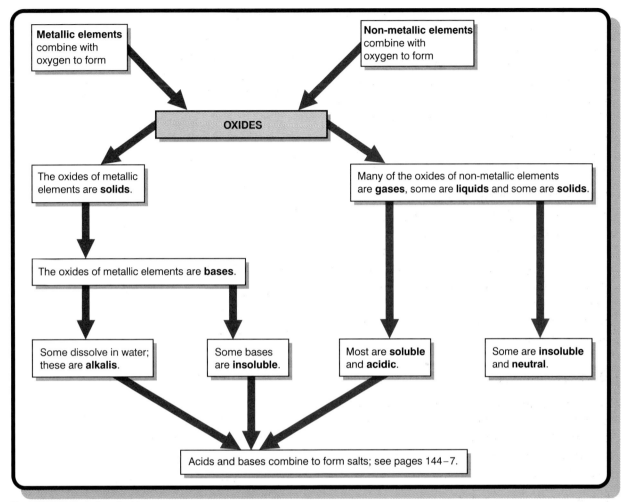

Concept map: properties of oxides

9.3 Oxidation and reduction

Fact file

★ **Oxidation** = gain of oxygen or loss of hydrogen

★ **Reduction** = loss of oxygen or gain of hydrogen

★ An **oxidising agent** gives oxygen or takes hydrogen.

★ A **reducing agent** takes oxygen or gives hydrogen.

★ Oxidation and reduction occur together in **oxidation–reduction reactions** or **redox reactions**.

Here is an example of a redox reaction:

lead(II) oxide + hydrogen → lead + water

$$PbO(s) + H_2(g) \rightarrow Pb(s) + H_2O(l)$$

In this reaction,

- hydrogen has gained oxygen: hydrogen has been oxidised
- lead(II) oxide has lost oxygen: lead(II) oxide has been reduced
- hydrogen has taken oxygen from another substance: hydrogen is a reducing agent
- lead(II) oxide has given oxygen to another substance: lead(II) oxide is an oxidising agent
- oxidation and reduction are occurring together.

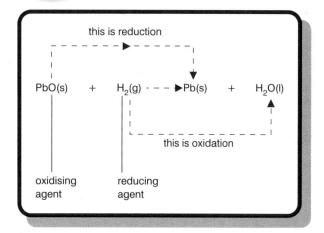

this is reduction

$$PbO(s) \quad + \quad H_2(g) \; - - - \blacktriangleright Pb(s) \quad + \quad H_2O(l)$$

this is oxidation

oxidising
agent

reducing
agent

You can also think of oxidation and reduction in terms of electron transfer:

Oxidation	Reduction
Is	**I**s
Loss	**G**ain
of electrons	of electrons

9.4 Nitrogen

Nitrogen is a gas which does not take part in many chemical reactions. It combines with hydrogen to form ammonia. This reaction is the basis of the fertiliser industry; see opposite. Many uses of nitrogen arise from its lack of reactivity.

★ Liquid nitrogen is used in the fast-freezing of foods.

★ Many foods are packed in an atmosphere of nitrogen to prevent oils and fats in the foods from being oxidised to rancid products.

★ Oil tankers, road tankers and grain silos are flushed out with nitrogen as a precaution against fire.

9.5 The nitrogen cycle

Nitrogen circulates from air to soil to living things and back again in a process called the **nitrogen cycle**, shown below.

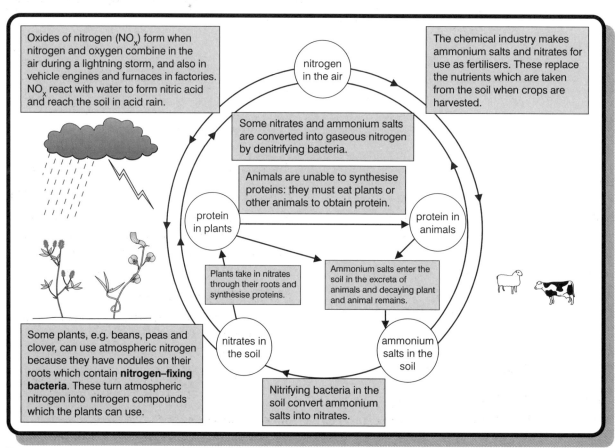

Oxides of nitrogen (NO_x) form when nitrogen and oxygen combine in the air during a lightning storm, and also in vehicle engines and furnaces in factories. NO_x react with water to form nitric acid and reach the soil in acid rain.

The chemical industry makes ammonium salts and nitrates for use as fertilisers. These replace the nutrients which are taken from the soil when crops are harvested.

nitrogen in the air

Some nitrates and ammonium salts are converted into gaseous nitrogen by denitrifying bacteria.

Animals are unable to synthesise proteins: they must eat plants or other animals to obtain protein.

protein in plants

protein in animals

Plants take in nitrates through their roots and synthesise proteins.

Ammonium salts enter the soil in the excreta of animals and decaying plant and animal remains.

Some plants, e.g. beans, peas and clover, can use atmospheric nitrogen because they have nodules on their roots which contain **nitrogen–fixing bacteria**. These turn atmospheric nitrogen into nitrogen compounds which the plants can use.

nitrates in the soil

ammonium salts in the soil

Nitrifying bacteria in the soil convert ammonium salts into nitrates.

The nitrogen cycle

9.6 Ammonia and fertilisers

Ammonia

The nitrogen in the air is used to make nitrogenous fertilisers. Under the conditions of the **Haber process** (named after the chemist Fritz Haber) nitrogen will combine with hydrogen.

nitrogen + hydrogen $\rightleftharpoons$ ammonia

$$N_2(g) + 3H_2(g) \rightleftharpoons 2NH_3(g)$$

The reaction is reversible: some of the ammonia formed dissociates into nitrogen and hydrogen. The product is a mixture of nitrogen, hydrogen and ammonia. Two factors increase the percentage of ammonia in the mixture: a **high pressure** and a **low temperature**. However, the reaction is very slow to reach equilibrium at a low temperature, and industrial plants use a compromise temperature and a catalyst to speed up the reaction, as shown in the flow diagram. The ammonia made by the Haber process can be oxidised to nitric acid.

NPK fertilisers

Ammonia solution can be used as a fertiliser. However, it is more common to use the solid fertilisers ammonium nitrate, ammonium sulphate and ammonium phosphate.

Mixtures of ammonium nitrate, ammonium phosphate and potassium chloride contain the elements nitrogen, phosphorus and potassium, which are essential for plant growth and are sold as **NPK fertilisers**.

9.7 Carbon dioxide

The carbon cycle

Plants are able to make sugars by the process of **photosynthesis**:

PHOTOSYNTHESIS Page 48.

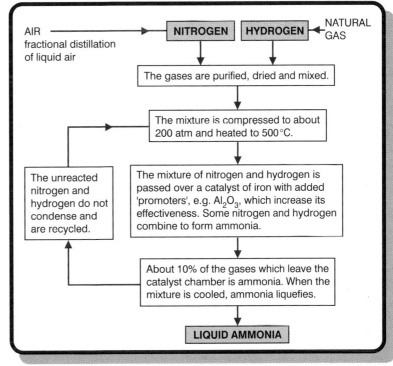

Flow diagram of the Haber process

$$\underset{\text{dioxide}}{\text{carbon}} + \text{water} + \text{sunlight} \xrightarrow{\text{catalysed by chlorophyll}} \text{glucose} + \text{oxygen}$$

The energy of sunlight is converted into the energy of the chemical bonds in the sugar glucose.

RESPIRATION Page 66.

Animals obtain energy by **cellular respiration**:

glucose + oxygen $\rightarrow$ carbon dioxide + water + energy

The balance between the processes which take carbon dioxide from the air and those which put carbon dioxide into the air is called the **carbon cycle**. The cycle is shown on the next page.

Uses of carbon dioxide

★ Soft drinks are made by dissolving carbon dioxide in water under pressure and adding sugar and flavourings.

★ Solid carbon dioxide sublimes (turns into a vapour on warming). It is used as the refrigerant 'dry ice'.

★ Carbon dioxide is used in fire extinguishers because it does not support combustion and is denser than air.

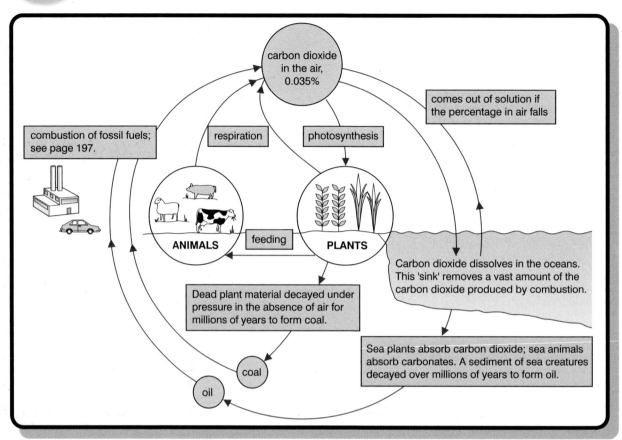

The carbon cycle

Test for carbon dioxide

Carbon dioxide reacts with a solution of calcium hydroxide (limewater) to form a white precipitate of calcium carbonate.

$$\text{carbon dioxide} + \text{calcium hydroxide} \rightarrow \text{calcium carbonate} + \text{water}$$

$$CO_2(g) + Ca(OH)_2(aq) \rightarrow CaCO_3(s) + H_2O(l)$$

The greenhouse effect

The Earth receives radiation from the Sun, and also radiates heat into space. Carbon dioxide and water vapour reduce the escape of heat energy from the Earth by means of the **greenhouse effect** (see diagram on opposite page). Without these 'blankets' of water vapour and carbon dioxide, the temperature of the Earth's surface would be at −40°C, and life on Earth would be impossible.

The combustion of fossil fuels is causing an increase in the level of carbon dioxide at a rate which could raise the average temperature of the Earth. One result would be that the massive icecaps of the Arctic and Antarctic regions would slowly begin to melt. The levels of oceans would rise, and coastal areas would be flooded. A rise in temperature could decrease food production over vast areas, e.g. the mid-west USA and Russia. Secondary effects would make matters worse. The increase in temperature would make more water vaporise from the oceans and drive out some of the carbon dioxide dissolved in the oceans to add to a still thicker greenhouse blanket. Other 'greenhouse gases' are methane, chlorofluorocarbons (CFCs), nitrogen oxides and ozone.

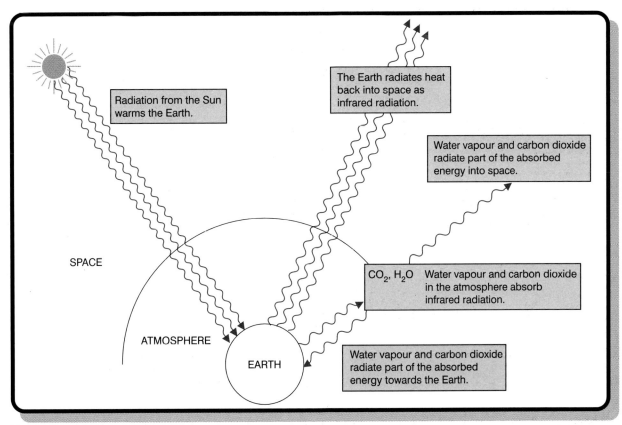

The greenhouse effect

9.8 The noble gases

GROUPS OF THE PERIODIC TABLE Page 139.

Helium, neon, argon, krypton and xenon are the noble gases.

★ Helium is used in airships because of its low density.

★ Neon and other noble gases are used in illuminated signs.

★ Argon is used to fill light bulbs.

9.9 The problem of pollution

Carbon monoxide

Source: most of the carbon monoxide in the air comes from vehicle engines, where it is formed by the incomplete combustion of petrol. Soil organisms remove carbon monoxide from the air.

However, in cities, where the concentration of carbon monoxide is high, there is little soil to remove it.

Effects: carbon monoxide combines with haemoglobin, the red pigment in the blood, and prevents haemoglobin from combining with oxygen. At a level of 1%, carbon monoxide will kill quickly; at lower levels, it causes headaches and dizziness and affects reaction times. Being colourless and odourless, carbon monoxide gives no warning of its presence.

Solutions to the problem may come from

• tuning vehicle engines to use more air and produce only carbon dioxide and water. However, this increases the emission of oxides of nitrogen.
• fitting vehicles with catalytic converters
• using fuels which burn more cleanly than hydrocarbons, e.g. ethanol.

9

Sulphur dioxide

Sources: major sources of the sulphur dioxide in the air are

- the extraction of metals from sulphide ores
- the burning of coal, which contains 0.5–5% sulphur, mostly in electricity power stations
- oil-burning power stations, because fuel oil contains sulphur compounds.

Effects: sulphur dioxide is a colourless gas with a very penetrating and irritating smell. Atmospheric sulphur dioxide is thought to contribute to bronchitis and lung diseases. It is a cause of acid rain.

Solutions to the problem: see below.

Acid rain

Rain is naturally weakly acidic because it dissolves carbon dioxide from the air. The pH of natural rainwater is 5.2. Rain with a pH below this is described as **acid rain**.

There are many effects of acid rain:

- damage to lakes and the fish and plants in them; see diagram below

- washing of nutrients out of topsoil, resulting in poor crops and damage to trees
- costly damage to building materials, e.g. limestone, concrete, cement and metal.

What can be done?

Sweden has tackled the problem by spraying tonnes of calcium hydroxide into acid lakes.

Members of the European Community (EC) have agreed to make a 60% to 70% cut in their emissions of sulphur dioxide by 2003. Power stations must make a big contribution to solving the problem. Some lines of attack are:

1. Coal can be crushed and washed with a solvent to remove much of the sulphur content.

2. Fuel oil can be purified at the refinery – at a cost.

3. Sulphur dioxide can be removed from the exhaust gases of power stations. In **flue gas desulphurisation** (**FGD**), jets of wet powdered limestone neutralise acidic gases as they pass up the chimney of the power station.

The tall chimneys of power stations and factories release sulphur dioxide and oxides of nitrogen into the atmosphere.

The pollutants travel long distances. They react with water vapour and oxygen to form sulphuric acid and nitric acid.

Cold countries receive acid snow for many months. The spring thaw sends a huge volume of acidic water into the lake. The soil has no chance to neutralise it.

When it rains or snows, sulphuric acid and nitric acid fall to earth as acid rain or acid snow.

Vehicles emit nitrogen oxides.

The acidity and the concentration of metal salts in the lake increase. Fish die.

Acid rain washes salts out of the topsoil, robbing trees of nourishment.

Acidic water and metal salts run into the lake. Rocks such as limestone neutralise part of the acidity.

Acid rain; its source and its effect on lake water

4 In a **pulverised fluidised bed combustion** (**PFBC**) furnace, the coal is pulverised (broken into small pieces) and burnt on a bed of powdered limestone, which is 'fluidised' (kept in motion by an upward flow of air). As the coal burns, sulphur dioxide reacts with the limestone.

5 Nuclear power stations do not send pollutants into the air. However, they create the problem of storing radioactive waste.

RADIOACTIVITY
Pages 237–42.

Smoke, dust and grit

Particles enter the air from natural sources such as dust storms, forest fires and volcanic eruptions. Coal-burning power stations, incinerators, industries and vehicles add to the pollution. When smoke particles mix with fog, **smog** is formed. Smog contains sulphuric acid, which has been formed from sulphur dioxide in the smoke. Breathing smog makes the lungs produce mucus, making it more difficult to breathe.

Methods of removing particles include:

* using sprays of water to wash out particles from waste gases
* passing exhaust gases through filters
* using electrostatic precipitators which attract particles to charged plates.

The exhaust gases of vehicles are not treated by any of these methods.

ELECTROSTATIC
PRECIPITATORS
Page 288.

Oxides of nitrogen

Source: when fuels are burned in air, the temperature rises. Some of the nitrogen and oxygen in the air combine to form nitrogen monoxide, NO, and nitrogen dioxide, NO_2. This mixture (shown as NO_x) is emitted by power stations, factories and vehicles.

Effects: nitrogen monoxide is soon converted into nitrogen dioxide which is highly toxic, and which contributes to the formation of acid rain (see previous page).

Solution to the problem: the presence of a catalyst (platinum) brings about the reaction:

$$\text{nitrogen monoxide} + \text{carbon monoxide} \rightarrow \text{nitrogen} + \text{carbon dioxide}$$

$$2NO(g) + 2CO(g) \rightarrow N_2(g) + 2CO_2(g)$$

The **catalytic converters** which are now fitted in the exhausts of cars reduce the emission of oxides of nitrogen in this way. Unleaded petrol must be used because lead compounds in the exhaust gases would stop the catalyst working.

Hydrocarbons

Sources: the hydrocarbons in the air come from natural sources, such as the decay of plant material (85%), and from vehicles (15%).

Effects: in sunlight, hydrocarbons react with oxygen and oxides of nitrogen to form **photochemical smog**. This contains irritating and toxic compounds.

Solutions to the problem: if the air supply in a vehicle engine is increased, the petrol burns completely. However, at the same time, the formation of NO_x increases. A solution may be found by running the engine at a lower temperature and employing a catalyst to promote combustion.

Lead

Sources: lead compounds enter the air from the combustion of coal, the roasting of metal ores and from vehicle engines. Since the introduction of unleaded petrol, the level of lead in the atmosphere has fallen.

Effects: lead causes depression, tiredness, irritability and headaches. Higher levels of lead cause damage to the brain, liver and kidneys.

round-up

How much have you improved?
Work out your improvement index on pages 206–7.

1 zinc oxide + carbon → zinc + carbon monoxide
$$ZnO(s) + C(s) \rightarrow Zn(s) + CO(g)$$
a) In this reaction, name **(i)** the oxidising agent and
(ii) the reducing agent. [2]
b) Say which substance is **(i)** oxidised
(ii) reduced. [2]

2 State which is **(i)** the oxidising agent and
(ii) the reducing agent in each of these reactions:
a) aluminium + iron oxide → iron + aluminium oxide [2]
b) tin sulphide + oxygen → tin oxide + sulphur dioxide [2]
c) tin oxide + carbon → tin + carbon monoxide [2]

3 a) Why is air not used for 'airships'? [1]
b) Helium has a density twice that of hydrogen.
Why is helium used in preference to hydrogen
for filling airships? [2]

4 Explain the danger to health from the presence in the
air of **a)** carbon monoxide **b)** sulphur dioxide and
c) particles of smoke and dust.
Say how nature removes each of these pollutants
from the air. [6]

5 a) How do oxides of nitrogen get into the air?
b) What damage do they cause?
c) What is the solution to this problem? [3]

6 a) Explain how the 'greenhouse effect' makes
life on Earth possible. [2]
b) Explain why people are worried about an
'enhanced greenhouse effect'. [2]
c) If Earth warms up, what do people predict
will happen
(i) at the North Pole **(ii)** in Thailand
(iii) in the mid-west of the USA? [3]

7 Explain why power stations have tall chimneys.
Would the problem of pollution from power
stations be solved by still taller chimneys? [2]

8 a) Why do cold countries, e.g. Sweden, suffer
badly from acid rain? [1]
b) In Sweden, the base calcium hydroxide is
added to acid lakes. Write a word equation
and a chemical equation for the reaction
between calcium hydroxide and sulphuric acid
in the lake water. [4]
c) What name is given to this type of reaction? [1]

9 What chemical reactions take place between acid
rain and **a)** iron railings **b)** marble statues
c) fresh mortar? [2, 3, 2]

10 a) In petrol engines and diesel engines,
hydrocarbons burn to form a number of products.
What are these products? [4]
b) What other substances are present in vehicle
exhaust gases? [3]

Can you summarise this topic in a Mind Map?
To start you off …

Mind Maps

Electrolysis (Topic 5)

Acids, bases and salts (Topic 8)

Air (Topic 9)

Water (Topic 10)

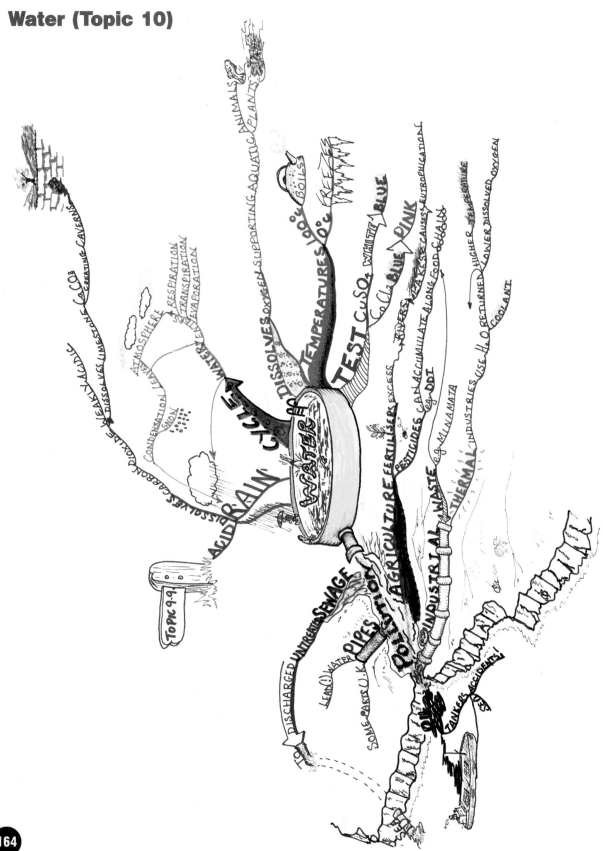

Metals and alloys (Topic 12)

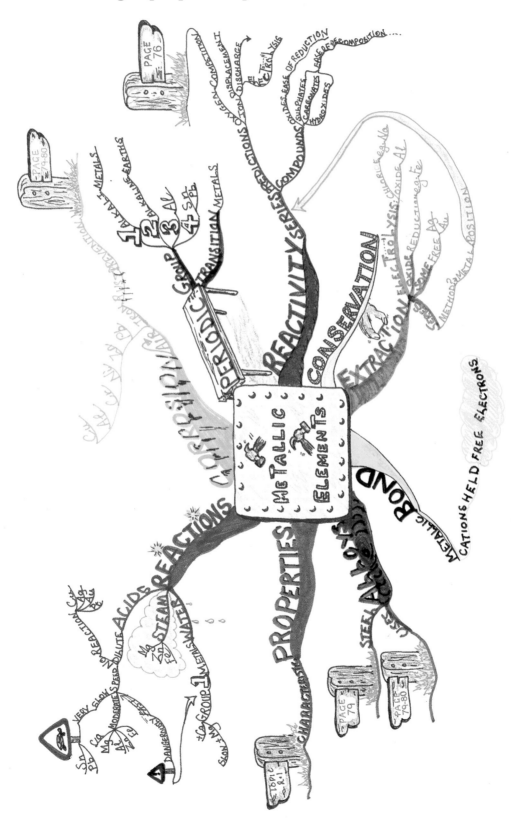

Reaction speeds (Topic 13)

Fuels (Topic 15)

Alkenes and plastics (Topic 16)

Water

preview

At the end of this topic you will:

- **appreciate the importance of the water cycle**
- **know how to purify water and how to test for water**
- **appreciate the dangers of water pollution.**

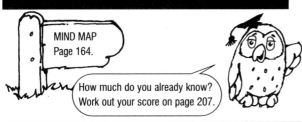

MIND MAP
Page 164.

How much do you already know?
Work out your score on page 207.

10

Test yourself

1 Name three processes which send water vapour into the atmosphere. [3]

2 Explain why rainwater is weakly acidic. [1]

3 Explain how weakly acidic rainwater leads to the formation of underground caves in limestone regions. Write a word equation and a chemical equation for the process. [5]

4 State **a)** a test to find out whether a liquid contains water **b)** a test to show whether a liquid is pure water. [3]

5 Name three types of living things for which dissolved oxygen is important. [3]

10.1 The water cycle

The water cycle is shown in the diagram.

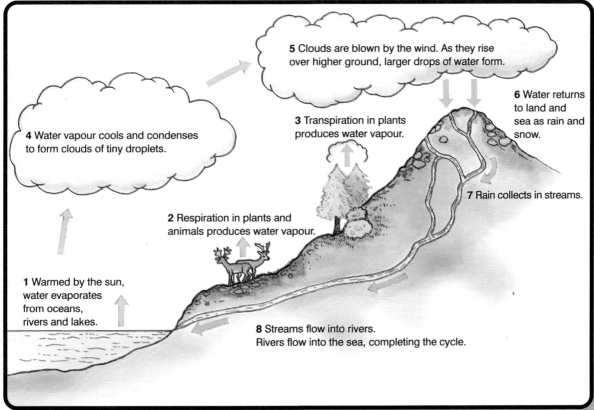

5 Clouds are blown by the wind. As they rise over higher ground, larger drops of water form.

6 Water returns to land and sea as rain and snow.

3 Transpiration in plants produces water vapour.

4 Water vapour cools and condenses to form clouds of tiny droplets.

7 Rain collects in streams.

2 Respiration in plants and animals produces water vapour.

1 Warmed by the sun, water evaporates from oceans, rivers and lakes.

8 Streams flow into rivers. Rivers flow into the sea, completing the cycle.

The water cycle

10.2 Water underground

Rainwater dissolves carbon dioxide as it falls through the air, and natural rainwater is therefore weakly acidic. In limestone regions, rain trickles over rocks containing calcium carbonate and magnesium carbonate. The acidic rainwater reacts with the rocks:

$$\text{calcium carbonate} + \text{water} + \text{carbon dioxide} \rightarrow \text{calcium hydrogencarbonate}$$

$$CaCO_3(s) + H_2O(l) + CO_2(aq) \rightarrow Ca(HCO_3)_2(aq)$$

Over a period of thousands of years, calcium carbonate and magnesium carbonate have been dissolved out of the rocks to form the underground caves and potholes that occur in limestone regions.

The reverse reaction can take place. In an underground cavern, dissolved calcium hydrogencarbonate can turn into a grain of solid calcium carbonate. Over thousands of years, tiny grains of calcium carbonate can build up into **stalactites** and **stalagmites**.

10.3 Dissolved oxygen

The solubility of oxygen in water is 10 p.p.m. (parts per million), only about 10 g oxygen per tonne of water. Fish and other water-living animals and plants depend on this dissolved oxygen. **Aerobic** bacteria which feed on plant and animal debris in the water also depend on the dissolved oxygen. If the oxygen is used up, for example to oxidise untreated sewage, the aerobic bacteria die and **anaerobic** bacteria take over. They digest biomass to produce unpleasant-smelling decay products.

10.4 Pure water

Tests for water

or for any liquid that contains water:

1   Water turns white anhydrous copper(II) sulphate blue:

$$\text{copper(II) sulphate} + \text{water} \rightarrow \text{copper(II) sulphate-5-water}$$

$$CuSO_4(s) + 5H_2O(l) \rightarrow CuSO_4.5H_2O$$

2   Water turns blue anhydrous cobalt(II) chloride pink:

$$\text{cobalt(II) chloride} + \text{water} \rightarrow \text{cobalt(II) chloride-6-water}$$

$$CoCl_2(s) + 6H_2O(l) \rightarrow CoCl_2.6H_2O$$

The water in copper(II) sulphate-5-water and cobalt(II) chloride-6-water is combined as **water of crystallisation**. It gives these hydrates their crystalline form and their colour.

Tests for pure water

1   The boiling point is 100°C at 1 atm.
2   The freezing point is 0°C at 1 atm.

Methods of obtaining pure water

1   **Distillation** (see page 122).

2   **Deionisation**: water can be passed through an **ion-exchange column**, which contains a resin. An exchange takes place between cations (M^+) and anions (A^-) in the water and H^+ and OH^- ions bonded to the resin.

$$M^+(aq) + H^+(resin) \rightarrow M^+(resin) + H^+(aq)$$

$$A^-(aq) + OH^-(resin) \rightarrow A^-(resin) + OH^-(aq)$$

Then hydrogen ions and hydroxide ions combine to form water:

$$H^+(aq) + OH^-(aq) \rightarrow H_2O(l)$$

10.5 Pollution of water

Pollution by industry

Many industrial firms have their factories on the banks of rivers and estuaries and discharge waste into the water. The National Rivers Authority was set up in 1989 to watch over the quality of rivers and prosecute polluters. It does not watch over tidal waters, and much sewage and industrial waste is poured into coastal waters and estuaries.

Pollution by sewage

Much sewage is discharged into rivers and estuaries without being treated. This gives swimmers at some of Britain's bathing beaches some nasty surprises. Dozens of British beaches fail to meet European Community standards because they have too high a level of coliform bacteria and faecal bacteria in the water.

Pollution by agriculture

Fertilisers: when an excess of fertiliser is used, some of it is not absorbed by the crop. Rain washes it out of the soil, and it accumulates in groundwater. The water industry uses groundwater as a source of drinking water. There is concern that nitrates in drinking water can lead to the formation of nitrosoamines, compounds which cause cancer.

Fertiliser which plants fail to absorb may be carried into the water of a lake, where it nourishes the growth of algae and water plants. This accidental enrichment of the water causes algae to form a thick mat of **algal bloom**, and weeds flourish. When algae die and decay, they use up dissolved oxygen. The fish in the lake are deprived of oxygen and die. The lake becomes a 'dead lake'. This process is called **eutrophication**.

Pesticides: these may enter lakes and become part of a food chain.

FOOD CHAINS
Page 18.

Thermal pollution

Industries take water from rivers to use as a coolant and return it at a higher temperature. At the higher temperature, the solubility of oxygen in the water is decreased. At the same time, fish and aerobic bacteria become more active and need more oxygen. The **biochemical oxygen demand** has increased.

Pollution by oil

Modern oil tankers are huge, each carrying up to 500 000 tonnes of crude oil.

If a tanker has an accident at sea, oil is spilt, and a huge oil slick floats on the surface of the ocean. It is very slowly oxidised by air and decomposed by bacteria. While the oil slick remains, it poisons fish and glues the feathers of sea birds together so that they cannot fly. When the oil slick washes ashore, it fouls beaches. The following methods

can be used to deal with oil slicks:

1 **dispersants** – powerful detergents

2 **sinking** the oil by spreading it with e.g. powdered chalk

3 **absorption** in e.g. straw and polystyrene

4 **booms** placed in the water to prevent oil from spreading

5 **natural processes** if the oil spill occurs far out to sea.

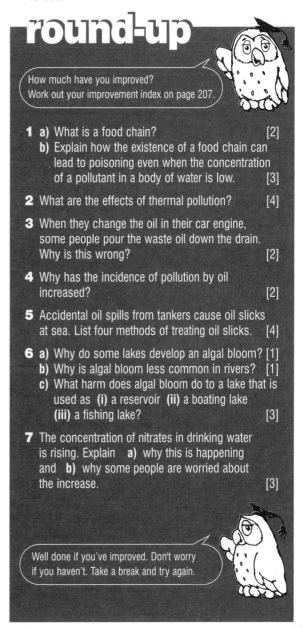

round-up

How much have you improved?
Work out your improvement index on page 207.

1 a) What is a food chain? [2]
b) Explain how the existence of a food chain can lead to poisoning even when the concentration of a pollutant in a body of water is low. [3]

2 What are the effects of thermal pollution? [4]

3 When they change the oil in their car engine, some people pour the waste oil down the drain. Why is this wrong? [2]

4 Why has the incidence of pollution by oil increased? [2]

5 Accidental oil spills from tankers cause oil slicks at sea. List four methods of treating oil slicks. [4]

6 a) Why do some lakes develop an algal bloom? [1]
b) Why is algal bloom less common in rivers? [1]
c) What harm does algal bloom do to a lake that is used as **(i)** a reservoir **(ii)** a boating lake **(iii)** a fishing lake? [3]

7 The concentration of nitrates in drinking water is rising. Explain **a)** why this is happening and **b)** why some people are worried about the increase. [3]

Well done if you've improved. Don't worry if you haven't. Take a break and try again.

Planet Earth

preview

At the end of this topic you will:

- **know how Earth and its atmosphere evolved**
- **understand the theory of plate tectonics**
- **know about the different types of rock**
- **know how useful materials are obtained from rocks.**

How much do you already know?
Work out your score on page 207.

Test yourself

1 The age of Earth is estimated to be
  A 46 000 years
  B 1000 million years
  C 460 000 years
  D 4 600 000 000 years. [1]

2 The average density of the whole Earth is
  A 1.0 g/cm³
  B 3.0 g/cm³
  C 5.5 g/cm³
  D 12.0 g/cm³. [1]

3 The diameter of the Earth is
  A 127 000 km
  B 12 700 km
  C 1270 km
  D 127 km. [1]

4 The Moho lies between
  A the inner and outer core
  B the crust and the mantle
  C the oceanic and continental crust
  D the outer core and the mantle. [1]

5 Name the following parts of the Earth:
  a) the solid zone made of nickel and iron [1]
  b) a zone which lies beneath ocean floors [1]
  c) a zone which forms continents [1]
  d) the zone of gases [1]
  e) the zone where Earth's magnetism arises [1]
  f) the outermost solid zone. [1]

6 Name
  a) the type of rock which is formed when lava solidifies
  b) the type of rock which is formed by compressing deposits of solid particles
  c) the type of rock formed by the action of heat and pressure on types **a** and **b**. [3]

7 Of which type of rock was the original crust of Earth made? [1]

8 The original atmosphere of Earth contained about 25% carbon dioxide by volume. Why is the percentage of carbon dioxide in today's atmosphere so much lower? [2]

9 Name three weathering agents which act on rocks and shape the landscape. [3]

10 What theory says that Earth's crust is made up of separate pieces? [1]

11 State three uses for limestone. [3]

12 Name two materials that can be made from silica (sand). [2]

11.1 Structure of the Earth

ATMOSPHERE
Pages 151–2.

The planet called Earth was formed as a molten mass of material cooled over a period of millions of years (see diagram opposite).

As Earth cooled, water vapour condensed and rivers, lakes and oceans formed on its surface.

Earth's crust is of two kinds: **continental crust** and **oceanic crust**.

continental crust	oceanic crust
forms continents and their shelves	beneath deep sea floors
50–70 km thick	6 km thick on average
density 2.7 g/cm³	density 3.0 g/cm³
aged up to 3700 million years	aged up to 210 million years
has the same composition as granite	has the same composition as basalt

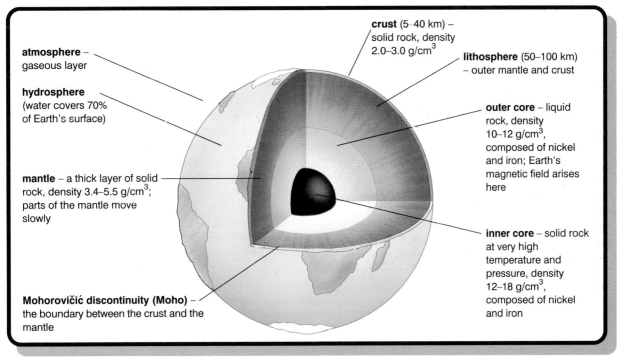

atmosphere –
gaseous layer

hydrosphere
(water covers 70%
of Earth's surface)

mantle – a thick layer of solid
rock, density 3.4–5.5 g/cm^3;
parts of the mantle move
slowly

Mohorovičić discontinuity (Moho) –
the boundary between the crust and the
mantle

crust (5–40 km) –
solid rock, density
2.0–3.0 g/cm^3

lithosphere (50–100 km)
– outer mantle and crust

outer core – liquid
rock, density
10–12 g/cm^3,
composed of nickel
and iron; Earth's
magnetic field arises
here

inner core – solid rock
at very high
temperature and
pressure, density
12–18 g/cm^3,
composed of nickel
and iron

The layered structure of the Earth

11.2 Plate tectonics

Earthquakes and volcanoes occur in belts of
activity, which run

- along chains of high mountains, e.g. the Alps
  and the Andes. Deep **oceanic trenches** in the
  sea floor run alongside mountain ranges near
  the edges of continents.
- along chains of high mountains beneath the
  sea called **oceanic ridges**
- through chains of volcanic islands, e.g. the
  Philippines. Oceanic trenches run close to
  these belts.

Why do earthquakes and volcanoes occur in some
parts of Earth's crust and not others? The theory
of **plate tectonics** holds that the lithosphere (crust
+ outer mantle) is made up of a number of
separate **plates** (see diagram on next page).
Movements in the mantle make the plates move
very slowly, at a rate of about 5 cm a year. As a
result, plates may push against each other,
creating stress. As the stress builds up, the plates
may bend more and more until suddenly and
violently they spring back into shape. Then the

shock is felt as an earthquake. The energy
required for the movements of the mantle comes
from the decay of radioactive elements in the
lithosphere.

Plate boundaries

There are three types of boundaries
between plates.

★ **Destructive boundaries** occur where plates are in
  collision. The edge of the oceanic plate slides
  beneath the less dense continental plate. As the
  oceanic plate moves downwards it melts and
  becomes part of the mantle. The process is called
  subduction. It causes oceans to shrink in size.

★ **Constructive boundaries** occur where lava erupts
  from volcanoes along the oceanic ridges and cools
  to form new oceanic crust. The new crust adds to
  the plates on each side and pushes them apart,
  increasing the width of the ocean floor. The process
  is called **sea-floor spreading**.

★ **Conservative boundaries** occur where two plates
  slide past one another, e.g. the San Andreas fault in
  California. No lithosphere is added or lost.

The plates that make up Earth's crust

The movement of plates

Material is subducted from plates at oceanic trenches and added at oceanic ridges. As a result, there is a movement of plates which has been described as a **conveyor belt** (see diagram below). As plates ride on the mobile mantle, the continents on them move. This has been happening for thousands of millions of years. Although continents move only a few centimetres a year, they have already travelled thousands of kilometres. About 300 million years ago, northern Europe was near the equator, and tropical forests grew there. These later decayed to form coal deposits.

Evidence for the theory of plate tectonics

There is a similarity between the east coastline of South America and the west coastline of Africa. This led scientists to suggest the theory of

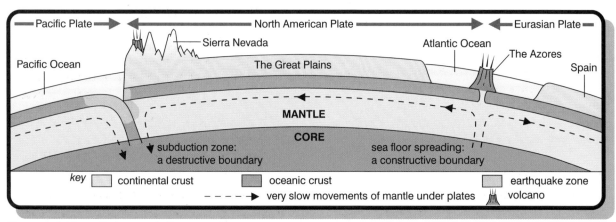

Movement of plates on the 'conveyor belt'

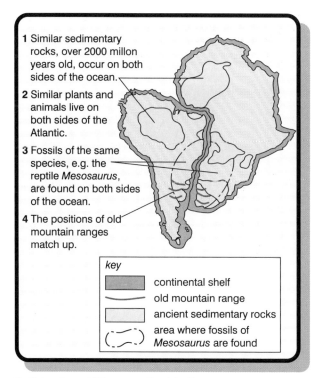

1 Similar sedimentary rocks, over 2000 millon years old, occur on both sides of the ocean.

2 Similar plants and animals live on both sides of the Atlantic.

3 Fossils of the same species, e.g. the reptile *Mesosaurus*, are found on both sides of the ocean.

4 The positions of old mountain ranges match up.

key

continental shelf

old mountain range

ancient sedimentary rocks

area where fossils of *Mesosaurus* are found

South America and Africa – were they joined?

continental drift. There is evidence that geological ages ago the two continents were joined together, and later split up and slowly drifted apart.

According to the theory of continental drift, there was one original land mass, Pangaea, which split 180 million years ago into two parts. The two land masses, Laurasia and Gondwanaland, drifted apart. Oceans widened between them. Over millions of years the original land masses split up and drifted apart to form the five continents that we have today. What was the source of the energy needed to drive the continents apart? An enormous quantity of heat is produced by radioactive decay inside the Earth. Some of the heat drives convection currents in the magma. These currents power the continental drift.

11.3 Types of rock

Igneous rocks

Molten rock beneath Earth's crust is called **magma**. Magma tends to rise, and, when cracks appear in the Earth's crust, magma is forced out from the mantle as lava. It erupts on to the surface of the Earth as a volcano. When volcanic lava cools, it crystallises to form **extrusive igneous rocks**. The faster the rate of cooling, the smaller the crystals that are formed. When magma crystallises below Earth's surface, **intrusive igneous rocks** are formed. Igneous rocks include

- basalt, an extrusive igneous rock formed by free-flowing mobile lava
- granite, an intrusive igneous rock
- pumice, formed from a foam of lava and volcanic gases.

Sedimentary rocks

The rocks on Earth's surface are worn down by weathering and by erosion. The fragments that are worn away are carried by winds, ice and rivers and eventually deposited as a **sediment**. A bed of sediment may form on a sea shore, on an ocean floor or in a desert. As more material is deposited on top, the pressure makes the sediment **lithify** – form a sedimentary rock. Sedimentary rocks may contain fossils – imprints of dead plants or animals which were included in the rocks as they formed. Fossils are used to date rocks. If a rock contains the marks of creatures known to have been alive 250 million years ago, the rock must be 250 million years old. Sedimentary rocks include

- limestone, formed from the shells of dead animals
- coal, formed from the remains of dead plants
- sandstone, compacted grains of sand.

Metamorphic rocks

Metamorphic rocks are formed from igneous and sedimentary rocks at high temperature or high pressure. Included among metamorphic rocks are

- marble, formed from limestone at high temperature
- slate, formed from clay, mud and shale at high pressure.

Earth's crust is composed of 8% sedimentary rocks, 65% igneous rocks and 27% metamorphic rocks.

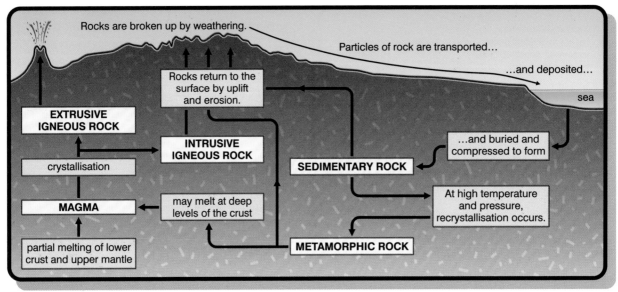

The rock cycle

The rock cycle

The interconversion between igneous rocks, sedimentary rocks and metamorphic rocks is called the **rock cycle** (see diagram above).

11.4 The landscape

Rocks are constantly being slowly broken down into smaller particles by **physical forces**, such as the wind, and **chemical reactions** which attack rocks. These processes are called **weathering**. When rocks are broken down and the particles are carried away by an agent such as water or wind, the process is called **erosion**. Weathering and erosion shape the landscape. The following agents shape the landscape:

- rainwater enters cracks in a rock, freezes, expands and opens the cracks wider
- rivers and streams carry material in solution and in suspension
- erosion happens when minerals dissolve slightly in water
- chemical reactions occur, e.g. between acidic water and limestone rocks
- glaciers move slowly over a landscape, wearing down rocks
- wind has a landscaping effect which is strongest in desert areas.

11.5 Materials from rocks

Many useful materials are obtained from rocks. Metals are extracted from compounds which occur in rocks; see page 182. Limestone and silica are important rocks.

Limestone

The concept map opposite shows the uses of limestone.

A lime kiln

The reaction that takes place in a lime kiln is

calcium carbonate → calcium oxide + carbon
(limestone)   (quicklime)   dioxide

$$CaCO_3(s) \rightarrow CaO(s) + CO_2(g)$$

This reaction is **reversible**; it can take place in the reverse direction as well as in the forward direction:

calcium oxide + carbon dioxide → calcium carbonate
(a base)   (an acid)   (a salt)

In the lime kiln, a draught of air blowing through the kiln carries away carbon dioxide so that it cannot recombine with calcium oxide.

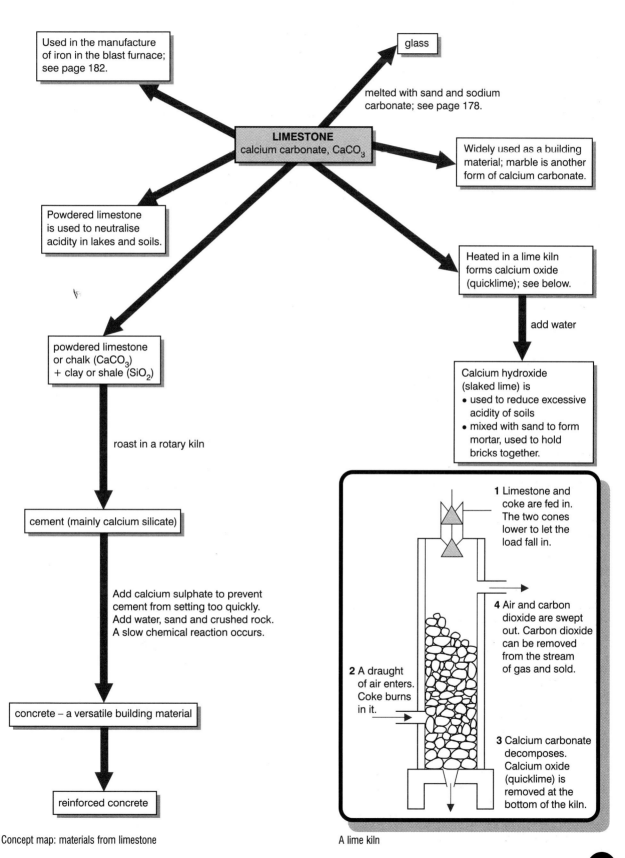

Used in the manufacture of iron in the blast furnace; see page 182.

glass

melted with sand and sodium carbonate; see page 178.

LIMESTONE
calcium carbonate, $CaCO_3$

Widely used as a building material; marble is another form of calcium carbonate.

Powdered limestone is used to neutralise acidity in lakes and soils.

Heated in a lime kiln forms calcium oxide (quicklime); see below.

add water

powdered limestone or chalk ($CaCO_3$) + clay or shale (SiO_2)

Calcium hydroxide (slaked lime) is
• used to reduce excessive acidity of soils
• mixed with sand to form mortar, used to hold bricks together.

roast in a rotary kiln

cement (mainly calcium silicate)

Add calcium sulphate to prevent cement from setting too quickly. Add water, sand and crushed rock. A slow chemical reaction occurs.

concrete – a versatile building material

reinforced concrete

1 Limestone and coke are fed in. The two cones lower to let the load fall in.

4 Air and carbon dioxide are swept out. Carbon dioxide can be removed from the stream of gas and sold.

2 A draught of air enters. Coke burns in it.

3 Calcium carbonate decomposes. Calcium oxide (quicklime) is removed at the bottom of the kiln.

Concept map: materials from limestone

A lime kiln

11

Silica

The concept map below shows the uses of silicon(IV) oxide (silica).

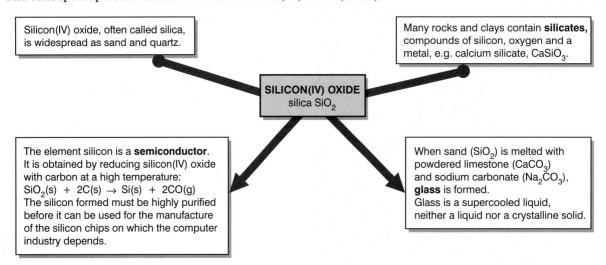

Silicon(IV) oxide, often called silica, is widespread as sand and quartz.

Many rocks and clays contain **silicates,** compounds of silicon, oxygen and a metal, e.g. calcium silicate, $CaSiO_3$.

SILICON(IV) OXIDE
silica SiO_2

The element silicon is a **semiconductor**. It is obtained by reducing silicon(IV) oxide with carbon at a high temperature:
$$SiO_2(s) + 2C(s) \rightarrow Si(s) + 2CO(g)$$
The silicon formed must be highly purified before it can be used for the manufacture of the silicon chips on which the computer industry depends.

When sand (SiO_2) is melted with powdered limestone ($CaCO_3$) and sodium carbonate (Na_2CO_3), **glass** is formed. Glass is a supercooled liquid, neither a liquid nor a crystalline solid.

Concept map: silica

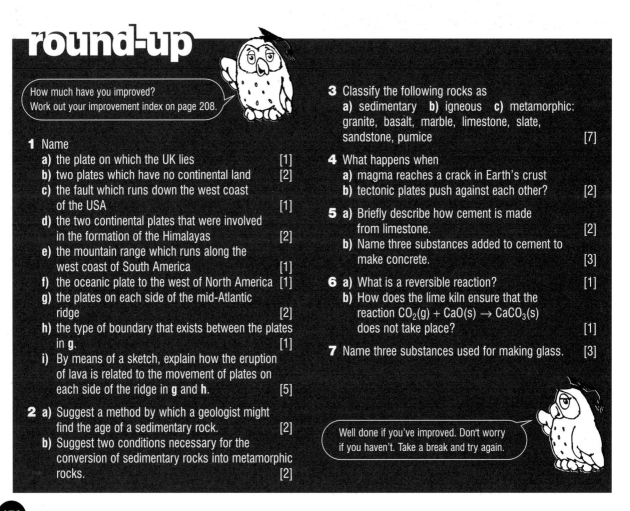

round-up

How much have you improved? Work out your improvement index on page 208.

1 Name
  a) the plate on which the UK lies [1]
  b) two plates which have no continental land [2]
  c) the fault which runs down the west coast of the USA [1]
  d) the two continental plates that were involved in the formation of the Himalayas [2]
  e) the mountain range which runs along the west coast of South America [1]
  f) the oceanic plate to the west of North America [1]
  g) the plates on each side of the mid-Atlantic ridge [2]
  h) the type of boundary that exists between the plates in **g**. [1]
  i) By means of a sketch, explain how the eruption of lava is related to the movement of plates on each side of the ridge in **g** and **h**. [5]

2 a) Suggest a method by which a geologist might find the age of a sedimentary rock. [2]
  b) Suggest two conditions necessary for the conversion of sedimentary rocks into metamorphic rocks. [2]

3 Classify the following rocks as
  a) sedimentary b) igneous c) metamorphic:
  granite, basalt, marble, limestone, slate, sandstone, pumice [7]

4 What happens when
  a) magma reaches a crack in Earth's crust
  b) tectonic plates push against each other? [2]

5 a) Briefly describe how cement is made from limestone. [2]
  b) Name three substances added to cement to make concrete. [3]

6 a) What is a reversible reaction? [1]
  b) How does the lime kiln ensure that the reaction $CO_2(g) + CaO(s) \rightarrow CaCO_3(s)$ does not take place? [1]

7 Name three substances used for making glass. [3]

Well done if you've improved. Don't worry if you haven't. Take a break and try again.

Metals and alloys

12

preview

At the end of this topic you will:

- **understand the nature of the metallic bond**

- **be familiar with the chemical reactions of metals**

- **use the reactivity series to make predictions about metals and their compounds and methods used for extracting metals**

- **know methods of preventing the rusting of iron.**

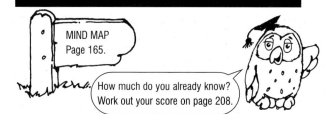

MIND MAP
Page 165.

How much do you already know?
Work out your score on page 208.

Test yourself

1 List three characteristics of metals that are explained by the metallic bond. [3]

2 Name three metals that burn in air to form oxides. [3]

3 Name two metals that do not react when heated in air. [2]

4 Name three metals that react with cold water and say what products are formed. [5]

5 What is formed when a metal reacts with hydrochloric acid? [2]

6 In which groups of the periodic table do you find
a) sodium **b)** magnesium **c)** transition metals? [3]

7 What method is used to extract very reactive metals from their ores? [2]

8 How is iron extracted from its ore? [3]

9 Name two metals which become coated with a film of oxide on exposure to the air. [2]

12.1 The metallic bond

A block of metal consists of positive metal ions and free electrons, as shown in the diagram.

The presence of free electrons explains how metals can conduct electricity. Electrons can be supplied at one end of a piece of metal and removed at the other end. The nature of the metallic bond also explains how metals can change their shape without breaking.

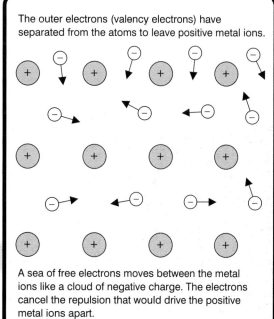

The outer electrons (valency electrons) have separated from the atoms to leave positive metal ions.

A sea of free electrons moves between the metal ions like a cloud of negative charge. The electrons cancel the repulsion that would drive the positive metal ions apart.

The metallic bond

12.2 Reactions of metals

Most metals react slowly with air to form a surface film of metal oxide. This reaction is called **tarnishing**. Gold and platinum do not tarnish in air. Aluminium rapidly forms a surface layer of aluminium oxide and only shows its true reactivity if this layer is removed. The table on the next page shows some of the reactions of metals.

metal	reaction when heated in oxygen	reaction with cold water	reaction with dilute hydrochloric acid
potassium sodium lithium calcium magnesium aluminium zinc iron	burn to form the oxides	displace hydrogen; form alkaline hydroxides.	react dangerously fast to form hydrogen and the metal chloride
		reacts slowly do not react, except for slow rusting of iron; all react with steam	displace hydrogen; form metal chlorides
tin lead copper	slowly form oxides without burning	do not react even with steam	react very slowly to form hydrogen and the metal chloride
silver gold platinum	do not react		do not react

Reactions of metals

Here are equations for some of the reactions mentioned in the table:

sodium + water → hydrogen + sodium hydroxide

$$2Na(s) + 2H_2O(l) \rightarrow H_2(g) + 2NaOH(aq)$$

(Sodium must be kept under oil to prevent it being attacked by water in the air.)

calcium + water → hydrogen + calcium hydroxide

$$Ca(s) + 2H_2O(l) \rightarrow H_2(g) + Ca(OH)_2(aq)$$

magnesium + water → hydrogen + magnesium hydroxide

$$Mg(s) + 2H_2O(l) \rightarrow H_2(g) + Mg(OH)_2(aq)$$

magnesium + steam → hydrogen + magnesium oxide

$$Mg(s) + H_2O(g) \rightarrow H_2(g) + MgO(s)$$

zinc + steam → hydrogen + zinc oxide

$$Zn(s) + H_2O(g) \rightarrow H_2(g) + ZnO(s)$$

iron + steam → hydrogen + tri-iron tetraoxide

$$3Fe(s) + 4H_2O(g) \rightarrow 4H_2(g) + Fe_3O_4(s)$$

zinc + hydrochloric acid → hydrogen + zinc chloride

$$Zn(s) + 2HCl(aq) \rightarrow H_2(g) + ZnCl_2(aq)$$

The metals can be placed in an order of reactivity which is called the **reactivity series**:

potassium	K		
sodium	Na		
lithium	Li	increase in	
calcium	Ca	reactivity	
magnesium	Mg		
aluminium	Al	increase in	increase in
zinc	Zn	the ease	the ease of
iron	Fe	with which	discharge
tin	Sn	metals	of metal ions
lead	Pb	react to	in electrolysis
copper	Cu	form ions	
silver	Ag		
gold	Au		
platinum	Pt		

Part of the reactivity series of metals

12.3 Metals in the periodic table

PERIODIC TABLE
Page 139.

In Group 1 of the periodic table are the **alkali metals**, and in Group 2 are the **alkaline earths**. Aluminium is in Group 3. The less reactive metals tin and lead are in Group 4. The metals in the block between Group 2 and Group 3 are called the **transition metals**, e.g. iron, nickel, copper and zinc. For the differences between the physical and chemical properties of metallic and non-metallic elements, see page 118.

12.4 Making predictions

Competition between metals for oxygen

When aluminium is heated with iron(III) oxide, the two metals are in competition for oxygen. Aluminium wins because it is above iron in the reactivity series.

aluminium + iron(III) oxide → iron + aluminium oxide

$$2Al(s) + Fe_2O_3(s) \rightarrow 2Fe(s) + Al_2O_3(s)$$

The reaction that occurs is highly exothermic. It is called the **thermit reaction**. Since the iron forms in a molten state, it can be used to weld pieces of metal together.

Competition between metals to form ions

Metals high in the reactivity series form ions with ease. A metal which is higher in the reactivity series will displace a metal which is lower in the reactivity series from a salt. Examples are:

copper + silver nitrate solution → silver + copper(II) nitrate solution
(colourless solution) (silver crystals, turn black in light) (blue solution)

$$Cu(s) + 2AgNO_3(aq) \rightarrow 2Ag(s) + Cu(NO_3)_2(aq)$$

or $$Cu(s) + 2Ag^+(aq) \rightarrow Cu^{2+}(aq) + 2Ag(s)$$

zinc + copper(II) sulphate → copper + zinc sulphate
(blue solution) (reddish brown solid) (colourless solution)

$$Zn(s) + CuSO_4(aq) \rightarrow Cu(s) + ZnSO_4(aq)$$

or $$Zn(s) + Cu^{2+}(aq) \rightarrow Zn^{2+}(aq) + Cu(s)$$

Discharge of ions in electrolysis

When metal ions are discharged in electrolysis, the ions of metals high in the reactivity series are difficult to discharge, and the ions of metals low in the reactivity series are easy to discharge. For example:

* when a solution containing copper ions and iron ions is electrolysed, copper is formed at the cathode, while iron ions remain in solution

* when a solution containing copper ions and silver ions is electrolysed, silver is discharged at the cathode, while copper ions remain in solution.

Compounds and the reactivity series

The higher a metal is in the reactivity series,

* the more readily it forms compounds
* the more difficult it is to split up its compounds.

Oxides

★ Hydrogen will reduce the oxides of metals which are low in the reactivity series, e.g.

copper(II) oxide + hydrogen $\xrightarrow{heat}$ copper + water

$$CuO(s) + H_2(g) \rightarrow Cu(s) + H_2O(l)$$

★ Carbon, when heated, will reduce the oxides of metals which are low in the reactivity series, e.g.

lead(II) oxide + carbon $\xrightarrow{heat}$ lead + carbon monoxide

$$PbO(s) + C(s) \rightarrow Pb(s) + CO(g)$$

★ Carbon monoxide is used to reduce hot iron oxide to iron.

iron(III) oxide + carbon monoxide $\xrightarrow{heat}$ iron + carbon dioxide

$$Fe_2O_3(s) + 3CO(g) \rightarrow 2Fe(s) + 3CO_2(g)$$

★ The oxides of metals which are high in the reactivity series, e.g. aluminium, are not reduced by hydrogen or carbon or carbon monoxide.

★ Silver and mercury are very low in the reactivity series. Their oxides decompose when heated.

Other compounds

The position of the metal in the reactivity series ties in with the stability of its compounds to heat, as shown in the table on the next page.

cation	anion				
	oxide	**chloride**	**sulphate**	**carbonate**	**hydroxide**
potassium sodium calcium magnesium aluminium zinc iron lead	no decomposition	no decomposition	no decomposition		
			oxide + sulphur trioxide, $MO + SO_3$ some also give SO_2	oxide + carbon dioxide, $MO + CO_2$	oxide + water, $MO + H_2O$
copper silver	metal + oxygen		metal + O_2 + SO_3	metal + O_2 + CO_2	do not form hydroxides
gold	not formed				

Action of heat on compounds

12.5 Extracting metals

The method chosen for extracting a metal from its ore depends on the position of the metal in the reactivity series; see table opposite.

Iron

The chief ores of iron are haematite, Fe_2O_3, magnetite, Fe_3O_4, and iron pyrites, FeS_2. The sulphide ore is roasted in air to convert it into an oxide. The oxide ores are reduced to iron in a blast furnace (see diagram below). The blast furnace is run continuously. The low cost of extraction and the plentiful raw materials make iron cheaper than other metals.

potassium, sodium, calcium, magnesium — Anhydrous chloride is melted and electrolysed.

aluminium — Molten anhydrous oxide is electrolysed.

zinc, iron, lead — Sulphides are roasted to give oxides which are reduced with carbon; oxides are reduced with carbon.

copper — Sulphide ore is heated with a controlled volume of air.

silver, gold — Found 'native' (as the free metals).

Methods used for the extraction of metals from their ores

1 A load of iron ore, limestone and coke is tipped in. The two cones lower in turn to let the load fall into the furnace.

4 Carbon monoxide reduces iron oxides to iron.
$Fe_2O_3(s) + 3CO(g) \rightarrow 2Fe(s) + 3CO_2(g)$

3 Carbon dioxide rises up the furnace and reacts with coke to form carbon monoxide.
$CO_2(g) + C(s) \rightarrow 2CO(g)$

2 A blast of hot air enters. Coke burns in it to form carbon dioxide.
$C(s) + O_2(g) \rightarrow CO_2(g)$

8 Molten slag is run off.

5 Exhaust gases leave. They are used to heat incoming air.

6 Limestone decomposes to form calcium oxide and carbon dioxide.
$CaCO_3(s) \rightarrow CaO(s) + CO_2(g)$

Calcium oxide combines with acidic impurities in the ore to form 'slag'
$CaO(s) + SiO_2(s) \rightarrow CaSiO_3(l)$

7 Molten iron is run off.

A blast furnace

12.6 Corrosion of metals

★ **Copper**: the green roofs you see on some buildings are of copper, which has corroded in the air to copper carbonate hydroxide, $Cu(OH)_2.CuCO_3$.

★ **Aluminium**: as soon as a fresh surface of aluminium meets the air, it is corroded to form a thin film of the oxide, which prevents air from reaching the metal below.

★ **Chromium** forms a protective oxide layer in the same way as aluminium. Stainless steel cutlery is made of a chromium–steel alloy (mixture).

★ **Nickel** forms a protective oxide layer as soon as a fresh surface of nickel meets the air. Nickel-plated steels are very useful.

★ **Lead** water pipes were used for centuries. However, water attacks lead slowly to form soluble lead compounds.

★ **Zinc** corrodes quickly in air to form a film of zinc carbonate. This protects the zinc beneath from further attack. Iron can be coated with zinc (**galvanised**) to protect it from rusting.

Rusting of iron and steel

The corrosion of iron and steel is called rusting. Rust has the formula $Fe_2O_3.nH_2O$, where n, the number of water molecules in the formula, varies.

The combination of reagents that attacks iron is water, air and acid. The carbon dioxide in the air provides the acidity. If the water contains salts, the speed of rusting is increased. In a warm climate, rusting is more rapid than at lower temperatures.

The rusting of iron is an expensive problem. The table below lists some of the methods used to protect iron and steel against rusting.

12.7 Conservation

The Earth's resources of metals are limited. It makes sense to collect scrap metals and recycle them. In addition, there is a saving in fuel resources because less energy is needed for recycling than for extracting metals from their ores. There is another reason for conserving metals: the impact which mining has on the environment. Before recycling, scrap metals must be collected, sorted and stored until there is enough to process.

method	where used	comment
1 a coat of paint	large objects, e.g. ships and bridges	If the paint is scratched, the iron beneath it starts to rust.
2 a film oil or grease	moving parts of machinery	The protective film must be renewed.
3 a coat of metal **a)** chromium plating	trim on cars, cycle handlebars, taps	Applied by electroplating, decorative as well as protective.
b) galvanising (zinc plating)	galvanised steel girders are used in buildings	Even if the layer of zinc is scratched, the iron underneath does not rust. Zinc cannot be used for food cans because zinc and its compounds are poisonous.
c) tin plating	food cans	If the layer of tin is scratched, the iron beneath it rusts.
4 stainless steel	cutlery, car accessories	Steels containing chromium (10–25%) or nickel (10–20%) do not rust.
5 sacrificial protection	ships	Bars of zinc attached to the hull of a ship corrode and protect the ship from rusting.
	underground pipes	Bags of magnesium scrap attached to underground iron pipes corrode in preference to the pipes. The scrap must be replaced from time to time.

Rust prevention

12

TAKE A BREAK

12.8 Uses of metals and alloys

The strengths of metals and **alloys** (mixtures of metals) find them thousands of uses; the table below lists just some of these.

metal/alloy	characteristics	uses
aluminium	low density good electrical conductor good thermal conductor reflector of light non-toxic resistant to corrosion	aircraft manufacture (Duralumin) overhead electrical cable saucepans, etc. car headlamps food packaging door frames, window frames, etc.
brass, an alloy of copper and zinc	golden colour, harder than copper, resists corrosion	ships' propellers, taps, screws, electrical fittings
bronze, an alloy of copper and tin	golden colour, hard, sonorous, resistant to corrosion	coins, medals, statues, springs, church bells
copper	good electrical conductor not corroded	electrical circuits water pipes and tanks
Duralumin, an alloy of aluminium	low density, stronger than aluminium	aircraft and spacecraft
gold	beautiful colour never tarnishes	jewellery, dentistry, electrical contacts
iron	hard, strong, inexpensive, rusts	construction, transport
lead	dense, unreactive, soft, not very strong	car batteries, divers' weights, roofing
magnesium	bright flame	flares and flash bulbs
mercury	liquid at room temperature	thermometers, dental amalgam for filling teeth
nickel	resists corrosion, strong, tough, hard	stainless steel
silver	beautiful colour and shine good electrical conductor good reflector of light	jewellery, silverware contacts in computers, etc. mirrors, dental amalgam
solder, alloy of tin and lead	low melting point	joining metals in an electrical circuit
steel, an iron alloy	strong	buildings, machinery, transport
tin	low in reactivity series	coating 'tin cans'
titanium	low in density, strong, very resistant to corrosion	high-altitude planes, nose-cones of spacecraft
zinc	high in reactivity series	protection of iron and steel by galvanising

The uses of some metals and alloys

12.9 Iron and steel

Cast iron

The iron that comes out of the blast furnace is called cast iron. It contains 3–4% carbon which lowers the melting point, making cast iron easier to melt and mould than pure iron. By casting, objects with complicated shapes can be made, such as the engine blocks of motor vehicles. The carbon content makes cast iron brittle.

Steel

Steel is made from iron by burning off carbon and other impurities in a stream of oxygen. A number of elements may be added to give different types of steel:

- chromium in stainless steels for cutlery, car accessories and tools
- cobalt steel in permanent magnets
- manganese in all steels to increase strength
- molybdenum steel for rifle barrels and propeller shafts
- nickel in stainless steel cutlery and industrial plants
- tungsten steel in high-speed cutting tools
- vanadium steel in springs.

round-up

PERIODIC TABLE
Page 139.

How much have you improved?
Work out your improvement index on pages 208–9.

1 Write equations for the reactions with oxygen of
   a) sodium (to form Na_2O) [3]
   b) magnesium [3]
   c) zinc [3]
   d) iron (to form Fe_3O_4) [3]
   e) tin (to form SnO) [3]
   f) lead (to form PbO) [3]
   g) copper (to form CuO). [3]

2 a) Write equations for the reactions of
      (i) magnesium and hydrochloric acid [4]
      (ii) iron and hydrochloric acid (to form $FeCl_2$) [4]
      (iii) tin and hydrochloric acid (to form $SnCl_2$). [4]
   b) Write equations for the reactions between
      (i) magnesium and sulphuric acid [4]
      (ii) iron and sulphuric acid (to give $FeSO_4$). [4]

3 Copy and complete these word equations. If there is no reaction, write 'no reaction'. [8]
   a) magnesium + sulphuric acid →
   b) platinum + sulphuric acid →
   c) silver + hydrochloric acid →
   d) gold + hydrochloric acid →
   e) zinc + sulphuric acid →
   f) tin + water →

4 Why are copper and its alloys used as coinage metals in preference to iron? [3]

5 The following metals are listed in order of reactivity:
      calcium > magnesium > iron > copper
   Describe how the metals follow this order in their reactions with
   a) water [4]
   b) dilute hydrochloric acid. [4]

6 What would you see if you dropped a piece of zinc into a test tube of
   a) copper(II) sulphate solution
   b) lead(II) nitrate solution?
   Write word equations and chemical equations for the reactions. [11]

7 A metal X displaces another metal Y from a solution of a salt of Y. X is displaced by a metal Z from a solution of a salt of X. List the metals in order of reactivity with the most reactive first. [2]

8 The following metals are listed in order of reactivity, with the most reactive first:
   Na Mg Al Zn Fe Pb Cu Hg Au
   List the metals which
   a) occur as the free elements in the Earth's crust [1]
   b) react at an observable speed with cold water [2]
   c) react with steam but not with cold water [2]
   d) react at an observable speed with dilute acids [4]
   e) react dangerously fast with dilute acids [1]
   f) displace lead from lead(II) nitrate solution. [4]

12

round-up

9 Suggest what method could be used to extract each of the metals A, B, C and D from a chloride ore or an oxide ore.
- Metal A reacts with cold water. [3]
- Metal B reacts only very, very slowly with water. [2]
- Metal C does not react with steam or with dilute hydrochloric acid. [2]
- Metal D when exposed to air immediately becomes coated with a layer of oxide. [3]

10 Predict the reaction of **a)** rubidium and cold water **b)** palladium and dilute hydrochloric acid. [5]

11 Copy and complete the following word equations. If no reaction occurs, write 'no reaction'.
- **a)** copper + oxygen → [1]
- **b)** aluminium + iron(III) oxide → [1]
- **c)** iron + aluminium oxide → [1]
- **d)** carbon monoxide + iron(III) oxide → [1]
- **e)** carbon monoxide + aluminium oxide → [1]
- **f)** zinc + copper(II) sulphate solution → [1]

12 List four different uses for aluminium. Say what property of aluminium makes it suitable for each use. [8]

13 What method of rust prevention is used on **a)** a bicycle chain **b)** bicycle handlebars **c)** steel girders **d)** cutlery **e)** parts of a ship above the waterline **f)** parts of a ship below the waterline **g)** food cans? [7]

14 List three savings which are made when metal objects are recycled. [3]

Well done if you've improved. Don't worry if you haven't. Take a break and try again.

Make your own Mind Map! This is only a starting point. The rest is up to you!

Reaction speeds

preview

At the end of this topic you will:

- **understand the factors which can change the speed of a chemical reaction.**

MIND MAP
Page 166.

How much do you already know?
Work out your score on page 209.

Test yourself

1 Which act faster to cure acid indigestion, indigestion tablets or indigestion powders? Explain your answer. [2]

2 a) Suggest three ways in which you could speed up the reaction between zinc and dilute sulphuric acid:

$$Zn(s) + H_2SO_4(aq) \rightarrow H_2(g) + ZnSO_4(aq)$$ [3]

b) Explain why each of these methods increases the speed of the reaction. [4]

3 Sketch an apparatus in which you could collect a gaseous product of a reaction and measure the rate at which it was formed. [5]

4 What is a catalyst? [2]

5 Why are catalysts important in industry? [2]

6 Name two reactions which depend on the absorption of light energy. [2]

13.1 Particle size

The reaction between a solid and a liquid is speeded up by using smaller particles of the solid reactant. The reason is that it is the atoms or ions at the surface of the solid that react, and the ratio of surface area:mass is greater for small particles than for large particles.

The diagram below shows an apparatus which you may have used to investigate the effect of particle size on the reaction:

$$\text{calcium carbonate} + \text{hydrochloric acid} \rightarrow \text{carbon dioxide} + \text{calcium chloride} + \text{water}$$

$$CaCO_3(s) + 2HCl(aq) \rightarrow CO_2(g) + CaCl_2(aq) + H_2O(l)$$

The effect of particle size on the speed of a reaction

As the reaction happens, carbon dioxide is given off and the mass of the reacting mixture decreases.

1 Note the mass of flask + acid + marble chips.

2 Add the marble chips to the acid, and start a stopwatch.

3 Note the mass after 10 seconds and then every 30 seconds for 5–10 minutes.

4 Plot the mass against time since the start of the reaction.

5 Repeat with the same mass of smaller chips.

13.2 Concentration

A precipitate of sulphur is formed in the reaction:

| sodium thiosulphate | + | hydrochloric acid | → sulphur + | sulphur dioxide | + | sodium chloride | + water |

$$Na_2S_2O_3(aq) + 2HCl(aq) \rightarrow S(s) + SO_2(g) + 2NaCl(aq) + H_2O(l)$$

1 Watch the precipitate of sulphur appear.

2 Note the time when the precipitate is thick enough to block your view of a cross on a piece of paper.

3 Repeat for various concentrations of acid and for various concentrations of thiosulphate.

The experiment shows that, for this reaction,

• rate of reaction is proportional to concentration of thiosulphate
• rate of reaction is proportional to concentration of acid.

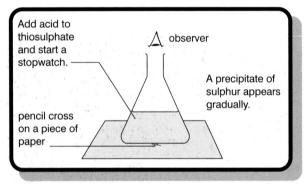

The effect of concentration on the speed of a reaction

13.3 Pressure

An increase in pressure increases the rates of reactions between gases. As the molecules are pushed more closely together, they react more rapidly.

13.4 Temperature

The reaction between thiosulphate and acid can be used to study the effect of temperature on the rate of a reaction, as shown in the following graphs. This reaction goes twice as fast at 30°C as it does at 20°C. At higher temperatures, ions have more kinetic energy and collide more often and more vigorously, giving them a greater chance of reacting.

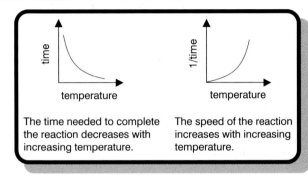

The time needed to complete the reaction decreases with increasing temperature.

The speed of the reaction increases with increasing temperature.

The effect of temperature on the speed of a reaction

13.5 Light

Heat is not the only form of energy that speeds up chemical reactions. Light energy enables many reactions to take place, e.g. photosynthesis and photography.

13.6 Catalysts

Hydrogen peroxide decomposes to form oxygen and water:

hydrogen peroxide → oxygen + water

$$2H_2O_2(aq) \rightarrow O_2(g) + 2H_2O(l)$$

The decomposition takes place very slowly unless a **catalyst**, e.g. manganese(IV) oxide, is present. The rate at which the reaction takes place can be found by collecting the oxygen formed and measuring its volume at certain times after the start of the reaction, as shown in the diagram.

Oxygen collects in the gas syringe. The volume is read at certain times after the reaction. The volume can be plotted against the time.

Collecting and measuring a gas

★ A catalyst is a substance which increases the rate of a chemical reaction without being used up in the reaction.

★ A catalyst will catalyse a certain reaction or group of reactions. Platinum catalyses certain oxidation reactions, and nickel catalyses some hydrogenation reactions.

★ Catalysts are very important in industry. They enable a manufacturer to make a product more rapidly or at a lower temperature.

13.7 Enzymes

Chemical reactions take place in the cells of living things. These reactions happen at reasonably fast

ENZYMES
Page 45.

rates at the temperatures which exist in plants and animals. They can do this because the cells contain powerful catalysts called **enzymes**.

Enzymes are proteins. They have large molecules which are twisted into complicated three-dimensional structures. The structures are damaged by temperatures above about 45°C. Here are some examples of enzyme-catalysed reactions:

• Enzymes in yeast catalyse the conversion of sugar into ethanol and carbon dioxide. The process is called **fermentation**. It is used to make ethanol (alcohol) by the fermentation of carbohydrates. It also produces bubbles of carbon dioxide which make bread rise.
• Enzymes in bacteria produce yoghurt from milk. They catalyse the conversion of lactose, the sugar in milk, into lactic acid.

round-up

How much have you improved?
Work out your improvement index on page 209.

1 The three graphs were obtained in experiments as described on page 187.
 a) Why is there a decrease in mass? [1]
 b) Which of the graphs relates to (i) small chips (ii) large chips (iii) medium-sized chips? [2]
 c) Explain why there is a difference. [1]

Graphs of mass of marble chips + acid against time

2 Suggest two ways of cooking potatoes faster. [2]

3 Someone tells you that there is an enzyme in potatoes that is better than manganese(IV) oxide as a catalyst for the decomposition of hydrogen peroxide. Describe the experiments you would do to find out whether this is true. [4]

4 You are asked to study the effect of temperature on the reaction:

magnesium + $\dfrac{\text{sulphuric}}{\text{acid}}$ → $\dfrac{\text{magnesium}}{\text{sulphate}}$ + hydrogen

Describe the measurements you would make and what you would do with your results. [6]

5 Catalysts A and B catalyse the decomposition of hydrogen peroxide.

time / minutes	0	3	6	9	12	15	18	21
volume of oxygen with A / cm³	0	4	8	12	16	17	18	18
volume of oxygen with B / cm³	0	5	10	15	16.5	18	18	18

 a) Plot a graph to show both sets of results. [4]
 b) Say which is the better catalyst, A or B. [1]
 c) Add a line to your graph to show the uncatalysed reaction. [1]

Well done if you've improved. Don't worry if you haven't. Take a break and try again.

Tackling chemical calculations

preview

At the end of this topic you will be able to:

- **calculate the relative molecular mass and molar mass of a compound**
- **understand 'the mole'**
- **calculate the empirical formula and molecular formula of a compound**
- **use the equation for a reaction to calculate the masses of solids that react.**

RELATIVE ATOMIC MASSES Page 194.

How much do you already know? Work out your score on page 209.

Test yourself

1 State the relative molecular masses of **a)** SO_2 **b)** SO_3 **c)** H_2SO_4 **d)** CH_3CO_2H **e)** $CuSO_4.5H_2O$. [5]

2 State the amount in moles of **a)** sodium in 46 g of sodium **b)** sulphur atoms in 64 g of sulphur **c)** S_8 molecules in 64 g of sulphur. [3]

3 State the mass of **a)** mercury in 0.100 mol of mercury **b)** sulphuric acid in 0.25 mol of H_2SO_4 **c)** magnesium oxide in 3.0 mol of MgO. [3]

4 Calculate the empirical formulas of
   a) the compound containing 55.5% mercury and 44.5% bromine by mass [1]
   b) the compound formed from 14.9 g of copper and 17.7 g of chlorine [1]
   c) the compound formed when 0.69 g of sodium forms 0.93 g of an oxide. [1]

5 Calculate the percentage by mass of sulphur in
   a) SO_2 **b)** SO_3 **c)** H_2SO_4. [3]

6 When a mixture of 8 g of iron and 4 g of sulphur is heated, the elements react to form iron(II) sulphide, FeS. How much iron will be left over at the end of the reaction? [1]

7 **a)** Calculate the mass of carbon dioxide formed by the action of acid on 15 g of calcium carbonate in the reaction [1]
   $$CaCO_3(s) + 2HCl(aq) \rightarrow CO_2(g) + CaCl_2(aq) + H_2O(l)$$
   b) State the volume at room temperature and pressure (rtp) of the carbon dioxide formed. [1]

8 A sulphuric acid plant uses 2500 tonnes of sulphur dioxide each day.
   a) What mass of sulphur must be burned to produce this quantity of sulphur dioxide? [1]
   b) What is the volume at rtp of this mass of sulphur dioxide? [1]

9 A company buys 100 kg of $Na_2CO_3.10H_2O$ at 30p/kg with the intention of selling it as bath salts. While standing in the warehouse, the bag punctures, and the crystals lose some of their water of crystallisation to form $Na_2CO_3.H_2O$. The company sells this powder at 50p/kg. Does the company make a profit or a loss? [2]

14.1 Some definitions

Relative atomic mass

Relative atomic mass A_r of element =

$$\frac{\text{mass of one atom of the element}}{\frac{1}{12}\text{ mass of one atom of carbon-12}}$$

Relative molecular mass

Relative molecular mass M_r of compound =

$$\frac{\text{mass of one molecule or formula unit}}{\frac{1}{12}\text{ mass of one atom of carbon-12}}$$

The relative molecular mass M_r of a compound is the sum of the relative atomic masses of all the atoms in a molecule of the compound. For sulphuric acid, H_2SO_4,

$$M_r = 2(A_r\ H) + 1(A_r\ S) + 4(A_r\ O) = 2 + 32 + 64 = 98$$

The mole

The amount of an element that contains 6.022×10^{23} atoms (the same number of atoms as 12 g of carbon-12) is called **one mole** (symbol mol) of that element.

Take the relative atomic mass expressed in grams of any element:

12 g of carbon	24 g of magnesium	56 g of iron
40 g of calcium	108 g of silver	238 g of uranium

All these masses contain the same number of atoms: 6.022×10^{23} atoms.

The ratio 6.022×10^{23}/mol is called the **Avogadro constant**. Each of these masses represents one mole (1 mol) of the element. One mole of sulphuric acid contains 6.022×10^{23} molecules of H_2SO_4, that is, 98 g of H_2SO_4 (the molar mass in grams). To write 'a mole of nitrogen' is imprecise: one mole of nitrogen atoms, N, has a mass of 14 g; one mole of nitrogen molecules, N_2, has a mass of 28 g.

Molar mass

The molar mass of a substance, symbol M, is defined by the equation:

$$\frac{\text{amount (in moles)}}{\text{of substance}} = \frac{\text{mass of substance}}{\text{molar mass of substance}}$$

The molar mass of carbon is 12 g/mol; that is the relative atomic mass expressed in grams per mole. The molar mass of sulphuric acid, H_2SO_4, is 98 g/mol. Notice the units: relative molecular mass has no unit; molar mass has the unit g/mol.

Make sure you understand each of the terms in the Mind Map:

Example 1

What is the amount of calcium present in 120 g of calcium?

A_r of calcium = 40; molar mass of calcium = 40 g/mol

$$\text{amount of calcium} = \frac{\text{mass of calcium}}{\text{molar mass of calcium}}$$

$$= \frac{120 \text{ g}}{40 \text{ g/mol}}$$

$$= 3.0 \text{ mol}$$

The amount of calcium is 3.0 mol.

Example 2

If you need 2.25 mol of magnesium carbonate, what mass of the substance do you have to weigh out?

$$\begin{aligned}\text{relative molecular} \\ \text{mass of } MgCO_3\end{aligned} = 24 + 12 + (3 \times 16)$$

$$= 84$$

molar mass of $MgCO_3$ = 84 g/mol

$$\text{amount of substance} = \frac{\text{mass of substance}}{\text{molar mass of substance}}$$

$$2.25 \text{ mol} = \frac{\text{mass}}{84 \text{ g/mol}}$$

$$\text{mass} = 84 \text{ g/mol} \times 2.25 \text{ mol} = 189 \text{ g}$$

You need to weigh out 189 g of magnesium carbonate.

14

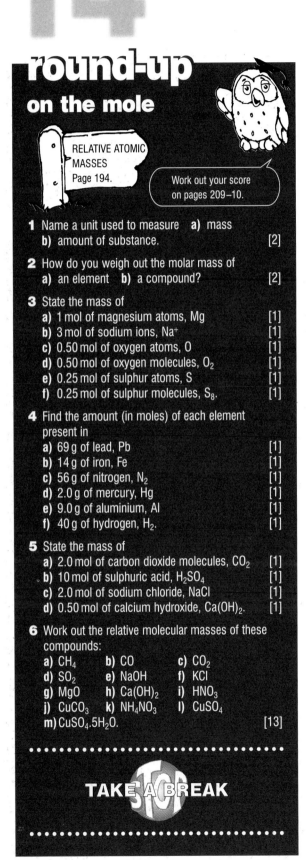

round-up
on the mole

RELATIVE ATOMIC
MASSES
Page 194.

Work out your score
on pages 209–10.

1 Name a unit used to measure **a)** mass
b) amount of substance. [2]

2 How do you weigh out the molar mass of
a) an element **b)** a compound? [2]

3 State the mass of
a) 1 mol of magnesium atoms, Mg [1]
b) 3 mol of sodium ions, Na^+ [1]
c) 0.50 mol of oxygen atoms, O [1]
d) 0.50 mol of oxygen molecules, O_2 [1]
e) 0.25 mol of sulphur atoms, S [1]
f) 0.25 mol of sulphur molecules, S_8. [1]

4 Find the amount (in moles) of each element
present in
a) 69 g of lead, Pb [1]
b) 14 g of iron, Fe [1]
c) 56 g of nitrogen, N_2 [1]
d) 2.0 g of mercury, Hg [1]
e) 9.0 g of aluminium, Al [1]
f) 40 g of hydrogen, H_2. [1]

5 State the mass of
a) 2.0 mol of carbon dioxide molecules, CO_2 [1]
b) 10 mol of sulphuric acid, H_2SO_4 [1]
c) 2.0 mol of sodium chloride, NaCl [1]
d) 0.50 mol of calcium hydroxide, $Ca(OH)_2$. [1]

6 Work out the relative molecular masses of these
compounds:
a) CH_4 **b)** CO   **c)** CO_2
d) SO_2 **e)** NaOH   **f)** KCl
g) MgO   **h)** $Ca(OH)_2$ **i)** HNO_3
j) $CuCO_3$ **k)** NH_4NO_3 **l)** $CuSO_4$
m) $CuSO_4.5H_2O$. [13]

• •

TAKE A BREAK

• •

14.2 Formulas

Molecular formula

The molecular formula of a compound shows the elements present and how many atoms of each element are present in a molecule or formula unit of the compound. For example, the molecular formula of ethanoic acid is $C_2H_4O_2$.

Empirical formula

The empirical formula of a compound shows the elements present and the **ratio** of the numbers of atoms of each element present in a molecule or formula unit of the compound. For example, the empirical formula of ethanoic acid is CH_2O. The empirical formula is calculated from the composition by mass of the compound. It is also possible to find the percentage composition by mass of the compound if its empirical formula is known.

Calculation of empirical formula

3.72 g of phosphorus react with 4.80 g of oxygen to form an oxide. What is the empirical formula of the oxide?

	phosphorus	**oxygen**
mass	3.72 g	4.80 g
A_r	31	16
amount (moles)	$\frac{3.72}{31}$	$\frac{4.80}{16}$
	= 0.12	0.30
ratio of amounts = 1	to	2.5
ratio of numbers of atoms = 2	to	5

Empirical formula is P_2O_5.

Calculation of percentage composition

Find the percentages by mass of carbon, hydrogen and oxygen in propanol, C_3H_7OH.

The empirical formula is C_3H_8O.

$M_r = (3 \times 12) + 8 + 16 = 60$

$$\text{percentage of carbon} = \frac{A_r(C) \times \text{no. of C atoms}}{M_r(C_3H_8O)} \times 100\%$$

$$= \frac{(12 \times 3)}{60} \times 100\% = 60.0\%$$

$$\text{percentage of hydrogen} = \frac{A_r(H) \times \text{no. of H atoms}}{M_r(C_3H_8O)} \times 100\%$$

$$= \frac{(1 \times 8)}{60} \times 100\% = 13.3\%$$

$$\text{percentage of oxygen} = \frac{A_r(O) \times \text{no. of O atoms}}{M_r(C_3H_8O)} \times 100\%$$

$$= \frac{(16 \times 1)}{60} \times 100\% = 26.7\%$$

You can check on your calculation by adding up the percentages:

carbon 60.0% + hydrogen 13.3% + oxygen 26.7% = 100%

Calculation of molecular formula

The molecular formula is a multiple of the empirical formula:

molecular formula = (empirical formula)$_n$

Therefore relative molecular mass = $n \times$ relative empirical formula mass.

For ethanoic acid:

empirical formula = CH_2O

relative empirical formula mass = (12 + 2 + 16) = 30

The relative molecular mass of ethanoic acid is found by experiment to be 60, therefore

molecular formula = 2 × empirical formula
$$= C_2H_4O_2.$$

14.3 Masses of reacting solids

The equation for a chemical reaction enables us to calculate the masses of solids that react together, and the masses of solid products that are formed.

Example 1

What mass of copper(II) oxide is formed by the complete oxidation of 3.175 g of copper?

Equation: $2Cu(s) + O_2(g) \rightarrow 2CuO(s)$

The equation shows that 2 mol of copper form 2 mol of copper(II) oxide; that is, 1 mol of copper forms 1 mol of copper(II) oxide.

round-up
on formulas

RELATIVE ATOMIC MASSES
Page 194.

Work out your score on page 210.

1 Which of the following shows the mass of each element present in one mole of aluminium oxide, Al_2O_3? [1]

	mass of aluminium / g	mass of oxygen / g
A	2	3
B	27	16
C	54	32
D	54	48

2 Calculate the empirical formulas of the following compounds. [5]
  A contains 0.72 g of magnesium and 0.28 g of nitrogen.
  B contains 1.68 g of iron and 0.64 g of oxygen.
  C contains 3.5 g of silicon and 4.0 g of oxygen.
  D contains 20.0% magnesium, 26.6% sulphur and 53.3% oxygen.
  E contains 60.0% carbon, 13.3% hydrogen and 26.7% oxygen.

3 Find the percentage by mass of
  a) carbon and hydrogen in ethane, C_2H_6 [2]
  b) sulphur and oxygen in sulphur trioxide, SO_3 [2]
  c) nitrogen, hydrogen and oxygen in ammonium nitrate, NH_4NO_3 [3]
  d) calcium and bromine in calcium bromide, $CaBr_2$. [2]

TAKE A BREAK

Putting in the values $A_r(Cu) = 63.5$, $A_r(O) = 16$, $M_r(CuO) = 79.5$:

63.5 g of copper form 79.5 g of copper(II) oxide

3.175 g of copper gives $(\frac{3.175}{63.5}) \times 79.5 = 3.975$ g of copper(II) oxide

Example 2

What mass of calcium carbonate must be decomposed to give 50 tonnes of calcium oxide? ($1 \text{ tonne} = 1 \times 10^3 \text{ kg} = 1 \times 10^6 \text{ g}$)

Equation: $CaCO_3(s) \rightarrow CaO(s) + CO_2(g)$

Putting in the values $A_r(Ca) = 40$, $A_r(C) = 12$, $A_r(O) = 16$:

M_r of $CaCO_3 = 40 + 12 + (3 \times 16) = 100$

M_r of $CaO = 40 + 16 = 56$

Therefore 56 g of CaO are formed from 100 g of $CaCO_3$.

50 tonnes of CaO are formed from $(50 \times 10^6/56) \times 100$ g of $CaCO_3 = 89$ tonnes of $CaCO_3$

element	symbol	relative atomic mass
aluminium	Al	27
bromine	Br	80
calcium	Ca	40
carbon	C	12
chlorine	Cl	35.5
copper	Cu	63.5
hydrogen	H	1
iron	Fe	56
lead	Pb	207
magnesium	Mg	24
mercury	Hg	200
nitrogen	N	14
oxygen	O	16
phosphorus	P	31
potassium	K	39
silicon	Si	28
sodium	Na	23
sulphur	S	64

Table of selected relative atomic masses

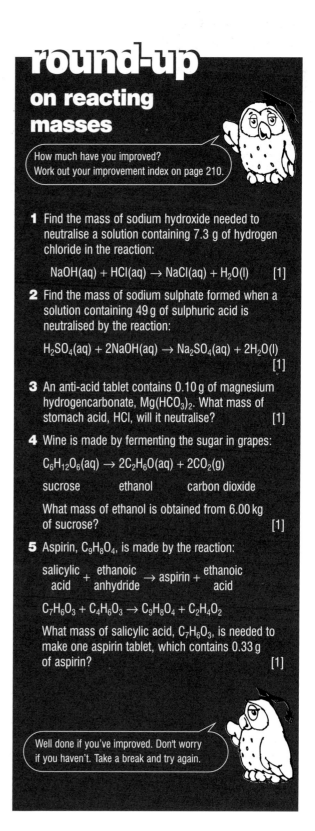

round-up
on reacting masses

How much have you improved? Work out your improvement index on page 210.

1 Find the mass of sodium hydroxide needed to neutralise a solution containing 7.3 g of hydrogen chloride in the reaction:

$$NaOH(aq) + HCl(aq) \rightarrow NaCl(aq) + H_2O(l) \quad [1]$$

2 Find the mass of sodium sulphate formed when a solution containing 49 g of sulphuric acid is neutralised by the reaction:

$$H_2SO_4(aq) + 2NaOH(aq) \rightarrow Na_2SO_4(aq) + 2H_2O(l) \quad [1]$$

3 An anti-acid tablet contains 0.10 g of magnesium hydrogencarbonate, $Mg(HCO_3)_2$. What mass of stomach acid, HCl, will it neutralise? [1]

4 Wine is made by fermenting the sugar in grapes:

$$C_6H_{12}O_6(aq) \rightarrow 2C_2H_6O(aq) + 2CO_2(g)$$

sucrose   ethanol   carbon dioxide

What mass of ethanol is obtained from 6.00 kg of sucrose? [1]

5 Aspirin, $C_9H_8O_4$, is made by the reaction:

$$\text{salicylic acid} + \text{ethanoic anhydride} \rightarrow \text{aspirin} + \text{ethanoic acid}$$

$$C_7H_6O_3 + C_4H_6O_3 \rightarrow C_9H_8O_4 + C_2H_4O_2$$

What mass of salicylic acid, $C_7H_6O_3$, is needed to make one aspirin tablet, which contains 0.33 g of aspirin? [1]

Well done if you've improved. Don't worry if you haven't. Take a break and try again.

Fuels

preview

At the end of this topic you will:

- **know about fossil fuels: coal, oil and natural gas**
- **know about the alkane hydrocarbons**
- **understand energy diagrams and heat of reaction.**

MIND MAP
Page 167.

How much do you already know?
Work out your score on page 210.

Test yourself

1 Why are coal and oil called 'fossil fuels'? [3]

2 What is most of the world's coal used for? [1]

3 Crude oil can be separated into useful fuels and other substances.
   a) Name the process which is used. [1]
   b) Name four fuels obtained from crude oil. [4]
   c) Name two other useful substances separated from crude oil. [2]

4 Name the compounds with formulas **a)** CH_4 **b)** C_2H_6 **c)** C_3H_8 **d)** and name the series to which they belong. [4]

5 Explain what is meant by 'cracking'. [4]

6 Divide the following list of reactions into **a)** exothermic reactions **b)** endothermic reactions: [4] photosynthesis, combustion, cracking of hydrocarbons, respiration.

15.1 Fossil fuels

Coal

Coal is one of the fuels we describe as **fossil fuels**. It was formed from dead plant material decaying slowly over millions of years under the pressure of deposits of mud and sand. Coal is a complicated mixture of carbon, hydrocarbons and other compounds. Much of the coal used in the world is burned in power stations. The main combustion products are carbon dioxide and water.

COMBUSTION
Page 152.

Petroleum oil and natural gas

Petroleum oil (usually called simply oil) and natural gas are fossil fuels: they are the remains of sea animals which lived millions of years ago. Decaying slowly under the pressure of layers of mud and silt, the organic part of the creatures' bodies turned into a mixture of hydrocarbons: petroleum oil. The sediment on top of the decaying matter became compressed to form rock, so oil is held in porous oil-bearing rock. Natural gas is always formed in the same deposits as oil.

The economic importance of oil

Industrialised countries depend on fossil fuels for transport, for power stations and for manufacturing industries. The petrochemicals industry makes a vast number of important chemicals from oil including fertilisers, herbicides, insecticides and the raw materials needed by the pharmaceutical industry. When we have used the Earth's deposits of coal, oil and gas, there will be no more forthcoming. The economies of all industrial countries will depend on alternative energy sources.

ENERGY SOURCES
Page 234.

15.2 Fuels from petroleum

FRACTIONAL DISTILLATION Page 123.

Fractional distillation

Crude oil is separated by fractional distillation into a number of important fuels. Each fraction is collected over a certain boiling point range. Each fraction is a mixture of hydrocarbons (compounds which consist of hydrogen and carbon only). The use that is made of each fraction depends on these factors, all of which increase with the size of the molecules:

- its boiling point range: the higher the boiling point range, the more difficult it is to vaporise in a vehicle engine.
- its viscosity: the more viscous a fraction is, the less easily it flows.
- its ignition temperature: the less easily a fraction ignites, the less flammable it is.

Cracking

We use more naphtha, petrol and kerosene than heavy fuel oil. The technique called **cracking** is used to convert the high boiling point range fractions into the lower boiling point range fractions petrol and kerosene.

vapour of hydrocarbon with large molecules and high boiling point $\xrightarrow[\text{e.g. } Al_2O_3 \text{ or } SiO_2]{\substack{\textit{cracking} \\ \text{passed over a} \\ \text{heated catalyst}}}$ mixture of hydrocarbons with smaller molecules and low boiling point, and hydrogen. The mixture is separated by fractional distillation.

15.3 Alkanes

Most of the hydrocarbons in crude oil belong to the **homologous series** called **alkanes**; they are shown in the table. A homologous series is a set of compounds with similar chemical properties in which one member of the series differs from the next by a $-CH_2-$ group. Physical properties such as boiling point vary gradually as the size of the molecules increases.

The column diagram:

below 25 °C — **Petroleum gases** are liquefied under pressure, and sold in cylinders as 'bottled gas' for use in gas cookers.

40–75 °C — **Petrol** (gasoline) vaporises easily at the temperature of vehicle engines.

75–150 °C — **Naphtha** is used in the manufacture of plastics, fabrics, medicines, agricultural chemicals, etc.

150–260 °C — **Kerosene** needs a higher temperature for combustion. It is used as aviation fuel.

260–340 °C — **Diesel oil** is used in the diesel engine which has a special fuel injection system to allow this fuel to burn. It is used in buses, lorries, etc.

340–500 °C — **Lubricating oil** is used as a lubricant to reduce engine wear.

vapour of crude oil →

>500 °C — **Fuel oil** is a viscous liquid with a high ignition temperature. It is used in ships, heating plants and power stations. To help it to ignite, fuel oil must be sprayed into the combustion chambers as a fine mist.

Bitumen is left as a residue at the bottom of the distillation column. It is used to waterproof roofs and pipes and to tar roads.

Petroleum fractions and their uses

FACTS

The alkanes	
name	formula
methane	CH_4
ethane	C_2H_6
propane	C_3H_8
butane	C_4H_{10}
pentane	C_5H_{12}
hexane	C_6H_{14}
general formula	C_nH_{2n+2}

Here are the structural formulas for the first three alkanes:

methane   ethane   propane

Alkanes do not take part in many chemical reactions. Their important reaction is combustion.

Alkanes contain only single bonds between carbon atoms. Such hydrocarbons are called **saturated hydrocarbons**. This is in contrast to the alkenes, which contain double bonds and are **unsaturated hydrocarbons**.

UNSATURATED HYDROCARBONS Page 199.

15.4 Energy and chemical reactions

Exothermic reactions

1 **Combustion**: the combustion of hydrocarbons is an exothermic reaction – heat is given out.

methane + oxygen → carbon dioxide + water;
heat is given out

$$CH_4(g) + 2O_2(g) \rightarrow CO_2(g) + 2H_2O(l)$$

octane + oxygen → carbon dioxide + water;
heat is given out

★ An oxidation reaction in which heat is given out is **combustion**.

★ Combustion accompanied by a flame is **burning**.

★ A substance which is oxidised with the release of energy is a **fuel**.

2 **Respiration**: our bodies obtain energy from the oxidation of foods, e.g. glucose, in cells. This process is called **cellular respiration**.

RESPIRATION Page 66.

glucose + oxygen → carbon dioxide + water;
energy is given out

$$C_6H_{12}O_6(aq) + 6O_2(g) \rightarrow 6CO_2(g) + 6H_2O(l)$$

3 **Neutralisation**

hydrogen ion + hydroxide ion → water;
heat is given out

$$H^+(aq) + OH^-(aq) \rightarrow H_2O(l)$$

Endothermic reactions

1 **Photosynthesis**: plants convert carbon dioxide and water into sugars in the process of photosynthesis.

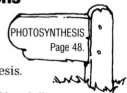

PHOTOSYNTHESIS Page 48.

catalysed by chlorophyll
carbon dioxide + water → glucose + oxygen;
energy of sunlight is taken in

$$6CO_2(g) + 6H_2O(l) \rightarrow C_6H_{12}O_6(aq) + 6O_2(g)$$

2 **Thermal decomposition**; for example the cracking of hydrocarbons and the decomposition of calcium carbonate:

calcium carbonate $\xrightarrow{\text{heat}}$ calcium oxide + carbon dioxide;
heat is taken in

$$CaCO_3(s) \rightarrow CaO(s) + CO_2(g)$$

15.5 Heat of reaction

The atoms, ions or molecules in a substance are held together by chemical bonds. Energy must be supplied if these chemical bonds are to be broken. When bonds are created, energy is given out. The reactants and the products possess different amounts of energy because they have different chemical bonds; see diagram below.

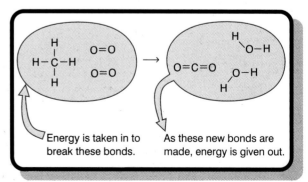

Energy is taken in to break these bonds.

As these new bonds are made, energy is given out.

Bonds broken and made when methane burns

In the reaction shown, the energy taken in is less than the energy given out: this reaction is exothermic.

The graphs below are energy diagrams, in which:

- H = energy content of a substance
- ΔH = heat of reaction = heat taken in or given out during a reaction
- ΔH = energy of products – energy of reactants
- In an **exothermic reaction**, the products of the reaction contain less energy than the reactants. When the reactants change into the products, they get rid of their extra energy by giving out heat to the surroundings.
- In an **endothermic reaction**, the reactants have to climb to a higher energy level to change into the products. To do this, they take energy from the surroundings: they cool the surroundings.

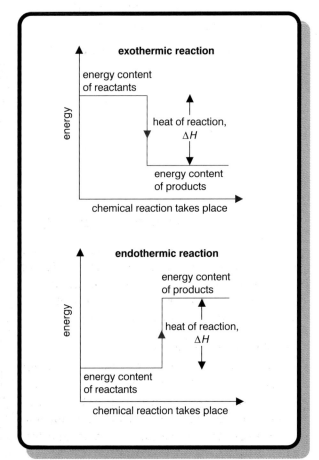

Energy diagrams for an exothermic reaction and an endothermic reaction

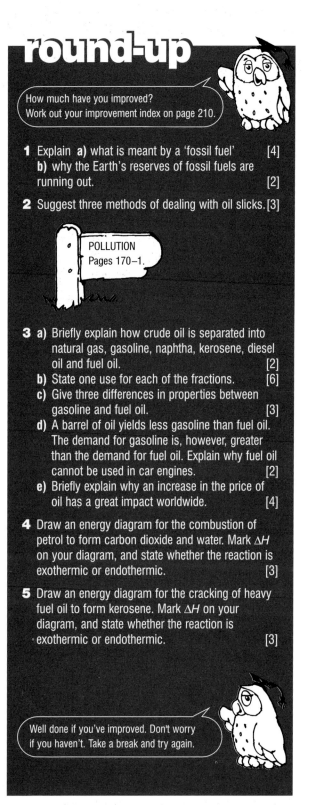

round-up

How much have you improved?
Work out your improvement index on page 210.

1 Explain **a)** what is meant by a 'fossil fuel' [4]
b) why the Earth's reserves of fossil fuels are running out. [2]

2 Suggest three methods of dealing with oil slicks. [3]

POLLUTION
Pages 170–1.

3 a) Briefly explain how crude oil is separated into natural gas, gasoline, naphtha, kerosene, diesel oil and fuel oil. [2]
b) State one use for each of the fractions. [6]
c) Give three differences in properties between gasoline and fuel oil. [3]
d) A barrel of oil yields less gasoline than fuel oil. The demand for gasoline is, however, greater than the demand for fuel oil. Explain why fuel oil cannot be used in car engines. [2]
e) Briefly explain why an increase in the price of oil has a great impact worldwide. [4]

4 Draw an energy diagram for the combustion of petrol to form carbon dioxide and water. Mark ΔH on your diagram, and state whether the reaction is exothermic or endothermic. [3]

5 Draw an energy diagram for the cracking of heavy fuel oil to form kerosene. Mark ΔH on your diagram, and state whether the reaction is exothermic or endothermic. [3]

Well done if you've improved. Don't worry if you haven't. Take a break and try again.

Alkenes and plastics

16

preview

At the end of this topic you will:

- **know the general formula and reactions of alkenes**
- **understand the differences between thermoplastic and thermosetting plastics**
- **know the names and uses of some poly(alkenes)**
- **appreciate the difficulties of disposing of plastics waste.**

MIND MAP
Page 168.

How much do you already know?
Work out your score on page 210.

Test yourself

1 Draw the functional group of an alkene. Say in what type of reactions this functional group takes part. [2]

2 Unlike alkanes, alkenes are not used as fuels. Why is this? [2]

3 Why does ethene decolorise a solution of bromine? Give the formula of the product. [1]

4 a) What is hydration? [1]
 b) What important compound is formed by the hydration of ethene? Give its name and formula. [1]

5 a) What is hydrogenation? [1]
 b) What is the industrial importance of hydrogenation? [1]

6 Explain what is meant by addition polymerisation. [2]

7 Name two sets of plastics which differ in their reaction to heat. Describe the difference in behaviour. [4]

8 By what types of process are the two different kinds of plastics moulded? [2]

16.1 Alkenes

The alkenes are a homologous series of hydrocarbons, as shown in the table.

The alkenes	
name	formula
ethene	C_2H_4
propene	C_3H_6
butene	C_4H_8
general formula	C_nH_{2n}

The double bond (see page 135) between the carbon atoms is the **functional group** of alkenes, and is responsible for their reactions. Alkenes are described as **unsaturated hydrocarbons**. They will react with hydrogen in an **addition reaction** to form saturated hydrocarbons (alkanes).

ethene + hydrogen → ethane

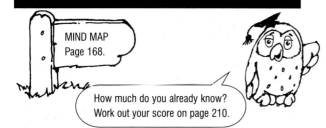

16.2 Reactions of alkenes

Alkenes are not used as fuels because they are an important source of other compounds. The double bond makes them chemically reactive, and they are starting materials in the manufacture of plastics, fibres, solvents and other chemicals.

Addition reactions

1 **Halogens add** to alkenes. A solution of bromine in an organic solvent is brown. If an alkene is bubbled through such a bromine solution, the solution loses its colour. Bromine has added to the alkene to form a colourless compound, for example:

ethene + bromine → 1, 2-dibromoethane

199

The decolorisation of a bromine solution is used to distinguish between an alkene and an alkane. Chlorine adds to alkenes in a similar way.

2 **Hydration**: a molecule of water will add across the double bond. Addition of water is called **hydration**.

ethene + water → ethanol

Ethene and steam are passed over a heated catalyst under pressure. The product is ethanol, an important industrial solvent.

3 **Hydrogenation**: animal fats, such as butter, are saturated compounds and are solid. Vegetable oils, such as sunflower seed oil, are unsaturated compounds and are liquid. An unsaturated vegetable oil can be converted into a saturated fat by hydrogenation (the addition of hydrogen):

$$\text{vegetable oil} + \text{hydrogen} \xrightarrow[\text{nickel catalyst}]{\text{pass over heated}} \text{solid fat}$$
(unsaturated)   (saturated)

The solid fat produced is sold as margarine.

4 **Addition polymerisation**: in this reaction, many molecules of the **monomer**, e.g. ethene, join together (**polymerise**) to form the **polymer**, e.g. poly(ethene).

The conditions needed are:

$$\text{ethene} \xrightarrow{\text{pass at high pressure over a heated catalyst}} \text{poly(ethene)}$$

$$n\text{CH}_2{=}\text{CH}_2 \longrightarrow (\text{–CH}_2\text{–CH}_2\text{–})_n$$

In poly(ethene), n is between 30 000 and 40 000. Poly(ethene) is used for making plastic bags, for kitchenware (buckets, bowls, etc.), for laboratory tubing and for toys. It is flexible and difficult to break. Polymers of alkenes are called poly(alkenes).

16.3 Uses of plastics

Plastics are
* strong
* low in density
* good insulators of heat and electricity
* resistant to attack by chemicals
* smooth
* able to be moulded into different shapes.

There are two kinds of plastics, **thermoplastics** and **thermosetting plastics**. The difference is shown in the diagram below.

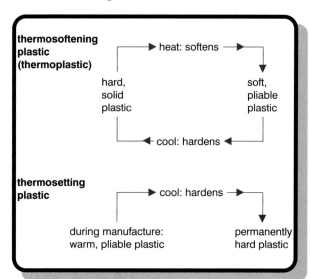

The reason for the difference in behaviour is a difference in structure, as shown.

(a) Thermoplastics consist of long polymer chains. The forces of attraction between chains are weak.

(b) When a **thermosetting plastic** sets, the chains react with one another. Cross-links are formed, and a huge three-dimensional structure is built up. This is why thermosetting plastics can be formed only once.

The structure of **(a)** a thermosoftening plastic
(b) a thermosetting plastic

Moulding of thermoplastics can be a **continuous process**: solid granules of the plastic are fed into one end of the moulding machine, softened by heat and then moulded to come out of the other end in the shape of tubes, sheets or rods. It is easy to manufacture coloured articles by adding a pigment to the plastic.

The moulding of thermosetting plastics is a **batch process**. The monomer is poured into the mould and heated. As it polymerises, the plastic solidifies and a press forms it into the required shape while it is setting.

Both types of plastic have their advantages. A material used for electrical fittings and counter tops must be able to withstand high temperatures without softening. For these purposes, 'thermosets' are used.

Sometimes gases are mixed with softened plastics to make low density plastic foam for use in car seats, thermal insulation, sound insulation and packaging. Plastics can be strengthened by the addition of other materials; for example the composite material **glass fibre-reinforced plastic** is used for the manufacture of boat hulls and car bodies.

round-up

How much have you improved?
Work out your improvement index on page 211.

1 a) Write **(i)** the molecular formulas **(ii)** the structural formulas of ethane and ethene. [4]
b) State the difference between the chemical bonding in the two compounds. [4]

2 a) Give two examples of substances which react with ethene but not with ethane. [2]
b) What name is given to the type of reactions in **a**? [1]
c) How can ethene be converted into ethane? [2]

3 Alkanes and alkenes burn in a similar way. Alkanes are important fuels.
a) What are the main products of combustion of alkanes and alkenes? [2]
b) Why are alkenes not used as fuels? [1]

4 a) Sketch the structural formulas of propane and propene. [2]
b) Which of the two compounds will decolorise bromine water? [1]
c) Sketch the structural formula of the product formed in the reaction between bromine and the compound in **b**. [1]

5 State the advantage that plastic has
a) over china for making cups and saucers and dolls [1]
b) over lead for making toy farmyard animals and soldiers [1]
c) over glass for making motorbike windscreens. [1]

6 The formula of propenamide is: Draw the formula of the polymer poly(propenamide).

$$H\!-\!C\!-\!CONH_2$$
$$\|$$
$$H\!-\!C\!-\!H$$ [1]

7 a) What does the word 'plastic' mean? [2]
b) There are two big classes of plastics, which behave differently when heated. Name the two classes. Describe the difference in behaviour. Say how this difference is related to the molecular nature of the plastics. [5]

8 Name two addition polymers, and give uses for them. [4]

9 a) What is meant by the statement that plastics are non-biodegradable? [1]
b) Why is this a disadvantage? [1]
c) What is wrong with burning plastic waste? [2]
d) Suggest an alternative to burning plastic waste. [1]

Answers

1 Test yourself (page 114)

Matter and the kinetic theory

1 solid (✓), liquid (✓), gas (✓).

2 A pure solid melts at a fixed temperature (✓); an impure solid melts over a range of temperature (✓).

3 Evaporation takes place over a range of temperature (✓). Boiling takes place at a certain temperature (✓).

4 Bubbles of vapour appear in the body of the liquid (✓).

5 In a pressure cooker, water boils at a temperature above 100°C (✓) and foods cook faster at higher temperature (✓).

6 On a high mountain, air pressure is lower than at sea level (✓), and water boils below 100°C (✓).

7 a) Both change shape when a force is applied (✓).
   b) When the force ceases, a plastic material retains its new shape (✓), but an elastic material returns to its previous shape (✓).

8 Crystals consist of a regular arrangement of particles (✓). As a result the surfaces are smooth (✓) and reflect light (✓).

9 The particles that make up the solid gain enough energy to break free from the attractive forces (✓) between particles which maintain the solid structure, and the particles move independently (✓).

10 In a gas, e.g. steam, the molecules are very much further apart (✓) than in a liquid (✓).

11 Particles (✓) of salt dissolve (✓) and spread out (✓) through the soup.

Your score: ☐ out of 25

1 Round-up (page 116)

Matter and the kinetic theory

1 At A, the temperature of the liquid is rising (✓). At B, the temperature stays constant because the liquid is boiling (✓) and all the heat is being used to convert liquid into gas (✓).

2 At C, the temperature of the solid is rising as it is heated (✓). At D the solid starts to melt (✓), and the temperature stays constant at the melting point (✓) while heat is used in the conversion of solid into liquid (✓). At E all the solid has melted (✓), and the temperature of the liquid rises as it is heated (✓). The sharp melting point shows that the solid is a pure substance (✓).

3 Under pressure, water boils at a temperature above 100°C (✓) and the hotter steam kills more bacteria than steam at 100°C (✓).

4 Most of a gas is space; the molecules are far apart (✓).

5 There is so much space between the molecules of a gas (✓) that it is easy for them to move closer together (✓) when the pressure is increased.

6 One example, e.g. heating a lump of bread dough, e.g. air in a hot air balloon expands and is less dense than the air outside the balloon (✓).

7 One example, e.g. increase in the pressure of air in car tyres, e.g. removing a dent from a table tennis ball by warming, e.g. a balloon filled with gas bursts if it is heated (✓).

8 The liquid vaporises (✓). A gas diffuses (✓) to occupy the whole of its container, i.e. the whole of the room (✓).

9 Liquids need energy to vaporise (see page 114) (✓). Aftershave lotion takes this energy from the skin (✓).

Your score: ☐ out of 22

Your improvement index: $\dfrac{\boxed{}/22}{\boxed{}/25} \times 100\% = \boxed{}$ %

2 Test yourself (page 117)

Elements, compounds and equations

1 An element is a pure substance (✓) that cannot be split up (✓) into simpler substances (✓).

2 Zinc reacts with dilute acids (✓) to form hydrogen (✓) and a salt (✓). It forms the cation Zn^{2+} (✓). The oxide and hydroxide are basic (✓) (and amphoteric). The chloride is a solid salt (✓). It forms no hydride (✓).

3 In diamond every carbon atom is covalently bonded to four other carbon atoms (✓). In graphite carbon atoms are covalently bonded together in layers (✓). The layers are joined by weak forces (✓), so one layer can slide over another (✓).

4 Thermal decomposition (✓), electrolysis (✓).

5 14 (✓)

6 $2Na(s) + 2H_2O(l) \rightarrow 2NaOH(aq) + H_2(g)$
   (✓✓✓✓ for state symbols, ✓✓✓✓ for balancing)

Your score: ☐ out of 25

2 Round-up (page 120)

Elements, compounds and equations

1 Metallic (✓)

2 Non-metallic (✓)

3 Metallic (✓)

4 Non-metallic (✓)

5 For example:
   a) Appearance: sulphur is dull, whereas copper is shiny (✓).
   b) Sulphur is shattered by hammering, whereas copper can be hammered into shape (✓).
   c) Sulphur does not conduct heat or electricity, whereas copper is a good thermal and electrical conductor (✓).
   d) Sulphur is not sonorous; copper is sonorous (✓).

6 The appearance of the mixture (speckled yellow and grey) is different from that of the compound (dark grey throughout) (✓). The iron in the mixture reacts with dilute acids to give hydrogen (✓). The compound, iron(II) sulphide, reacts with acids to give hydrogen sulphide (✓), with a characteristic smell. The iron in the mixture is attracted to a magnet (✓).

7 45 (✓)

8 $CaCO_3(s) + 2HCl(aq) \rightarrow CaCl_2(aq) + CO_2(g) + H_2O(l)$
(✓✓✓ for state symbols, ✓ for factor 2)

9 $Fe^{2+}(aq) + 2OH^-(aq) \rightarrow Fe(OH)_2(s)$ (✓✓✓)

Your score: ☐ out of 20

Your improvement index: $\dfrac{☐/20}{☐/25} \times 100\% = ☐\%$

3 Test yourself (page 121)

Separating substances

1 a) Use a coarse seive to hold back the gravel and let sand through (✓).
   b) Centrifuge (✓)
   c) Dissolve the mixture of A and B in hot water (✓). Cool (✓). Filter to obtain A (✓). Evaporate the solution to obtain B (✓).
   d) Use a separating funnel (✓). Olive oil forms a layer on top of vinegar.
   e) Stir with warm water to dissolve the salt (✓). Filter to obtain the diamonds (✓).
   f) Fractional distillation (✓)

Your score: ☐ out of 10

3 Round-up (page 123)

Separating substances

1 Use a magnet or a magnetic field (✓) to attract the steel cans but not the aluminium cans (✓).

2 Stir the mixture of C and D with ethanol (✓). Filter to obtain D (✓). Evaporate the solution to obtain C (✓). Ethanol is flammable (✓): evaporate over a water bath (✓).

3 By fractional distillation (✓) (see page 123). Fractions with low boiling points are collected from the top of the distillation column (✓), while fractions with high boiling points are collected from the bottom of the column (✓).

4 The chromatogram shows that P1 contains A and C (✓), while P2 contains A and B (✓).

5 Allow to settle in a tank so that the oil forms a layer on top of the water (✓). Then carefully withdraw the oil from the top of the tank (✓) by suction (✓).

Your score: ☐ out of 15

Your improvement index: $\dfrac{☐/15}{☐/10} \times 100\% = ☐\%$

4 Test yourself (page 124)

The structure of the atom

1 The number of protons = number of electrons (✓) and the positive charge on a proton has the same value as the negative charge on an electron (✓).

2 a) 19 (✓) b) 20 (✓)

3 Their chemical reactions are identical because it is the electrons that determine the chemical behaviour (✓), and isotopes have the same electron arrangement (✓).

4 a) The number of protons (= number of electrons) in an atom of the element (✓).
   b) The number of protons + neutrons in an atom of the element (✓✓).

5 a) $^{31}_{15}P$ (✓✓) b) $^{39}_{19}K$ (✓✓)

6 Two in the first shell (✓), four in the second shell (✓).

Your score: ☐ out of 15

4 Round-up (page 126)

The structure of the atom

1 a) 27 (✓) b) 5 (✓) c) 0.7 (✓) d) 4 (✓)

2 a) $^{75}_{33}As$ (✓) b) $^{235}_{92}U$ (✓), $^{238}_{92}U$ (✓), $^{239}_{92}U$ (✓)

3 a) 63.6 (✓) b) 69.8 (✓)

4

(✓)

5

a)

B
5p

b)

N
7p

c)

F
9p

d)

Al
13p

(✓✓✓✓)

Your score: ☐ out of 15

Your improvement index: $\dfrac{☐/15}{☐/15} \times 100\% = $ ☐ %

5 Test yourself (page 128)

Electrolysis

1 A (✓) C (✓)

2 A (✓) B (✓) D (✓)

3 a) A compound which conducts electricity (✓) when molten (✓) or in solution (✓) and is split up in the process (✓).
   b) An object which conducts electricity into or out of a cell (✓).

4 a) Cation – a positively charged atom or group of atoms (✓).
      Anion – a negatively charged atom or group of atoms (✓).
      For examples see table on page 129 (✓✓✓✓).
   b) Ions are charged (✓) and move towards the electrode of opposite charge (✓).
   c) In the solid the ions are held in place in a crystal structure (✓). In solution, they are free to move (✓).

5 If water is present, hydrogen ions are discharged in preference to sodium (see page 130) (✓).

6 Chromium plate is not easily chipped off, as paint would be on door handles, etc. (✓).

7 a) Gold plate is cheaper than gold (✓).
   b) Gold does not tarnish as brass does (✓).

8 a) The melting point of the mixture is much lower than that of aluminium oxide (✓).
   b) Cathode: $Al^{3+}(l) + 3e^- \rightarrow Al(l)$ (✓✓)
      Anode: $O^{2-}(l) \rightarrow O(g) + 2e^-$ (✓✓)
      followed by: $2O(g) \rightarrow O_2(g)$ (✓)
   c) It requires a lot of energy (✓).

Your score: ☐ out of 31

5 Round-up (page 133)

Electrolysis

1 a) Copper(II) ions are discharged in preference to the ions of more reactive metals (see page 130) (✓).
   b) Metals which are less reactive than copper, e.g. silver and gold, do not go into solution (✓); they are part of the anode sludge (✓).

2 a) The coating is even (✓) and it can be as thin as required (✓).
   b) Your diagram should similar to be the one on page 129, using an iron nail as cathode and a solution of e.g. nickel(II) sulphate as electrolyte (✓✓).

3 a) Bromine (✓) b) Positive electrode/anode (✓)
   c) Hydrogen (✓) d) Hydroxide ion (✓)
   e) Cathode: $H^+(aq) + e^- \rightarrow H(g)$ (✓✓)
      followed by: $2H(g) \rightarrow H_2(g)$ (✓)
      Anode: $Br^-(aq) \rightarrow Br(aq) + e^-$ (✓✓)
      followed by: $2Br(aq) \rightarrow Br_2(aq)$ (✓)

4 a) Cathode: copper (✓), anode: oxygen (✓).
   b) Cathode: $Cu^{2+}(aq) + 2e^- \rightarrow Cu(s)$ (✓✓)
      Anode: $OH^-(aq) \rightarrow OH(aq) + e^-$ (✓✓)
      followed by: $4OH(aq) \rightarrow O_2(g) + 2H_2O(l)$ (✓✓✓)
   c) Oxygen is not evolved at the anode (✓). Copper dissolves from the anode (✓).
   d) Cathode: $Cu^{2+}(aq) + 2e^- \rightarrow Cu(s)$ (✓✓)
      Anode: $Cu(s) \rightarrow Cu^{2+}(aq) + 2e^-$ (✓✓)

Your score: ☐ out of 32

Your improvement index: $\dfrac{☐/32}{☐/31} \times 100\% = $ ☐ %

6 Test yourself (page 134)

The chemical bond

1 Positive (✓), negative (✓), electrostatic (✓), crystal (✓).

2 Each atom of E loses two electrons to become E^{2+} (2.8) (✓).
Each atom of Q gains one electron to become Q^-(2.8.8) (✓).
The compound EQ_2 is formed (✓).

3

T (✓) T_2 (✓)

4 a) Magnesium bromide (✓)   **b)** Iron(II) chloride (✓)
c) Iron(III) chloride (✓)   **d)** Sodium oxide (✓)
e) Barium sulphate (✓)

5 a) KBr (✓)   **b)** $CaCO_3$ (✓)   **c)** PbO (✓)   **d)** $PbSO_4$ (✓)
e) AgCl (✓)

Your score: ☐ out of 19

6 Round-up   (page 138)

The chemical bond

1 a) Sodium ions, Na^+ (✓) and chloride ions, Cl^- (✓).
b) Electrostatic attraction (✓).
c) A three-dimensional arrangement (✓) of alternate Na^+ ions
and Cl^- ions (✓).

2

(✓✓)

3 For example, one of: **a)** O_2, CH_4 (✓)   **b)** $I_2(s)$, $CO_2(s)$ (✓)
c) Diamond, graphite, silcon(IV) oxide (✓).

4 a) Calcium hydroxide (✓)   **b)** Sodium sulphite (✓)
c) Copper(II) carbonate (✓)   **d)** Magnesium
hydrogencarbonate (✓)   hydrogencarbonate (✓)   **e)** Potassium nitrate (✓)

5 a) NH_4NO_3 (✓)   **b)** Na_2SO_4 (✓)   **c)** $(NH_4)_2SO_4$ (✓)
d) Al_2O_3 (✓)   **e)** $Zn(OH)_2$ (✓)

Your score: ☐ out of 20

Your improvement index: $\dfrac{\boxed{}/20}{\boxed{}/19} \times 100\% = \boxed{}\%$

7 Test yourself   (page 139)

The periodic table

1 a) He, Ne, Ar, Kr, Xe (✓), a set of very unreactive gases present
in air (✓).
b) Group 0 (✓)
c) (i) They have a full outer shell of electrons (✓).
(ii) They are very unreactive (✓). (Some take part in no
chemical reactions. Krypton and xenon react with
fluorine.)

2 Group 2 (✓)

3 Group 7 (✓)

4 Group 1 (✓)

5 a) Fluorine (✓), chlorine (✓), bromine (✓), iodine (✓).
b) Group 7 (✓)   **c)** Decreases (✓)
d) (i) NaF (✓), NaCl (✓), NaBr (✓), NaI (✓)
(ii) FeF_3 (✓), $FeCl_3$ (✓), $FeBr_3$ (✓), FeI_2 (✓)

6 a) An element in the block of the periodic table between Groups
2 and 3 (✓).
b) See page 140 (✓).

Your score: ☐ out of 24

7 Round-up   (page 142)

The periodic table

1 Magnesium chloride is a three-dimensional structure of ions (✓)
with strong forces of attraction between them (✓).
Tetrachloromethane consists of individual covalent molecules
(✓) with only weak forces of attraction between them (✓).

2 a) Na (✓), Mg (✓)   **b)** Na (✓), Mg (✓), Al (✓)
c) (i) Argon (✓)   **(ii)** Chlorine (✓)   **d)** Silicon (✓)

3 a) Na (✓)   **b)** S (✓)   **c)** Al (✓)   **d)** S (✓)

4 Na_2O (✓), MgO (✓), Al_2O_3 (✓), SiO_2 (✓)

5 They do not exist (✓).

6 They both have one electron in the outermost shell (✓).
It is the electrons in the outermost shell that decide chemical
reactions (✓).

7 a) Basic (✓), ionic solid (✓), formula RaO (✓).
b) Reacts readily to form hydrogen (✓) and the alkali radium
hydroxide (✓), $Ra(OH)_2$ (✓).
c) Reacts readily to form hydrogen (✓) and a solution of the
ionic compound (✓) radium chloride (✓), $RaCl_2$ (✓).

8 a) Hydrogen astatide is a gas (✓), a covalent compound (✓)
which forms an acidic solution in water (✓).
b) Astatine reacts slowly with sodium (✓) to form the ionic
solid (✓) sodium astatide (✓), NaAt (✓) .

Your score: ☐ out of 40

Your improvement index: $\dfrac{\boxed{}/40}{\boxed{}/24} \times 100\% = \boxed{}\%$

8 Test yourself   (page 143)

Acids, bases and salts

1 a) SA (✓)   **b)** WA (✓)   **c)** WB (✓)   **d)** WB (✓)
e) WA (✓)   **f)** N (✓)   **g)** SB (✓)

2 You could compare the rates (✓) at which hydrogen is given off
(✓) in the reactions of the two acids with magnesium or
another metal (✓),
or the rates (✓) at which carbon dioxide is given off (✓) in the
reactions of the acids with a carbonate or hydrogencarbonate
(✓).

3 a) Hydrochloric acid (✓)   **b)** For example, magnesium hydroxide (✓)   **c)** Citric acid (✓)   **d)** Ammonia (✓)

4 a) Sodium hydroxide converts grease into soap (✓).
  b) Sodium hydroxide is a stronger base than ammonia (✓).
  c) Wear glasses (✓) and rubber gloves (✓).
  d) Sodium hydroxide would be too dangerous or corrosive (✓).
  e) The saponification of fats by a weak base, e.g. ammonia, is very slow (✓).

Your score: [   ] out of 20

8 Round-up (page 150)

Acids, bases and salts

1 a) A solid base can be separated by filtration (✓).
  b) If any acid remains it will be concentrated in the evaporation step (✓).
  c) (i) Note when the evolution of hydrogen stops (✓).
   (ii) Test with indicator paper to find out when the solution is no longer acidic (✓).
   (iii) Note when the evolution of carbon dioxide stops (✓).

2 a) Zinc + sulphuric acid → zinc sulphate + hydrogen (✓✓)
  b) Cobalt oxide + sulphuric acid → cobalt sulphate + water (✓✓)
  c) Nickel carbonate + hydrochloric acid → nickel chloride + carbon dioxide + water (✓✓✓)
  d) Potassium hydroxide + nitric acid → potassium nitrate + water (✓✓)
  e) Ammonia + nitric acid → ammonium nitrate (✓✓)

3 a) Mix e.g. lead(II) nitrate solution and sodium sulphate solution (✓✓).
  b) Lead(II) nitrate + sodium sulphate → lead(II) sulphate + sodium nitrate (✓✓✓✓)
   $Pb(NO_3)_2(aq) + Na_2SO_4(aq) \rightarrow PbSO_4(s) + 2NaNO_3(aq)$ (✓✓✓✓)
   $Pb^{2+}(aq) + SO_4^{2-}(aq) \rightarrow PbSO_4(s)$ (✓✓✓)
  c) Do not touch the lead salts with your hands. Wash your hands after the experiment (✓).

4 a) Sodium sulphate + water (✓✓).
  b) Ammonium chloride, no other product (✓).
  c) Zinc chloride + hydrogen (✓✓).
  d) Copper(II) sulphate + water (✓✓).
  e) Calcium chloride + carbon dioxide + water (✓✓✓).

Your score: [   ] out of 40

Your improvement index: $\dfrac{[\ ]/40}{[\ ]/20} \times 100\% = [\ ]\%$

9 Test yourself (page 151)

Air

1 More water vapour (✓), more carbon dioxide (✓), no oxygen (✓), same amount of nitrogen (✓).

2 21% O_2 (✓), 78% N_2 (✓)

3 Two from, for example, oxyacetylene flame, steel-making, sewage treatment, combatting pollution (✓✓).

4 Combustion (✓)

5 It makes a glowing splint burn more brightly (✓).

6 A = S (✓),   B = Na (✓),   C = Mg (✓),   D = C (✓)

7 Gain (✓), loss (✓), loss (✓).

8 Two from, for example, lightning, vehicle engines, Haber process, fixation by bacteria (✓✓).

9 For example, dissolving in oceans, photosynthesis (✓✓).

10 Pass through limewater, $Ca(OH)_2(aq)$ (✓). A white precipitate shows that the gas is carbon dioxide (✓).

11 Four from, for example, carbon monoxide – vehicle engines; sulphur dioxide – combustion of fuels; hydrocarbons – combustion of fuels; NO_x – vehicle engines; dust – combustion of fuels, mining, factories; lead compounds – vehicle engines (✓✓✓✓✓✓✓).

Your score: [   ] out of 31

9 Round-up (page 160)

Air

1 a) (i) Zinc oxide (✓)   **(ii)** Carbon (✓)
  b) (i) Carbon (✓)   **(ii)** Zinc oxide (✓)

2 a) (i) Iron oxide (✓)   **(ii)** Aluminium (✓)
  b) (i) Oxygen (✓)   **(ii)** Tin sulphide (✓)
  c) (i) Tin oxide (✓)   **(ii)** Carbon (✓)

3 a) Airships need to be lighter than air (✓).
  b) Helium is a noble gas (✓); hydrogen forms an explosive mixture with air (✓).

4 a) Poisonous (✓); removed by soil bacteria (✓).
  b) Causes respiratory difficulties (✓); acid rain (✓).
  c) Causes respiratory difficulties (✓); washed out in rain (✓).

5 a) From vehicle exhausts, power stations, factories (✓).
  b) One of the causes of acid rain (✓).
  c) Catalytic converters (✓).

6 a) See pages 156–7 (✓✓).
  b) See pages 156–7 (✓✓).
  c) (i) Icecaps will melt (✓)   **(ii)** Flooding (✓)
   (iii) Decrease in wheat crop (✓).

7 Tall chimneys carry pollutants away from the area of the power station (✓). Taller chimneys do not prevent acid rain (✓).

8 a) Acidic water is released suddenly in the spring thaw (✓).
b) Calcium hydroxide + sulphuric acid → calcium sulphate + water (✓✓)
$Ca(OH)_2(s) + H_2SO_4(aq) \rightarrow CaSO_4(aq) + 2H_2O(l)$ (✓✓)
c) Neutralisation (✓)

9 a) Iron + sulphuric acid → iron(II) sulphate + water (✓✓)
b) Calcium carbonate + sulphuric acid → calcium sulphate + carbon dioxide + water (✓✓✓)
c) Calcium hydroxide + sulphuric acid → calcium sulphate + water (✓✓)
(Nitric acid can be stated instead of sulphuric acid.)

10 a) Carbon dioxide (✓), carbon monoxide (✓), carbon (✓), water (✓).
b) Oxides of nitrogen (✓), hydrocarbons (✓), sulphur dioxide (✓).

Your score: ☐ out of 51

Your improvement index: $\dfrac{☐/51}{☐/31} \times 100\% = ☐\%$

10 Test yourself (page 169)

Water

1 Evaporation (✓), respiration (✓), transpiration (✓).

2 Carbon dioxide dissolves in rainwater (✓).

3 Limestone reacts with acidic rainwater to form the soluble salt calcium hydrogencarbonate (✓).

Calcium carbonate + carbon dioxide + water → calcium hydrogencarbonate (✓✓)
$CaCO_3(s) + CO_2(aq) + H_2O(l) \rightarrow Ca(HCO_3)_2(aq)$ (✓✓).

4 a) Water turns anhydrous copper(II) sulphate (✓) from white to blue (✓) (or anhydrous cobalt(II) chloride from blue to pink).
b) Pure water boils at 100°C (or freezes at 0°C) (✓).

5 For example, aquatic plants (✓), fish (✓), aerobic bacteria (✓).

Your score: ☐ out of 15

10 Round-up (page 171)

Water

1 a) Small animals are eaten by predators (✓); larger predators eat the smaller predators (✓), and so on.
b) A pollutant in the water becomes incorporated into the bodies of small animals (✓). A predator which eats many small animals has a higher concentration of the pollutant in its body (✓). A larger predator eats many smaller predators and builds up a still higher concentration of the pollutant in its body, and so on up the food chain (✓).

2 A rise in temperature decreases the solubility of oxygen in water (✓). It makes fish (✓) and aerobic bacteria more active (✓) thus increasing the biochemical oxygen demand (✓).

3 Oil is discharged from sewers into waterways (✓). The oxidation of hydrocarbons in the oil uses up dissolved oxygen in the water (✓).

4 Modern tankers are very large (✓). Any accident that happens involves a large loss of oil (✓).

5 Disperse oil with detergents (✓), sink it with e.g. chalk (✓), absorb the oil in straw etc. (✓), contain the oil in booms and suck it up (✓).

6 a) Eutrophication leads to an increase in the growth of algae (✓).
b) Fertilisers do not accumulate as much in running water (✓).
c) (i) You cannot drink water full of algae (✓).
(ii) Propellers get entangled in algae (✓).
(iii) Fish die because decaying algae use up all the dissolved oxygen (✓).

7 a) Excess fertiliser washes off fields in the rain and passes into groundwater (✓).
b) Nitrates can be converted into nitrites which can cause 'blue baby syndrome' and stomach cancer (✓✓).

Your score: ☐ out of 25

Your improvement index: $\dfrac{☐/25}{☐/15} \times 100\% = ☐\%$

11 Test yourself (page 172)

Planet Earth

1 D (✓)
2 C (✓)
3 B (✓)
4 B (✓)
5 a) Outer core (✓) **b)** Oceanic crust (✓)
c) Continental crust (✓) **d)** Atmosphere (✓)
e) Outer core (✓) **f)** Crust (✓)
6 a) Igneous (✓) **b)** Sedimentary (✓)
c) Metamorphic (✓)
7 Igneous (✓)
8 Carbon dioxide is removed from the atmosphere by photosynthesis (✓) and by dissolution in oceans (✓).
9 Three from, for example, rain, rivers, glaciers, wind (✓✓✓).
10 Plate tectonics (✓)
11 Three from, for example, to neutralise acidity in lakes and soils; used as a building material; in the manufacture of cement, quicklime, glass and iron (✓✓✓).
12 For example, silicon, glass (✓✓).

Your score: ☐ out of 25

Materials and their properties

11 Round-up (page 178)
Planet Earth

1 a) Eurasian Plate (✓). b) Pacific and Nazca Plates (✓✓).
 c) San Andreas Fault (✓). d) Eurasian and Indo-Australian
 Plates (✓✓). e) Andes (✓). f) Pacific Plate (✓).
 g) American Plate and African Plate (✓✓).
 h) Constructive (✓) i) See page 174 (✓✓✓✓✓).

2 a) Look for fossils and date the fossils (✓✓).
 b) High pressure and temperature (✓✓).

3 a) Limestone (✓), sandstone (✓).
 b) Basalt (✓), granite (✓), pumice (✓).
 c) Marble (✓), slate (✓).

4 a) A volcanic eruption (✓).
 b) An earthquake (✓).

5 a) Powdered limestone is mixed with clay or shale (✓) in a
 rotary kiln (✓).
 b) Three from water, sand, crushed rock, calcium sulphate
 (✓✓✓).

6 a) The reaction can take place in the reverse direction as well
 as the forward direction (✓).
 b) Carbon dioxide is removed by air blowing through the kiln
 (✓).

7 Silicon(IV) oxide (silica), calcium carbonate, sodium carbonate
 (✓✓✓).

Your score: [ ] out of 39

Your improvement index: $\dfrac{[\ ]/39}{[\ ]/25} \times 100\% = [\ ]$%

12 Test yourself (page 179)
Metals and alloys

1 Metals can change shape without breaking (✓),
 conduct heat (✓), conduct electricity (✓).

2 Three from, for example, potassium, sodium, lithium, calcium,
 magnesium, aluminium, zinc, iron (✓✓✓).

3 Two from, for example, silver, gold, platinum (✓✓).

4 Three from, for example, lithium, sodium, potassium, calcium,
 magnesium (slowly) (✓✓✓). Products are hydrogen (✓) and
 the metal hydroxide (✓).

5 Hydrogen (✓) and the metal chloride (✓).

6 a) Group 1 (✓) b) Group 2 (✓)
 c) Between Group 2 and Group 3 (✓).

7 Electrolysis (✓) of the molten anhydrous chloride or oxide (✓).

8 The ore is heated with limestone and coke in a blast furnace
 (✓✓✓).

9 Two from, for example, aluminium, chromium, nickel (✓✓).

Your score: [ ] out of 25

12 Round-up (pages 185–6)
Metals and alloys

1 a) $4Na(s) + O_2(g) \rightarrow 2Na_2O(s)$ (✓✓✓, one for each symbol
 or formula)
 b) $2Mg(s) + O_2(g) \rightarrow 2MgO(s)$ (✓✓✓)
 c) $2Zn(s) + O_2(g) \rightarrow 2ZnO(s)$ (✓✓✓)
 d) $3Fe(s) + 2O_2(g) \rightarrow Fe_3O_4(s)$ (✓✓✓)
 e) Similar to b (✓✓✓)
 f) Similar to b (✓✓✓)
 g) Similar to b (✓✓✓)

2 a) (i) $Mg(s) + 2HCl(aq) \rightarrow MgCl_2(aq) + H_2(g)$ (✓✓✓✓,
 one for each)
 (ii) $Fe(s) + 2HCl(aq) \rightarrow FeCl_2(aq) + H_2(g)$ (✓✓✓✓)
 (iii) $Sn(s) + 2HCl(aq) \rightarrow SnCl_2(s) + H_2(g)$ (✓✓✓✓)
 b) (i) $Mg(s) + H_2SO_4(aq) \rightarrow MgSO_4(aq) + H_2(g)$ (✓✓✓✓)
 (ii) $Fe(s) + H_2SO_4(aq) \rightarrow FeSO_4(aq) + H_2(g)$ (✓✓✓✓)

3 a) Magnesium sulphate and hydrogen (✓✓).
 e) Zinc sulphate and hydrogen (✓✓).
 b), c), d) and f) No reaction (✓✓✓✓).

4 Copper alloys do not rust (✓). They are softer than iron (✓)
 and easier to mint (✓).

5 a) With water, calcium reacts steadily (✓), magnesium over
 several days (✓), iron rusts over a period of weeks (✓),
 and copper does not react (✓).
 b) With dilute hydrochloric acid, calcium reacts extremely
 vigorously (✓), magnesium reacts in minutes (✓), iron
 reacts at moderate speed with warm acid (✓), and copper
 does not react (✓).

6 a) The blue colour of the solution fades (✓) and a reddish
 brown solid is precipitated (✓).
 Zinc + copper(II) sulphate → copper + zinc sulphate (✓✓)
 $Zn(s) + CuSO_4(aq) \rightarrow Cu(s) + ZnSO_4(aq)$ (✓✓)
 b) Grey crystals appear (✓).
 Zinc + lead(II) nitrate → lead + zinc nitrate (✓✓)
 $Zn(s) + Pb(NO_3)_2(aq) \rightarrow Pb(s) + Zn(NO_3)_2(aq)$ (✓✓)

7 Z > X > Y (✓✓)

8 a) Au (✓) b) Na (✓), Mg (✓) c) Zn(✓), Fe (✓)
 d) Na (✓), Mg (✓), Zn (✓), Fe (✓) e) Na (✓)
 f) Mg (✓), Al (✓), Zn (✓), Fe (✓) (Na reacts with water
 instead of with Pb^{2+}).

9 A: electrolysis (✓) of the molten anhydrous (✓) chloride or
 oxide (✓).
 B: reduction of the oxide (✓) with carbon or carbon
 monoxide (✓).
 C: electrolysis of a solution of the chloride (✓) or reduction
 of the oxide (✓).
 D: electrolysis (✓) of the molten anhydrous (✓) chloride or
 oxide (✓).

10 a) Rubidium (Group 1) reacts vigorously with cold water
 (✓), bursting into flame because of the hydrogen formed
 (✓) and forming a solution of the alkali rubidium
 hydroxide (✓).
 b) Palladium (transition metal, resembling iron) reacts with
 warm dilute hydrochloric acid to form hydrogen and
 palladium chloride (✓✓).

11 a) Copper(II) oxide (✓) **b)** Aluminium oxide + iron (✓)
d) Carbon dioxide + iron (✓) **f)** Copper + zinc sulphate
solution (✓) **c)** and **e)** No reaction (✓✓).

12 For uses of aluminium related to properties, see table on
page 184. (✓✓✓✓ for four uses, ✓✓✓✓ for four
properties).

13 a) Oiling (✓) **b)** Chromium-plating (✓)
c) Galvanising (coating with zinc) (✓)
d) Stainless steel (✓) **e)** Painting (✓)
f) Sacrificial protection by e.g. zinc (✓)
g) Tin-plating (✓)

14 Saving of Earth's resources (✓), saving of energy used in
extracting the metal, (✓) limiting damage to the environment
through mining (✓).

Your score: ☐ out of 126

Your improvement index: $\dfrac{\boxed{}/126}{\boxed{}/25} \times 100\% = \boxed{}\%$

13 Test yourself (page 187)

Reaction speeds

1 Indigestion powders (✓) because the ratio
surface area : mass is greater (✓).

2 a) Use smaller pieces of zinc (✓), use a more concentrated
solution of acid (✓), raise the temperature (✓).
b) In smaller particles, the ratio surface area : mass is
larger (✓). At a higher concentration, collisions take place
more frequently between hydrogen ions and zinc (✓). At a
higher temperature, the hydrogen ions have higher energy
(✓), and collide more frequently with the particles of zinc
(✓).

3 An apparatus with a gas syringe, see page 188, and a clock
(✓✓✓✓✓).

4 A catalyst is a substance which increases the rate of a chemical
reaction without being used up in the reaction (✓✓).

5 Industrial manufacturers can make their product more rapidly or
at a lower temperature with the use of a catalyst (✓✓).

6 Photosynthesis, photography (✓✓).

Your score: ☐ out of 20

13 Round-up (page 189)

Reaction speeds

1 a) Carbon dioxide is given off (✓).
b) (i) C (ii) A (iii) B (✓✓).
c) The ratio of surface area : volume differs (✓).

2 Cut them into smaller pieces (✓). Use a higher temperature by
using a pressure cooker (✓).

3 Use an apparatus such as that shown on page 188 (bottom)
(✓). Using potato, measure the volume of oxygen formed at
certain times after the start of the reaction (✓). Plot volume
against time(✓). Repeat the measurement using manganese(IV)
oxide. Compare the two graphs (✓).

4 You could take pieces of magnesium ribbon of the same length
and therefore approximately the same mass (✓). You could find
out how long it took (✓) for a piece of magnesium ribbon to
react completely with a certain volume of acid (✓) of a certain
concentration (✓) at different temperatures (✓). You could plot
time against temperature or 1/time (rate) against temperature
(✓).

5 a) Axes labelled correctly and units shown (✓), points plotted
correctly (✓), points covering at least half of each scale (✓),
smooth lines drawn through the points (✓).
b) B (✓)
c) Your line should should show very slow evolution of oxygen
(✓).

Your score: ☐ out of 22

Your improvement index: $\dfrac{\boxed{}/22}{\boxed{}/20} \times 100\% = \boxed{}\%$

14 Test yourself (page 190)

Tackling chemical calculations

1 a) 64 (✓) **b)** 80(✓) **c)** 98 (✓) **d)** 60 (✓)
e) 249.5 (✓)

2 a) 2.0 mol (✓) **b)** 2 mol (✓) **c)** 0.25 mol (✓)

3 a) 20.1 g (✓) **b)** 24.5 g (✓) **c)** 120 g (✓)

4 a) $HgBr_2$ (✓) **b)** $CuCl_2$ (✓) **c)** Na_2O (✓)

5 a) 50% (✓) **b)** 40% (✓) **c)** 33% (✓)

6 1 g (✓)

7 a) 6.6 g (✓) **b)** 3.6 dm^3 at rtp (✓)

8 a) 1250 tonnes (✓) **b)** $9.4 \times 10^8 \, dm^3$ (✓)

9 Loss (✓) of £8.30 (✓)

Your score: ☐ out of 24

14 Round-up

The mole (page 192)

1 a) Gram, kilogram (✓) **b)** Mole (✓)

2 Weigh out **a)** the relative atomic mass in grams (✓)
b) the relative molecular mass in grams (✓).

3 a) 24 g (✓) **b)** 69 g (✓) **c)** 8 g (✓) **d)** 16 g (✓)
e) 8 g (✓) **f)** 16 g (✓)

4 a) 0.33 mol (✓) **b)** 0.25 mol (✓) **c)** 2.0 mol (✓)
d) 0.010 mol (✓) **e)** 0.33 mol (✓) **f)** 20 mol (✓)

5 a) 88 g (✓) **b)** 980 g (✓) **c)** 117 g (✓) **d)** 37 g (✓)

6 a) 16 (✓) **b)** 28 (✓) **c)** 44 (✓) **d)** 64 (✓) **e)** 40 (✓)
f) 74.5 (✓) **g)** 40 (✓) **h)** 74 (✓) **i)** 63 (✓)
j) 123.5 (✓) **k)** 80 (✓) **l)** 159.5 (✓) **m)** 249.5 (✓)

Your score: ☐ out of 33

Formulas (page 193)

1 D (✓)

2 A $= Mg_3N_2$ (✓), B $= Fe_3O_4$ (✓), C $= SiO_2$ (✓),
D $= MgSO_4$ (✓), E $= C_3H_8$ (✓)

3 a) C = 80%, H = 20% (✓✓)
b) S = 40%, O = 60% (✓✓)
c) N = 35%, H = 5%, O = 60% (✓✓✓)
d) Ca = 20%, Br = 80% (✓✓)

Your score: ☐ out of 15

Reacting masses (page 194)

1 8.0 g (✓)

2 71 g (✓)

3 0.05 g (✓)

4 3.06 kg (✓)

5 0.26 g (✓)

Your score: ☐ out of 5

Total round-up score: ☐ + ☐ + ☐ = ☐ out of 53

Your improvement index: $\dfrac{☐/53}{☐/24} \times 100\% = ☐ \%$

15 Test yourself (page 195)
Fuels

1 Coal and oil were formed from the remains of plants and trees (coal) (✓) and sea animals and plants (oil) (✓) which lived millions of years ago (✓) .

2 It is burnt in power stations (✓).

3 a) Fractional distillation (✓).
b) Four from: petroleum gas, gasoline, kerosene, diesel oil, fuel oil (✓✓✓✓).
c) Two from: lubricating oil, bitumen, naphtha (✓✓).

4 a) Methane (✓) **b)** Ethane (✓) **c)** Propane (✓)
d) The alkane series (✓).

5 Converting hydrocarbons with large molecules (✓) and high boiling points (✓) into hydrocarbons with smaller molecules (✓) and lower boiling points (✓).

6 a) Combustion (✓), respiration (✓).
b) Photosynthesis (✓), cracking of hydrocarbons (✓).

Your score: ☐ out of 23

15 Round-up (page 198)
Fuels

1 a) Fossil fuels are formed by the decay (✓) of the remains of plants (✓) and animals (✓) over long periods of time (✓).
b) Fossil fuels took millions of years to form (✓) and we are using them up much more quickly (✓).

2 Three of the five methods mentioned on page 171 (✓✓✓).

3 a) Fractional distillation (✓) separates the fractions on the basis of their different boiling point ranges (✓).
b) For uses see the diagram on page 196 (✓✓✓✓✓✓).
c) Gasoline has a lower boiling point (✓), lower ignition temperature (✓) and lower viscosity than fuel oil (✓).
d) It does not vaporise (✓) and does not ignite (✓).
e) Fuels from petroleum oil are important in transport (✓), industry (✓) and power generation (✓). Oil is a source of valuable petrochemicals (✓).

4 As for exothermic energy diagram on page 198 (✓✓), exothermic (✓).

5 As for endothermic energy diagram on page 198 (✓✓), endothermic (✓).

Your score: ☐ out of 32

Your improvement index: $\dfrac{☐/32}{☐/23} \times 100\% = ☐ \%$

16 Test yourself (page 199)
Alkenes and plastics

1 $>C=C<$ (✓), addition reactions (✓).

2 Alkenes are reactive (✓) and are therefore the starting materials for the manufacture of many other compounds (✓).

3 Bromine adds across the double bond to form $BrCH_2CH_2Br$ (✓).

4 a) Addition of water across the double bond (✓).
b) Ethanol, C_2H_5OH (✓).

5 a) Addition of hydrogen across a double bond (✓).
b) Catalytic hydrogenation is used to convert unsaturated oils (vegetable oils) into saturated fats, which are solid, in the manufacture of margarine (✓).

6 The addition of many identical small molecules to form a large molecule (✓). The substance with small molecules is the monomer; the substance with large molecules is the polymer (✓).

7 Thermosetting plastics can be softened by heat and hardened by cooling (✓) many times (✓). Thermosetting plastics are softened by heat (✓) only during manufacture (✓).

8 For thermosoftening plastics a continuous process is used (✓). For thermosetting plastics, a batch process is used (✓).

Your score: ☐ out of 17

16 Round-up   (page 201)

Alkenes and plastics

1 a) **(i)** Ethane C_2H_6 (✓), ethene C_2H_4 (✓)
(ii)

ethane   ethene

(✓✓)

b) Ethane has only single bonds (✓); it is a saturated compound (✓). Ethene has a carbon–carbon double bond (✓); it is an unsaturated compound (✓).

2 a) Two from: hydrogen, bromine, water, sulphuric acid (✓✓).
b) Addition reactions (✓).
c) Hydrogen with a nickel catalyst (✓✓).

3 a) Carbon dioxide (✓) and water (✓).
b) Alkenes are a source of valuable chemicals (✓).

4 a)

propane   propene

(✓✓)

b) Propene (✓)
c)

(✓✓)

5 a) Less breakable (✓).
b) Cheaper, less breakable, non-toxic (✓).
c) Much less breakable (✓).

6

(✓)

7 a) When deformed, a plastic changes shape (✓) and retains the new shape when the deforming force is removed (✓).
b) Thermoplastic – can be softened by heat (✓) many times (✓).
Thermosetting – can be moulded only once (✓).
Thermoplastic – individual chains can move with respect to one another (✓).
Thermosetting – chains are cross-linked (✓).

8 Two from, for example, poly(ethene), poly(chloroethene), poly(propene) (✓✓). Uses: poly(ethene) for plastic bags, kitchenware, laboratory tubing, toys; poly(chloroethene) for plastic bottles, wellington boots, raincoats, electrical insulation, gutters; poly(propene) for hospital equipment that must be sterilised, as fibres for ropes and fishing nets (✓✓).

9 a) Most plastics cannot be decomposed by natural biological processes (✓).
b) Plastic rubbish accumulates in landfill sites and never decomposes (✓).
c) Some plastics form toxic combustion products (✓). Also, burning them is a waste of Earth's resources (✓).
d) Recycling (✓).

Your score: ☐ out of 40

Your improvement index: $\dfrac{\boxed{}/40}{\boxed{}/17} \times 100\% = \boxed{}\%$

THE PERIODIC TABLE OF THE ELEMENTS

Group								
1	2	3	4	5	6	7	0

H hydrogen 1

1	2												3	4	5	6	7	0
																		He helium 2
Li lithium 3	**Be** beryllium 4												**B** boron 5	**C** carbon 6	**N** nitrogen 7	**O** oxygen 8	**F** fluorine 9	**Ne** neon 10
Na sodium 11	**Mg** magnesium 12												**Al** aluminium 13	**Si** silicon 14	**P** phosphorus 15	**S** sulphur 16	**Cl** chlorine 17	**Ar** argon 18
K potassium 19	**Ca** calcium 20	**Sc** scandium 21	**Ti** titanium 22	**V** vanadium 23	**Cr** chromium 24	**Mn** manganese 25	**Fe** iron 26	**Co** cobalt 27	**Ni** nickel 28	**Cu** copper 29	**Zn** zinc 30		**Ga** gallium 31	**Ge** germanium 32	**As** arsenic 33	**Se** selenium 34	**Br** bromine 35	**Kr** krypton 36
Rb rubidium 37	**Sr** strontium 38	**Y** yttrium 39	**Zr** zirconium 40	**Nb** niobium 41	**Mo** molybdenum 42	**Tc** technetium 43	**Ru** ruthenium 44	**Rh** rhodium 45	**Pd** palladium 46	**Ag** silver 47	**Cd** cadmium 48		**In** indium 49	**Sn** tin 50	**Sb** antimony 51	**Te** tellurium 52	**I** iodine 53	**Xe** xenon 54
Cs caesium 55	**Ba** barium 56	**La** lanthanum 57	**Hf** hafnium 72	**Ta** tantalum 73	**W** tungsten 74	**Re** rhenium 75	**Os** osmium 76	**Ir** iridium 77	**Pt** platinum 78	**Au** gold 79	**Hg** mercury 80		**Tl** thallium 81	**Pb** lead 82	**Bi** bismuth 83	**Po** polonium 84	**At** astatine 85	**Rn** radon 86
Fr francium 87	**Ra** radium 88	**Ac** actinium 89																

lanthanum series: elements 58–71
actinium series: elements 90–103

Physical processes

Mind Maps

Earth in space (Topic 1)

Energy (Topic 2)

Radioactivity (Topic 3)

RELATIVE		
	MASS	CHARGE
P	1	+1
n	1	0
e	0	-1

Waves (Topics 4 and 5)

Light (Topics 6 and 7)

Force (Topics 8 and 9)

Electricity (Topics 10 and 11)

Electromagnetism (Topic 12)

Beyond the Earth

1

preview

At the end of this topic you will be able to:

- explain what causes day and night, the seasons, and the rising and setting of the Sun, Moon and stars
- describe and explain the phases of the Moon and solar and lunar eclipses
- recall the main features of the planets
- use the theory of gravity to explain the motion of the planets, the Moon, satellites and comets
- describe the life cycle of a star
- describe evidence for the expansion of the Universe.

MIND MAP
Page 214.

How much do you already know?
Work out your score on page 307.

MIND MAP Page 214.

Test yourself

1 List the planets Mars (M), Jupiter (J), Neptune (N), Uranus (U) and Venus (V) in order of *increasing* distance from the Sun. [5]

2 When it is summer in the northern hemisphere, it is winter in the southern hemisphere. Why? [2]

3 What causes a lunar eclipse? [2]

4 Why can you see different constellations in the night sky during the year? [2]

5 a) Of the planets Mercury, Venus, Mars and Jupiter, which one is rocky and further from the Sun than Earth is? [1]
   b) Which of the above four planets does not have a solid surface? [1]

6 A comet X orbits the Sun once every 76 years. It was last seen from Earth in 1985 when it was visible for about a year. By the year 2050, is it likely to be
   a) slowing down or speeding up [1]
   b) moving towards or away from the Sun? [1]

7 What is the name of the process that releases energy in the core of a star? [1]

8 What is a supernova? [2]

9 What is meant by 'red shift'? [2]

10 What did the astronomer Edwin Hubble discover? [2]

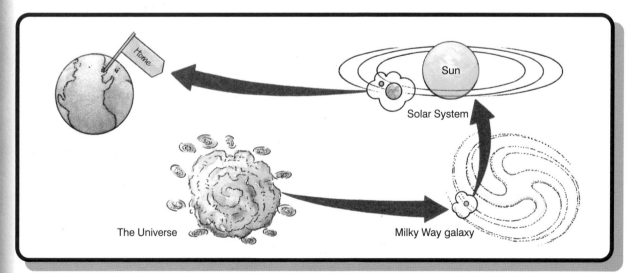

Home

Sun

Solar System

The Universe

Milky Way galaxy

Where do you fit in?

1.1 About the Earth

Did you know?

The Earth is one of nine planets in orbit round a star we call the Sun. It takes about 8 minutes for light to reach Earth from the Sun. It takes over four years for light to reach Earth from the next nearest star, Proxima Centauri.

One day in your life

FACTS

★ The Earth spins steadily on an axis passing through its poles.

★ One full day is the time it takes for the Earth to spin one full turn.

★ At night, our part of the Earth faces away from the Sun.

★ Sunrise happens when our part of the Earth moves into daylight.

★ Sunset happens when our part of the Earth moves out of daylight.

One year in your life

FACTS

★ The Earth moves round the Sun on an orbit which is almost circular.

★ The Earth takes $365\frac{1}{4}$ days to orbit the Sun once.

★ The Earth's axis is tilted and always points towards the Pole star in the northern sky.

★ In the northern summer, the North Pole is tilted towards the Sun.

★ In the northern winter, the North Pole is tilted away from the Sun.

What's on tonight?

The stars are mapped out in patterns called **constellations**. As the Earth moves round the Sun, the constellations we see at night change. Orion the Hunter is a spectacular constellation that we can see in the winter night sky, when the night side of Earth faces towards it.

Daily News

Happy Birthday Mary

Mary Davis is a sprightly 84-year-old who has just celebrated her twenty-first birthday. She was born on the 29th February 1912 and has a birthday every leap year.

Question

What difference would it make if leap years were abolished and we had 365 days in every calendar year?

Answer
The seasons would fall back by one day every four years. After a century, midwinter would be 25 days later than 21 December.

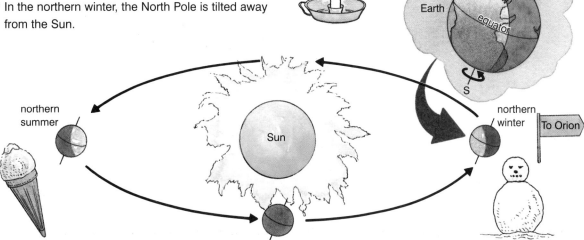

You are here at nightfall in winter. Brr!

N

Earth

equator

S

northern summer

Sun

northern winter

To Orion

The Earth in orbit

1.2 Over the Moon

The Moon in perspective

★ The Moon orbits the Earth once every $27\frac{1}{4}$ days.

★ Its orbit is tilted a few degrees to the Earth's orbit.

★ Its diameter is about $\frac{1}{4} \times$ the diameter of Earth.

★ Its distance from Earth is about 30 Earth diameters.

★ Its gravity is too weak to retain an atmosphere.

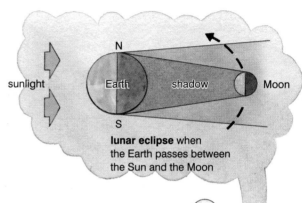

lunar eclipse when the Earth passes between the Sun and the Moon

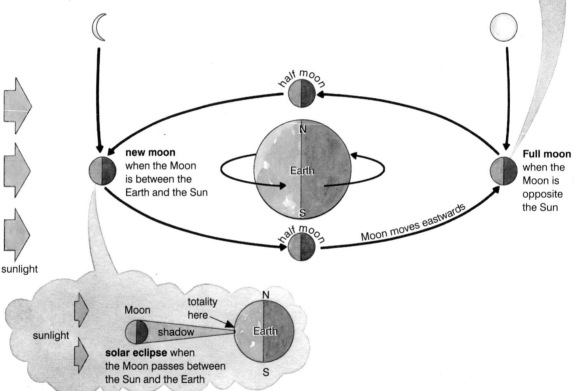

Phases and eclipses

Question

Why don't eclipses happen every month?

Larger than life

The Sun is 400 times further away from Earth than the Moon is. The Sun's diameter is also 400 times greater than the Moon's. This is why the Sun and the Moon look about the same size.

Answer The Moon's orbit is at about 7° to the Earth's orbit. An eclipse can only happen if the Moon is exactly on the line between the Earth and the Sun. Usually, the Moon is below or above this line because of the tilt of its orbit.

1.3 The Solar System

Planets in perspective

★ The planets all move round the Sun in the same direction.

★ Their orbits are almost circular, except for Pluto, and in the same plane as the Earth's orbit.

★ The planets reflect sunlight, which is why we can see them.

★ The further a planet is from the Sun, the longer it takes to go round its orbit.

★ When we observe the planets from Earth, they move through the constellations as they go round the Sun.

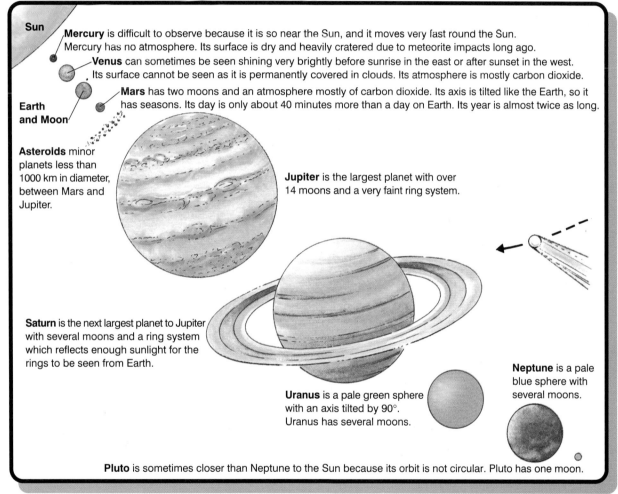

Sun

Mercury is difficult to observe because it is so near the Sun, and it moves very fast round the Sun. Mercury has no atmosphere. Its surface is dry and heavily cratered due to meteorite impacts long ago.

Venus can sometimes be seen shining very brightly before sunrise in the east or after sunset in the west. Its surface cannot be seen as it is permanently covered in clouds. Its atmosphere is mostly carbon dioxide.

Mars has two moons and an atmosphere mostly of carbon dioxide. Its axis is tilted like the Earth, so it has seasons. Its day is only about 40 minutes more than a day on Earth. Its year is almost twice as long.

Earth and Moon

Asteroids minor planets less than 1000 km in diameter, between Mars and Jupiter.

Jupiter is the largest planet with over 14 moons and a very faint ring system.

Saturn is the next largest planet to Jupiter with several moons and a ring system which reflects enough sunlight for the rings to be seen from Earth.

Uranus is a pale green sphere with an axis tilted by 90°. Uranus has several moons.

Neptune is a pale blue sphere with several moons.

Pluto is sometimes closer than Neptune to the Sun because its orbit is not circular. Pluto has one moon.

The planets

On another planet

Mercury and **Venus** are called the 'inner planets' because they are closer to the Sun than Earth is. They are rocky, without moons. **Mars** is a rocky planet like the Earth and the inner planets. **Jupiter**, **Saturn**, **Uranus** and **Neptune** are giant spinning balls of fluid. **Pluto** is a small rocky planet .

Handy hint

To remember the order of the planets from the Sun, use the mnemonic '**M**ake **V**ery **E**asy **M**ash, **J**ust **S**tart **U**sing **N**ew **P**otatoes'!

1.4 Gravity

A mysterious force

Any two objects attract each other. This force of attraction is called **gravity**. The greater the masses of the two objects or the closer they are, the stronger the force of gravity between them. The planets, the Moon, satellites and comets all stay in their orbits because of the force of gravity. You stay on the Earth because of the force of gravity between you and the Earth.

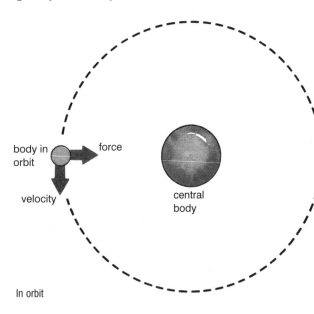

In orbit

Comets

★ Comets move round the Sun in elliptical orbits, usually in a different plane from the Earth's orbit.

★ As a comet approaches the Sun, it moves faster because the Sun's gravity is stronger closer in.

★ It also becomes visible near the Sun because solar heating raises the comet's temperature until it glows.

★ A comet usually develops a tail when it is near the Sun, as particles streaming from the Sun 'blow' glowing matter away from the comet.

★ Comets disappear into darkness as they move away from the Sun, but the Sun's gravity pulls them back towards the Sun again.

Scaling down

If the Sun was represented by a football, the Earth would be a pea 50 metres away from it. Pluto would be a small seed over 2 km away, still held in the Solar System by the force of gravity between it and the Sun.

Satellites

★ **Artificial satellites** are kept in their orbits because of the Earth's gravity. The greater the radius of orbit, the longer its **time period** (the time it takes to go round Earth once).

★ **Communication satellites** orbit the Earth at a certain height above the equator, with a time period of 24 hours. This means that they are always in the same place as seen from the Earth.

★ **Polar satellites** are in low orbits which take them over both poles once every few hours. They have a wide range of uses, including weather forecasting, surveying and spying.

★ **The Moon** is a natural satellite of the Earth. Its radius of orbit is so great that it takes over 27 days to orbit the Earth once.

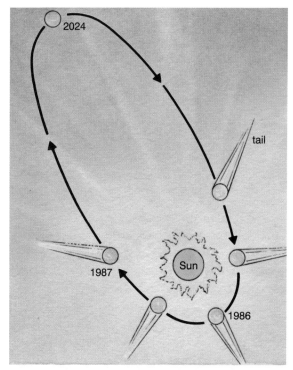

A comet orbit

1.5 Life as a star

The stars we see in the night sky are at different stages of evolution and they vary in size and brightness. Massive bright stars last no more than a few million years. Small dim stars shine for thousands of millions of years. The Sun is thought to be a typical middle-aged star about half-way through its life cycle of about 10 000 million years.

Formation – The star forms from dust and gas in space being pulled together by their own gravity. As the density rises, the star becomes hotter and hotter due to the release of gravitational energy. The planets are thought to have formed from dust clouds left over at this stage when the Sun was formed.

Birth – at a temperature of about 10 million degrees, the nuclei of hydrogen atoms fuse together releasing nuclear energy. This energy keeps the temperature of the star high enough for nuclear fusion to continue. A star is born!

Equilibrium – for most of its life, the star gradually fuses the hydrogen nuclei in its core into heavier nuclei such as helium. The nuclear reactions in the core release vast amounts of electromagnetic and particle radiation. The inward gravitational attraction on the core is balanced by outward pressure due to this radiation.

Expansion – eventually, the hydrogen in the core is used up and the star expands to become a **red giant**. This is thought to happen because the helium nuclei and other light nuclei formed in the star fuse to form heavier nuclei, releasing more radiation which forces the star to swell out.

dust cloud

Collapse – once there are no more light nuclei to fuse together, the star collapses due to its own gravity. It becomes very hot, very dense and very small. It is now a **white dwarf**.

low mass

high mass

oblivion as a dark object

Explosion – if the star is massive enough, it will explode, releasing huge amounts of matter and radiation in a very short time. This supernova event is thought to leave behind an extremely dense object known as a neutron star.

The life cycle of a star

Sandaluk II

Supernovae are rare events. The Crab Nebula in the constellation Taurus is thought to be the remnants of an eleventh century supernova. In 1987, a supernova was observed in the Andromeda galaxy. It was thought to be the death throes of a star called Sandaluk II.

In a supernova explosion, large heavy nuclei are formed from the fusion of lighter nuclei. Dense elements like uranium found in the Earth mean that the Earth and the Sun probably formed from the debris of a supernova explosion.

Question

When a star forms from dust clouds, it becomes so hot that its nuclei fuse together and release more energy. Why does it become so hot when it forms from dust?

Answer The dust clouds attract each other because of their own gravity, and become more and more dense. Gravitational potential energy is converted into kinetic energy of the dust particles, which become very hot when they collide with each other.

1.6 The expansion of the Universe

Local galaxies

Galaxies

FACTS

★ The Sun is just one of billions of stars in the Milky Way galaxy.

★ There are many other galaxies.

★ The nearest galaxy is about 10 million light years away.

★ The furthest is about 12 000 million light years away.

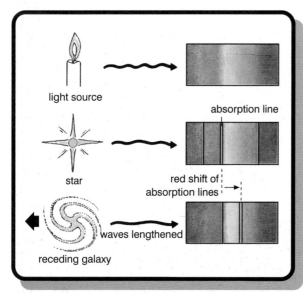

Starlight spectra

The red shift

The spectrum of light from a star is crossed by dark vertical lines. These are caused by the star's outer layers absorbing light of certain wavelengths. **Edwin Hubble** discovered that the absorption lines in the light spectra of distant galaxies are red-shifted towards longer wavelengths in the spectrum. This is because these galaxies are moving away from us very quickly so their light waves are lengthened.

Hubble made precise measurements and discovered that the speed of a galaxy is greater the more distant the galaxy is. This important discovery is known as **Hubble's law**.

The Big Bang

All the distant galaxies are rushing away from us. Scientists think the Universe is expanding. This would explain why distant galaxies are moving away faster and faster the further away they get. The expansion started billions of years ago in a huge explosion called the **Big Bang**. At present, it is not known whether the expansion will continue indefinitely or reverse – ending perhaps in the Big Crunch!

In the beginning

The edge of the Universe

No object can travel faster than light. Light from the Big Bang defines the edge of the Universe, which is expanding at present. Hubble estimated that the edge of the Universe is about 12 000 million light years away!

Question

If the age of the Universe was scaled down to start 24 hours ago, when would life on Earth (one million years ago) have started?

Answer ɟ seconds ago

round-up

How much have you improved?
Work out your improvement index on page 307.

1 A student made two sketches of the Moon one week apart.
   a) Explain why the Moon appears different in each sketch. [2]
   b) Make a further sketch to show how you think the Moon appeared after one more week. [1]

2 During the night, the constellations move across the sky. Explain why this happens. [2]

3 a) Stars produce their own light but planets do not. Explain why we can see the planets. [1]
   b) The diagram shows the planet Venus in two different positions on its orbit relative to the Earth. A sketch was made of Venus in each of these positions, viewed through a large telescope. Decide which sketch is for which position, and explain your reasons. [2]

position 1

Sun

orbit of Venus

sketch A

position 2

Earth

sketch B

4 a) Sketch a diagram to show how an eclipse of the Sun occurs. [2]
   b) The next total eclipse of the Sun visible from Britain will be in 1999. The last one was many years ago. Why is an eclipse of the Sun such a very rare event? [2]

5 a) Draw a sketch to show the relative positions of the Sun, the Earth and Jupiter when Jupiter is easily visible in the night sky. [1]
   b) State four differences between the Earth and (i) Mars (ii) Jupiter (iii) Saturn. [12]

6 a) Mercury is very difficult to observe. Why? [3]
   b) Pluto is the most distant planet, yet it can be closer than Neptune to the Sun. Why? [2]
   c) Uranus is closer to the Sun than Neptune is. Which takes longer to go round the Sun? [1]
   d) Why do comets disappear then return? [3]

7 a) Betelgeuse is a red giant star. Why is it described as a red giant? [2]
   b) Describe what will happen to the Sun when it uses up all the hydrogen nuclei in its core. [4]
   c) What is a supernova? [2]

8 a) Why is it difficult to launch satellites into orbit? [3]
   b) The Earth's surface gravity is 10 N/kg. The Moon's surface gravity is 1.6 N/kg. Why is the Moon's gravity smaller? [2]

9 The Universe is thought to be expanding. Describe the evidence for this. [4]

10 a) Write a short account of a space mission to a planet. [4]
   b) Light takes 8 minutes to reach the Earth from the Sun, and about 4 years from Proxima Centauri, the nearest star to the Sun. Do you think a space mission to this star is feasible? Explain your answer. [4]

Well done if you've improved. Don't worry if you haven't. Take a break and try again.

Energy resources and energy transfer

preview

At the end of this topic you will be able to:

- **describe different forms of energy**
- **explain what is meant by work, energy and power**
- **describe the energy changes when work is done or when heat transfer takes place**
- **explain what is meant by conservation of energy, efficiency and energy waste**
- **carry out calculations using the formulae for kinetic energy, potential energy, power and efficiency.**

MIND MAP
Page 214.

How much do you already know?
Work out your score on pages 307–8.

Test yourself

Assume $g = 10$ N/kg where necessary.

1 A cyclist freewheels down a road and eventually comes to rest. Which one of the following sequences **A** to **D** best describes the energy changes in this process?
  A Chemical $\longrightarrow$ potential $\longrightarrow$ kinetic
  B Potential $\longrightarrow$ kinetic $\longrightarrow$ thermal
  C Potential $\longrightarrow$ chemical $\longrightarrow$ kinetic
  D Chemical $\longrightarrow$ kinetic $\longrightarrow$ thermal   [1]

2 State the correct units for weight and power respectively.   [2]

3 A weightlifter raises an object of mass 60 kg from the floor to a height of 2.0 m. Calculate the gain of potential energy of the object.   [1]

4 An object of weight 2.0 N is held 4.0 m above a floor and then released. Calculate its kinetic energy and its potential energy in joules
  a) when it is 1.0 m above the floor   [2]
  b) just before it hits the floor.   [2]

5 A person uses a 1.0 kW electric heater for 4 hours and a 3.0 kW electric oven for 2 hours. Calculate the total number of kilowatt hours used.   [2]

6 A trolley of mass 20 kg is released at the top of a slope of height 10 m and allowed to run down the slope. Its speed at the bottom of the slope is 5.0 m/s. Calculate the ratio of the trolley's loss of potential energy to its gain of kinetic energy.   [3]

7 Why are metals good conductors of heat?   [3]

Home heating bills may be reduced by installing
a) double glazed windows instead of ordinary windows
b) felt insulation in the loft
c) draught excluders round the door frames.

8 Which of the above measures reduces heat loss due to thermal conduction and thermal radiation?   [2]

9 Which of the above measures reduces heat loss due to thermal convection?   [1]

10 A falling weight is used to turn an electricity generator which is used to light a bulb, as shown in the diagram. Complete the energy flow diagram.   [5]

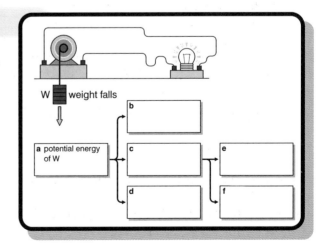

2.1 Work and energy

Time for work

Work is done when a force makes an object move. The greater the force or the further the movement, the greater the amount of work done. For example, the work done to lift a box to a height of 2 m is twice the work done to lift the same box to a height of 1 m.

Energy is the capacity to do work. A battery-operated electric motor used to raise a weight does work on the weight. The battery therefore contains energy because it has the capacity to make the motor do work.

Heat is energy transferred due to a difference of temperature. Heat and work are two methods by which energy can be transferred to or from a body. Work is energy transferred due to force and heat is energy transferred due to temperature difference. Heat as a method of transferring energy is discussed in more detail on page 231.

Energy can be changed from any one form into other forms. In other words, it can be transformed from one form into other forms.

Forms of energy

Energy exists in different forms, including

- **kinetic energy** which is the energy of a moving body due to its motion
- **potential energy** which is the energy of a body due to its position
- **chemical energy** which is energy released by chemical reactions
- **light energy** which is energy carried by light
- **elastic energy** which is energy stored in an object by changing its shape
- **electrical energy** which is energy due to electric charge
- **nuclear energy** which is energy released in nuclear reactions
- **sound energy** which is energy carried by sound waves
- **thermal energy** which is the energy of an object due to its temperature.

Make an anagram of the first letter of each line to help remember all these forms of energy. No doubt you can do better than 'KP Cleenst' or 'NT Speckle'!

Measuring energy

Work and energy are measured in joules (J), where one joule is defined as the work done when a force of one newton acts over a distance of one metre in the direction of the force.

The following equation is used to calculate the work done (or energy transferred) by a force:

work done (or energy transferred) = force × distance moved in the direction of the force

$$W = F \times s$$
$$\text{(in joules)} \quad \text{(in newtons)} \quad \text{(in metres)}$$

Question

a) A student applies a force of 600 N to a wardrobe and pushes it a distance of 2.0 m across a floor. Calculate the work done by the student.
b) If the wardrobe had been emptied, it could have been pushed across the floor using a force of 200 N. How far could it have been moved for the same amount of work?

Transferring energy

Energy can be transferred from one object to other objects. A raised weight has the capacity to do work and therefore contains energy. For example, it could be used to keep a clock running.

weight falls slowly

Transferring energy

Answers a) 1200J b) 6.0m

227

2

2.2 More about kinetic and potential energy

Gravitational potential energy (GPE)

For an object of mass m raised through a height h,

$$\text{its gain of potential energy} = mgh$$

where g is the gravitational field strength.

Note that for an object of mass m, its **weight** $= mg$ because g is the force of gravity per unit mass on an object. Also, the mass must be in kilograms and the height gain in metres to give the gain of potential energy in joules. The value of g on the Earth is 10 N/kg.

Kinetic energy (KE)

For an object of mass m moving at speed v,

$$\text{kinetic energy} = \tfrac{1}{2}mv^2$$

Proof of this formula is not required at GCSE. Note that the mass must be in kilograms and the speed in metres per second to give the kinetic energy in joules.

Questions

1 How much gravitational potential energy does a 60 kg swimmer gain as a result of climbing a height of 15 m?

2 a) If the swimmer in question 1 dives from a diving board 15 m above the water, how much kinetic energy does the swimmer have just before impact?
   b) Calculate the swimmer's speed just before impact.

15 m

Diving in!

A Very Important Principle

The principle of conservation of energy states that in any change, the total energy before the change is equal to the total energy after the change. In other words, the total amount of energy is conserved, even though it may change from its initial form into other forms as a result of the change.

Consider the energy changes if a 100 N weight is released at a height of 1.0 m above the floor.

- Its initial potential energy (relative to the floor) $= mgh = 100\,\text{N} \times 1.0\,\text{m} = 100\,\text{J}$.
- Its potential energy (relative to the floor) just before impact = 0, since its height is effectively zero just before impact.

It loses 100 J of potential energy as a result of falling to the floor. Just before impact, its kinetic energy is therefore 100 J since it had no kinetic energy at the start and all its potential energy is transformed into kinetic energy – assuming no air resistance!

But

The trouble with energy is that it tends to spread out when it changes from one form into other forms. For example, in a bicycle freewheeling down a slope, friction at the wheel bearings causes the bearings to become warm. Some of the initial potential energy is therefore converted into thermal energy. Such thermal energy is lost to the surroundings and can never be recovered and used to do work. The thermal energy is therefore wasted.

Even where energy is concentrated, such as when a car battery is charged, energy is wasted in the process. For example, the electric current passing through a car battery when it is being charged would warm the circuit wires a little.

Answers 1 9000 J 2 a) 9000 J b) 17 m/s

TAKE A BREAK

2.3 Power and efficiency

Power is defined as the work done or energy transferred per second.

$$\frac{\text{power}}{\text{(in watts)}} = \frac{\text{energy transferred (in joules)}}{\text{time taken (in seconds)}}$$

The unit of power is the **watt** (W), equal to one joule per second. Note that one kilowatt (kW) equals 1000 W and one megawatt (MW) equals 1 000 000 W.

> **Question**
>
> **1** Calculate the muscle power of a student of mass 50 kg who climbs a height of 5.0 m up a rope in 10 s.
> (Hint: remember that weight = mass × g where g = 10 N/kg. Also, the student uses both arms to climb the rope.)

Electrical power

The electrical power supplied to an electrical appliance is the electrical energy transferred per second to the appliance. For example, a 1000 W electrical heater is supplied with 1000 J of electrical energy each second. This is changed into thermal energy by the heater.

The electrical power of an appliance depends on the current and potential difference (i.e. voltage), in accordance with this equation:

electrical power = current × potential difference
| P | I | V |
| (in watts) | (in amperes) | (in volts) |

The unit of electrical energy used to cost mains electricity is the **kilowatt hour**, sometimes written as kWh. One kilowatt hour is the electrical energy supplied to a 1000 W appliance in one hour and is equal to 3.6 million joules (1000 W × 3600 s).

Machines at work

A machine is a device designed to do work. The diagram shows some examples of machines at work. In each case, energy is supplied to the machine enabling it to do **useful work**. The useful work done by a machine is always less than the energy supplied to it because of friction between its moving parts. This causes heating and therefore wastes energy. Energy may be wasted in other ways in a machine as well as through friction.

Machines at work

Efficiency

The efficiency of a machine is the proportion of the energy supplied to the machine which is transferred to useful work. This may be expressed as an equation:

$$\text{efficiency} = \frac{\text{useful work done by the machine}}{\text{energy supplied to the machine}}$$

Notes

1 *Efficiency is sometimes expressed as a percentage (the fraction above multiplied by 100).*

2 *The efficiency of any machine is always less than 100% because of friction.*

3 *Efficiency may be expressed in terms of power as*

$$\frac{\text{output power}}{\text{input power}}$$

> **Question**
>
> **2** A pulley system is used to raise a crate of weight 500 N through a height of 2.4 m. To do this, the operator must pull on the rope with a force of 300 N through a distance of 4.8 m.
> **a** Calculate **(i)** the work done by the operator **(ii)** the potential energy gain of the crate.
> **b** Hence calculate the efficiency of the pulley system and give two reasons why it is not 100%.

> **Answers**
> **1** 125 W
> **2 a) (i)** 1440 J **(ii)** 1200 J **b)** 83%

2

2.4 Temperature and heat

Temperature scales

Temperature is a measure of 'hotness'. If a solid substance is heated and heated, its temperature rises until it reaches the melting point of the substance. At this point the solid changes its physical state into a liquid without a change of temperature. Continued heating of the liquid raises its temperature to the boiling point.

A **scale of temperature** is defined by using fixed points which are easily reproduced 'degrees of hotness', such as the temperature of melting ice (the ice point), or of water boiling at atmospheric pressure (the steam point).

★ The **Celsius** scale of temperature, in °C, is defined in terms of the ice point (0°C) and the steam point (100°C). **FACTS**

★ The **absolute** scale of temperature, in kelvins (K), is defined in terms of the lowest possible temperature (0 K) as one fixed point, and the temperature of ice and water in equilibrium with water vapour (273 K) as the other fixed point. This scale is used for scientific work and is defined as

absolute temperature = Celsius temperature + 273
 (in kelvin)   (in °C)

Thermal energy

Thermal energy is the energy gained by a substance when its temperature rises or it melts or vaporises.

★ **When a substance is heated and its temperature rises**, its atoms gain kinetic energy. In a solid, the atoms vibrate more; in a liquid or a gas, the atoms move about faster.

★ **When a substance is heated and its physical state changes**, the potential energy of its atoms changes. When a solid melts, energy is required to let the atoms break free from each other. In a liquid, the atoms move about at random, with weak forces of attraction acting between them. When a liquid vaporises, the atoms or molecules break away from each other completely and only come into contact with each other when they collide.

★ **The thermal energy of a substance can also be changed by doing work**. For example, the work done by the frictional force between two moving parts in a machine causes the moving parts to gain thermal energy (warm up).

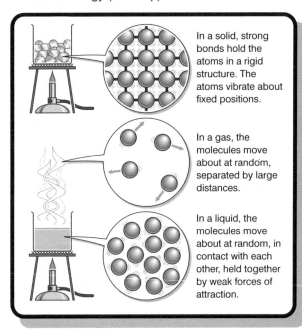

In a solid, strong bonds hold the atoms in a rigid structure. The atoms vibrate about fixed positions.

In a gas, the molecules move about at random, separated by large distances.

In a liquid, the molecules move about at random, in contact with each other, held together by weak forces of attraction.

States of matter

Question

The graph shows how the temperature of a hot substance, initially in the liquid state, changed as it cooled.
a) Use the graph to estimate the melting point of the substance.
b) Describe how the arrangement of the atoms of the substance changed during the cooling process.

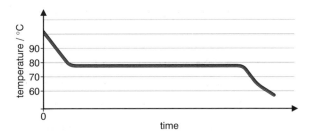

Answers **a)** 78°C **b)** Above 78°C, the atoms move about at random in contact with each other; at 78°C, they take up fixed positions into which they are locked below this temperature.

2.5 Heat transfer

Heat transfer occurs by means of thermal **conduction**, **convection** and **radiation**. Cooling also takes place during **evaporation** from a hot liquid, and matter as well as heat is transferred in this process, which is not the case with conduction, convection or radiation. (Evaporation is discussed on the next page).

Thermal conduction – five facts

1 Thermal conduction is heat transfer through a substance without the substance moving.

2 Solids, liquids and gases all conduct heat.

3 Good thermal conductors are also good electrical conductors. They contain free electrons which can transport both energy and charge through the substance.

4 Metals and alloys are the best conductors of heat.

5 Insulating materials such as wood, fibreglass and air are very poor conductors of heat. The presence of air pockets in an insulating material improves its insulating properties.

Thermal conduction in a metal

Thermal convection – five facts

1 Thermal convection is heat transfer in a liquid or a gas due to internal circulation of particles.

2 Thermal convection occurs only in fluids (liquids or gases).

3 Natural convection occurs because hot fluids, being less dense than cold fluids, rise, whereas cold fluids sink. When a fluid is heated, circulation is caused by hot fluid rising and cold fluid sinking.

4 Forced convection happens when a cold fluid is pumped over a hot surface and takes away energy from the surface.

5 Cooling fins on an engine increase the surface area of the engine and therefore enable more thermal convection to occur.

Thermal convection in water

Thermal radiation – five facts

1 Thermal radiation is electromagnetic radiation emitted by any surface at a temperature greater than absolute zero.

2 The hotter a surface is, the more thermal radiation it emits.

3 Thermal radiation can pass through a vacuum and does not need a substance to carry it.

4 A black surface is a better emitter and absorber of thermal radiation than a white surface.

5 A matt (rough) surface is a better emitter and absorber of thermal radiation than a shiny surface.

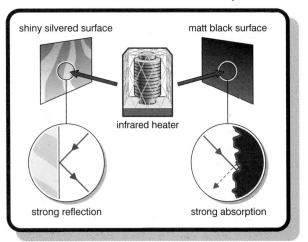

Thermal radiation

2.6 Evaporation

Four facts about evaporation

1 Evaporation is the process of a liquid vaporising below its boiling point.

2 A hot liquid in an open container cools mainly by evaporation.

3 Wet clothing on a washing line dries as water evaporates from it.

4 Cooling by evaporation involves transfer of mass as well as transfer of energy from the liquid state.

Drink up before it goes cold!

$E = mc^2$

How it happens

4 **The more energetic molecules can escape from the surface of the liquid**. A molecule at the surface of the liquid must do work to overcome the attraction between it and the other molecules there. Only fast-moving molecules have sufficient kinetic energy to break free of these forces of attraction.

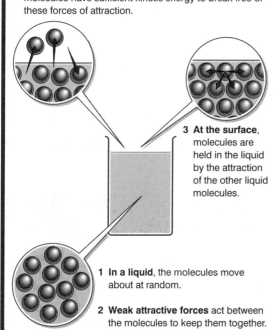

3 **At the surface**, molecules are held in the liquid by the attraction of the other liquid molecules.

1 **In a liquid**, the molecules move about at random.

2 **Weak attractive forces** act between the molecules to keep them together.

The process of evaporation

Cooling by evaporation

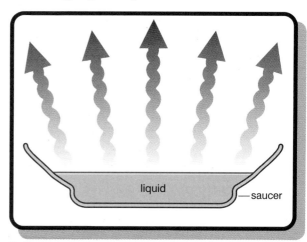

liquid —saucer

Cooling by evaporation

If the vapour formed above a liquid is carried away by a draught of air, the molecules in the vapour state are unable to return to the liquid. The faster-moving molecules in the liquid continuously leave the liquid. Without any supply of heat, the average kinetic energy of the remaining liquid molecules becomes lower and the liquid becomes colder. This process is called **cooling by evaporation**. Two examples of this process are

- the chill factor, experienced by someone outdoors in wet clothing on a windy day
- dabbing a volatile liquid on the skin to numb it before an inoculation.

Questions

1 Why do wet clothes on a washing line dry faster
  a) in warm weather b) on a windy day?
2 Why is it difficult to dry wet clothes on a washing line
  a) on a humid day b) on a very cold day?

Answers

1 a) The molecules in the liquid have more kinetic energy at a higher temperature, so they leave the liquid at a faster rate.
  b) The wind carries vapour molecules away as they leave the liquid, so they cannot re-enter the liquid.
2 a) The vapour content of the air is high, so molecules re-enter the liquid as fast as they leave it.
  b) The molecules in the liquid do not have sufficient kinetic energy to leave the liquid.

2.7 Controlling heat transfer

Designers need to take account of the thermal properties of materials when considering what materials to use in any given device or situation.

★ A car radiator transfers heat from the engine to the surroundings. Forced convection occurs as water pumped round the engine block carries away heat to the radiator. Heat is conducted through the radiator walls so the outside of the radiator becomes hot. Air circulates round the outside of the radiator, carrying away heat, and the radiator surface is blackened so it emits thermal radiation.

hot water from engine

heat transfer

cool water to engine

A car radiator

★ A domestic hot water tank is fitted with an insulating jacket to reduce heat losses. The outer surface of the jacket is shiny to reduce heat losses due to thermal radiation.

Keeping warm in winter

Home heating bills can be greatly reduced by fitting loft insulation and double glazing. The picture of the house shows these and other measures that can be taken to reduce fuel bills.

Question

1 Tick boxes in the table to show which heat transfer processes have been reduced by each measure.

Maintaining body temperature

If you are outdoors in winter, you need warm dry clothing made of fibres which trap layers of air. Since air is a very poor conductor of heat, it reduces heat transfer from the body to the surroundings. A white outer surface reduces thermal radiation. A smooth shiny surface would be even better but might be expensive! In addition, the outer surface needs to be waterproof and the inner layers need to prevent water vapour caused by sweat penetrating the fibres.

Question

2 List the materials you would use to make a winter coat, giving a reason for each material chosen.

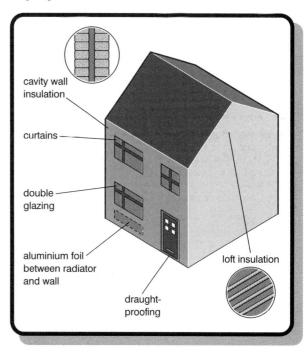

cavity wall insulation

curtains

double glazing

aluminium foil between radiator and wall

draught-proofing

loft insulation

Reducing home heating bills

Answer
1 conduction ✓✗✗✗ convection ✗✓✓✓✗✗ radiation ✗✓✓✗✗✗

	loft insulation	double glazing	cavity wall insulation	radiator foil	heavy curtains	draught excluder
conduction						
convection						
radiation						

233

2.8 Energy resources

Demand and supply

The total energy demand for the United Kingdom in one year is about 10 million million million joules. This works out at about 5000 joules per second for every person in the country. The pie charts show how the total energy is obtained and how it is used.

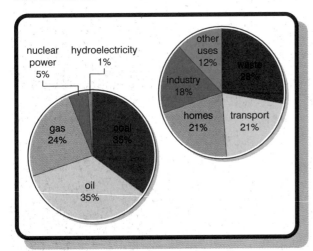

UK energy supplies   UK energy demands

Fuels are substances which release energy as a result of changing into another substance. Fuels cannot be reused.

- fossil fuels – coal, oil, gas, wood
- nuclear fuels – uranium, plutonium

Renewable energy resources are sources of useful energy which do not change the substances involved, allowing them to be reused. The energy usually comes from the Sun.

- solar-driven resources – solar panels for water heating, solar cells
- weather-driven resources (indirectly powered by the Sun's heating effect on the atmosphere) – hydroelectricity, aerogenerators (wind), wave powered generators
- tidal generators (powered by the gravitational potential energy between the Earth and the Moon)
- geothermal power (powered by thermal energy in the Earth's interior)

Energy efficiency

Reasons why energy should not be wasted:

1 Fuel supplies are finite and cannot be renewed once used.

2 Fossil fuels release carbon dioxide gas which is thought to be causing global warming, resulting in melting icecaps and rising sea levels. Sulphur dioxide from power stations is a cause of acid rain.

3 Nuclear fuel creates radioactive waste which must be stored safely for hundreds of years to prevent it harming us.

4 Small-scale renewable resources may damage the environment, for example turbine noise from aerogenerators and effects on plant and animal life when tidal power stations are made.

5 It costs money to make energy useful and to distribute it.

How to use energy resources more efficiently

★ Use machines and vehicles more efficiently.

★ Replace inefficient machines and vehicles with more efficient ones.

★ Improve thermal insulation in buildings.

★ Fit automatic lighting and temperature sensors to reduce unnecessary lighting and heating.

★ Supply waste heat from power stations for district heating (combined heat and power stations).

★ Use more pumped storage schemes.

★ Make energy-efficient lifestyle choices, for example teleworking, car sharing, better public transport.

A pumped storage station. Electricity is used to pump water uphill when the demand for electricity is low. Electricity is generated by allowing water to flow downhill when demand is high.

round-up

How much have you improved?
Work out your improvement index on page 308.

1 Describe the energy changes that take place when
 a) the alarm sounds on a battery-operated clock [1]
 b) a parachutist jumps from a plane and descends
  safely to the ground. [2]

2 An elevator is used in a factory to lift packages each
 weighing 200 N through a height of 4.0 m from the
 production line to a loading platform. The elevator is
 designed to deliver three packages per minute to the
 loading bay.

a) Calculate
  (i) the potential energy gain of each package [1]
  (ii) the work done per second by the elevator to
   lift the packages. [1]
 b) A 200 W electric motor is used to drive the
  elevator. Calculate the efficiency of the elevator
  and motor system. [1]

3 a) An athlete of mass 55 kg is capable of running
  at a top speed of 10 m/s. Calculate the athlete's
  kinetic energy at this speed. [1]
 b) If the athlete could convert all the kinetic energy in
  a into potential energy, how much would the
  athlete's centre of gravity rise? [1]

4 A passenger aeroplane of mass 25 000 kg accelerates
 on a level run from rest to reach its take-off speed of
 80 m/s in a time of 50 s. Calculate
 a) its kinetic energy at take-off [1]
 b) the power developed by its engines to achieve this
  speed in 50 s. [1]

5 A student records the usage of electrical appliances
 in her household over a period of 24 hours.

> 2.0 kW electric heater for 2.5 hours
>
> 100 W electric light for 3 hours
>
> 40 W electric light for 5 hours
>
> 750 W microwave oven for 20 minutes
>
> 3.0 kW electric kettle used 4 times
> for 5 minutes each time

a) Calculate the number of units of electricity (kWh)
  used by each appliance. [1]
 b) Calculate the total cost of using all these
  appliances if each unit of electricity costs 6.0p. [1]

6 A 12 V 25 W electric heater designed for use in a car
 is capable of heating a flask of tea from 20 °C to
 50 °C in 15 minutes.
 a) Calculate the energy supplied by a 25 W electric
  heater in 15 minutes. [1]
 b) A student decides to test the heater by filling the
  flask with 0.20 kg of water. She has discovered in
  a separate test that 4200 J of energy are needed
  to raise the temperature of 1.0 kg of water by 1 °C.
  She finds that the heater takes 650 s to heat the
  water from 20 °C to 40 °C.
  (i) Calculate the energy needed to heat 0.20 kg of
   water from 20 °C to 40 °C. [1]
  (ii) Calculate the power of the heater. [1]

7 a) Explain whether hot tea in a china teapot would
  cool faster than hot tea in a shiny metal teapot. [2]
 b) Explain why hot tea cools faster in a wide-
  brimmed cup than in a narrow cup. [3]
 c) Explain why heat loss through a single-glazed
  window can be reduced by fitting double glazing. [2]
 d) **(i)** Condensation often forms on single-glazed
   classroom windows in winter. Explain how this
   happens. [2]
  (ii) Double glazing reduces condensation. Why?
   [2]

Well done if you've improved. Don't worry
if you haven't. Take a break and try again.

Radioactivity

preview

At the end of this topic you will be able to:

- **explain the structure of the atomic nucleus and the term isotope**
- **explain radioactivity in simple terms**
- **describe the characteristics of the three main types of emission from radioactive substances**
- **explain what is meant by background radioactivity**
- **explain the term half-life and interpret half-life graphs and related data**
- **know that emissions from radioactive substances have harmful effects**
- **describe uses of radioactivity.**

MIND MAP
Page 215.

How much do you already know?
Work out your score on page 308.

Test yourself

1 State whether each of the following particles carries positive charge, negative charge or is uncharged.
a) the electron b) the proton c) the neutron
d) the alpha particle e) the beta minus particle   [5]

2 State how many protons and how many neutrons are present in each nucleus of the following isotopes.
a) $_2^4$He b) $_{92}^{235}$U   [4]

3 What type of charge does the nucleus of the atom carry?   [1]

4 State the three types of emissions from naturally occurring radioactive substances, and state which type of radioactive emission is most easily absorbed.   [4]

5 What is background radioactivity?   [1]

6 Name a scientific instrument used to measure radioactivity.   [1]

7 The *half-life* of the *isotope* of carbon $_6^{14}$C is 5500 years. Explain what is meant by the terms in italics. [2]

8 What is meant by nuclear fission?   [2]

9 Why is it important to store radioactive waste from a nuclear reactor for thousands of years?   [2]

10 State two uses of radioactive isotopes.   [2]

yellow

black

Symbol for radioactive sources

A scientific puzzle

Radioactivity was discovered in 1896 by **Henri Becquerel**. When he developed an unused photographic plate, he found an image of a key on it. He realised this was caused by radiation from a packet containing uranium salts, which had been on top of a key with the photographic plate underneath. The puzzle of explaining the radiation was passed by Becquerel to a young research worker, **Marie Curie**. She painstakingly analysed the uranium salts and discovered the radiations were emitted from the uranium atoms, which formed other types of atoms in the process. She and her husband Pierre discovered and named two new radioactive elements, polonium and radium. It was shown that the emissions contained two types of radiation, alpha radiation which is positively charged and easily absorbed, and beta radiation which is negatively charged and much less easily absorbed. Later gamma radiation was discovered which is uncharged and much more penetrating.

3.1 Inside the atom

The structure of the atom

	charge/ proton charge	mass/ proton mass
proton	1	1
neutron	0	1
electron	−1	0

A lithium atom

Ernest Rutherford used alpha radiation to probe the atom. He knew that alpha radiation consisted of positively charged particles. He found that when a beam of alpha particles was directed at a thin metal foil, some of the particles bounced back off the foil. He deduced that

- the atom contains a tiny positively charged nucleus, where most of its mass is located
- the rest of the atom consists of empty space through which negatively charged electrons move as they orbit the nucleus.

Further investigations showed that the nucleus contains two types of particles, **protons** and **neutrons**.

Atoms and molecules

1 An **element** is a substance which cannot be split into simpler substances. A **compound** is a substance containing two or more elements combined in fixed proportions.

2 An **atom** is the smallest particle of an element which is characteristic of that element.

3 A **molecule** is formed when two or more atoms join together.

4 The lightest atom is hydrogen. The heaviest naturally occurring atom is uranium.

5 The **periodic table of the elements** places the elements in order of increasing **atomic number** (symbol Z). The atomic number of an element is the number of protons in its nucleus.

PERIODIC TABLE Pages 139–42.

Isotopes

★ The number of protons in the atomic nucleus of an element (the **atomic number Z** of the element) is constant for that element.

★ The number of neutrons in the atomic nuclei of a given element can vary from one atom to another.

★ The term **isotope** describes a particular type of atom of a given element. For example, chlorine has two isotopes, one with 17 protons and 18 neutrons, and the other with 17 protons and 20 neutrons.

★ Since protons and neutrons each have a mass of one atomic mass unit, the total number of protons and neutrons in a nucleus gives the mass of the nucleus in atomic mass units. This is called the **mass number A** of the nucleus. Because electrons have very little mass in comparison, the mass of an atom in atomic mass units is equal to A.

★ An isotope is defined by the symbol

$$_{Z}^{A}X$$

where X is the chemical symbol of the element, Z is the number of protons in the nucleus (the atomic number) and A is the number of protons and neutrons in the nucleus (the mass number).

Why doesn't the nucleus fly apart due to repulsion of the positive protons? The nucleus is held together by the **strong nuclear force**.

Question

Work out the number of protons and neutrons in each of the following isotopes. **a)** $_{92}^{235}U$ **b)** $_{6}^{14}C$ **c)** $_{10}^{22}Ne$

Answers a) 92p + 143n b) 6p + 8n c) 10p + 12n

3.2 Radioactive isotopes

Stable and unstable nuclei

A nucleus is **stable** if the strong nuclear force between its neutrons and protons is much greater than the electrostatic force of repulsion between the protons. Some nuclei are **unstable** because the electrostatic forces of repulsion are larger than the strong attractive forces.

An unstable nucleus

★ A large nucleus with **too many protons and neutrons** is unstable. It becomes stable by emitting an **alpha particle**. This is a particle consisting of two protons and two neutrons.

★ A smaller nucleus with **too many neutrons** is unstable. It becomes stable by emitting a **beta particle**. This is an electron created in the nucleus and instantly emitted.

★ A nucleus may still possess **excess energy** after an alpha or beta particle has been emitted. It may then release the excess energy as **gamma radiation**. This is electromagnetic radiation of very short wavelength.

★ The daughter nucleus might itself be radioactive, and may emit a further alpha or beta particle.

★ An unstable nucleus is said to **disintegrate** when it emits an alpha particle or beta particle. When it emits gamma radiation, it is said to **de-excite**.

★ The **activity** of a radioactive source is the number of nuclei per second that disintegrate.

The Geiger counter

This consists of a Geiger tube connected to an electronic counter. Each particle from a radioactive source that enters the tube is registered on the electronic counter as one count. If the Geiger tube is pointed at a radioactive source, the activity of the source can be monitored by counting the number of particles entering the tube in a measured time interval and calculating the **count rate** (the number of counts per second), which is proportional to the activity.

Using a Geiger counter

Background radioactivity

A Geiger counter will detect a low level of radioactivity even with no source present. This is called **background radioactivity** and is due to cosmic radiation and naturally occurring radioactive isotopes in rocks such as granite.

> **Question**
>
> A Geiger counter records 1980 counts in 300 seconds when it is held at a fixed distance from a radioactive source. Without the source present, it records 120 counts in 300 seconds.
> a) Why does the Geiger tube count when no source is present?
> b) Calculate the count rate due to the source.
> c) Give two reasons why the count rate is less than the activity of the source.

$E = mc^2$

This famous equation was first derived by **Albert Einstein**. He showed that if energy E is given to (or taken away from) an object, the mass of the object increases (or decreases) by a mass m in accordance with the equation $E = mc^2$, where c is the speed of light. The energy given out when a nucleus disintegrates can be calculated from the difference in mass of the parent nucleus and its products.

> **Answers**
> a) background radioactivity
> b) 6.2 counts per second
> c) The radiation spreads out from the source in all directions so most of it misses the tube; absorption by the air between the tube and the source.

3.3 Radioactive emissions

Ionisation

Ions are atoms that have become charged, either by removing electrons or by adding them. When the particles produced from radioactive substances pass through a gas, they cause the gas molecules to ionise. In a **cloud chamber**, tiny droplets form along the path of an alpha particle due to the trail of ions created by the particle. The path of each alpha particle is visible in the cloud chamber.

Alpha-particle tracks in a cloud chamber

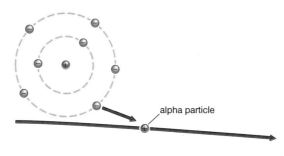

alpha particle

Ionisation

The properties of alpha, beta and gamma radiation

	alpha	beta	gamma
charge	+2	−1	0
absorption	thin paper	few mm of aluminium	several cm of lead
range in air	fixed, up to 10 cm	variable, up to 1 m	spreads without limit
ionising effect	strong	weak	very weak

Equations for radioactive change

★ Alpha emission

An alpha particle (symbol $^4_2\alpha$) consists of two protons and two neutrons. An unstable nucleus that emits an alpha particle therefore loses two units of charge and four units of mass. (Remember each proton has a mass of 1 atomic mass unit and a charge of +1 and a neutron has the same mass as a proton and is not charged.)

An unstable nucleus $^A_Z X$ has Z protons and $(A-Z)$ neutrons in its nucleus. If it emits an alpha particle, it becomes a nucleus with two fewer protons and two fewer neutrons.

$$^A_Z X \longrightarrow {}^{A-4}_{Z-2} Y + {}^4_2\alpha$$

★ Beta minus emission

A beta particle (symbol β) is an electron created in an unstable nucleus, then instantly emitted. A neutron in the nucleus suddenly becomes a proton, creating the beta particle at the same time. The total number of neutrons and protons in the nucleus is therefore unchanged, but there is one more proton.

$$^A_Z X \longrightarrow {}^A_{Z+1} Y + {}^0_{-1}\beta$$

The mass number of the beta particle is 0 because it is an electron. Its charge is opposite to that of a proton, so its proton number is written as −1.

Note
In both equations, the numbers balance along the top and along the bottom.

Question

a) Write down the equation representing
   (i) alpha emission from the unstable nucleus $^{238}_{92}$ U to form a nucleus of thorium (Th)
   (ii) beta emission from the unstable nucleus $^{27}_{12}$ Mg to form a nucleus of aluminium (Al).
b) State how many protons and how many neutrons are present in each nucleus in your equations.

Answers
a) (i) $^{238}_{92} U \longrightarrow {}^{234}_{90}Th + {}^4_2\alpha$
(ii) $^{27}_{12} Mg \longrightarrow {}^{27}_{13}Al + {}^0_{-1}\beta$
b) U-238 = 92 p + 146 n; Th-234 = 90p +144n;
Mg-27 = 12p + 15n; Al-27 = 13p + 14n

3.4 Half-life

The **half-life** of a radioactive isotope is the time taken for half its atoms to disintegrate. This time is a characteristic of the isotope. Long-lived radioactive isotopes have nuclei that are less unstable than short-lived isotopes. For example, uranium-238 has a half-life of more than 4500 million years.

The **number of atoms** of a radioactive isotope decreases with time. Radioactive disintegration is a **random** process, and the number of atoms that disintegrate per second is proportional to the number of radioactive atoms present at that time. For example, suppose 10% of the atoms of a certain radioactive isotope X disintegrate every 10 seconds. The table below shows how the number of atoms of X changes, starting with 10 000.

A graph showing how the number of atoms of X decreases with time is shown below. This type of curve is called a **decay curve**.

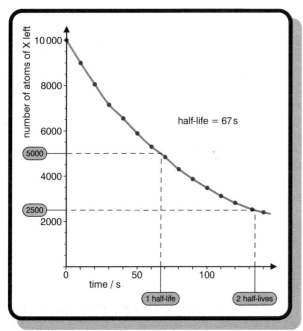

A decay curve

Question

a) Use the graph to estimate the half-life of X.
b) Use a calculator to estimate the time taken for the number of atoms to fall to 25% of 10 000. This should be equal to 2 half-lives.

The **activity** of a radioactive isotope decreases with time. This is because the activity is proportional to the number of atoms of the isotope left. The shape of the activity–time curve is the same as the decay curve, provided the 'daughter' isotope is stable.

Radioactive dating

Rocks formed millions of years ago can be dated using radioactivity. Ancient materials can also be dated using radioactivity.

★ Some igneous rocks contain the uranium isotope U-238, formed by volcanic activity long ago. These can be dated by measuring the proportion of an isotope of lead, Pb-206, relative to U-238. The uranium isotope has a half-life of 4500 million years, emitting alpha particles and forming the stable isotope Pb-206 via a series of relatively short-lived radioactive isotopes. A decay curve like the one here may be used to work out the age of a rock from the proportion of U-238 remaining.

★ Rocks containing trapped argon gas can be dated by measuring the proportion of the gas to the radioactive potassium isotope, K-40, which produces the gas as a result of radioactive change. K-40 is an unstable isotope with a half-life of 1250 million years, producing the argon isotope Ar-40. This gas is trapped when the molten rock solidifies. Hence the age of the rock can be determined by measuring the relative proportions of the two isotopes and then using a decay curve.

Answer   a) 66 s

Time/s	0	10	20	30	40	50	60	70
Number of atoms left	10 000	9000	8100	7290	6561	5905	5314	4783
Decrease in number of atoms of X	1000	900	810	729	656	591	531	478

3.5 Using radioactivity

In each of the uses of radioactivity described below, think about the choice of the radioactive isotope in terms of

1 the half-life of the isotope

2 absorption of radioactive emissions

3 whether or not the daughter isotope is stable.

Medical uses

Tracers for diagnosis: the cause of certain illnesses can be pinpointed using **radioactive tracers**. For example, an underactive thyroid gland can be detected by giving the patient food containing the radioactive isotope iodine-131. This is a beta emitter with a half-life of 8 days. A correctly functioning thyroid gland will absorb iodine and store it. A Geiger tube pointed at the neck will therefore show an increased reading if the patient's thyroid gland is functioning correctly. The amount of radioactivity is too small to harm the gland, and the isotope decays after a few weeks.

Treating cancer

Question

1 a) Why is a beta emitter chosen?
  b) Why is an isotope with a half-life of a few minutes not chosen?

Gamma therapy: gamma radiation from the radioactive isotope cobalt-60 is used to destroy cancerous tissues. The gamma radiation penetrates the body and passes into the diseased tissue. A lead collimator (filter) is used to direct the gamma radiation onto the cancer cells. The half-life of cobalt-60 is 5 years.

Question

2 a) Why is a gamma emitter chosen?
  b) Why is an isotope with a half-life of a few years chosen?

Industrial uses

Thickness of metal foil: a detector measures the amount of beta radiation passing through the metal foil feeding out of a production line. If the foil becomes too thick, the detector reading falls and feeds a signal back to increase the pressure on the foil and make it thinner.

Pipeline cracks: the crack in a leaking underground pipe can be located by putting a radioactive tracer into the flow. A Geiger counter is then moved on the ground along the pipeline. Its reading is higher where the fluid in the pipe leaks into the ground. A beta-emitting isotope with a half-life of a few hours would be suitable for this purpose.

Some other uses

Food radiation: gamma radiation is used to kill the bacteria responsible for food poisoning in certain foods. This makes the food safer to eat, and prolongs its shelf-life.

Answers

1 a) Beta radiation from the thyroid can be detected outside the body.
  b) There would be no radioactivity left in the iodine by the time it reached the thyroid.
2 a) Gamma radiation easily penetrates the body.
  b) The source only needs to be replaced every few years.

3.6 Nuclear reactors

2 The **moderator** slows down the neutrons from each fission event, so they can produce fission of more U-235. Otherwise they are absorbed by U-238 without producing fission.

concrete case

coolant

3 The **control rods** absorb excess neutrons to ensure only one neutron per fission produces further fission.

steam out

steam out

1 The **fuel rods** contain enriched uranium which is 97% U-238 and 3% U-235.

4 Energy released by fission is removed as heat by a **coolant**, which is pumped through the reactor core. The energy released is colossal – 1 kg of U-235 releases more energy than 200 tonnes of coal.

water in

water in

coolant pumps

6 The **spent fuel** is highly radioactive and must be stored for many years after removal from the reactor.

5 The **core** is in a thick-walled steel vessel encased in concrete to prevent neutrons and radioactive particles from escaping.

Inside a nuclear reactor

Releasing energy from the nucleus

★ The uranium-235 nucleus is unstable and splits into two approximately equal 'daughter' nuclei, and two or three neutrons. This splitting process is called **fission**.

Fission

★ Energy is released when a U-235 nucleus splits, which is carried away as kinetic energy by the daughter nuclei and neutrons.

★ Fission can be induced by bombarding U-235 nuclei with neutrons.

★ A controlled **chain reaction** is created if there are sufficient U-235 nuclei. One neutron from each fission event goes on to cause the fission of another nucleus.

Radioactive waste

Radioactive waste from a nuclear reactor is classified as

- **low level waste** such as clothing worn by personnel – the clothing fibres may contain radioactive dust particles
- **intermediate level waste** such as metal cladding from spent fuel rods – the cladding becomes radioactive inside the reactor
- **high level waste** such as fission products, unused uranium and plutonium.

Treatment and storage of radioactive waste

★ Low level radioactive waste from Britain's nuclear reactors is stored in sealed containers in a shallow trench at Sellafield.

★ Intermediate level waste is stored in sealed drums at several sites in Britain. An underground storage site at Sellafield is being developed to store all Britain's intermediate level and low level waste.

★ High level waste includes spent fuel rods, which are highly radioactive because the nuclei produced by fission of uranium-235 are unstable. The spent fuel rods therefore generate heat due to radioactive decay. The rods are placed initially in cooling ponds until they are cool enough to be transported safely to Sellafield. There they are reprocessed to recover unused uranium and plutonium. The rest of the high level waste is stored in sealed containers at Sellafield.

Why radioactivity is harmful

Radiation from radioactive substances produces ions. Ionising radiation damages living cells in two ways:

1 by penetrating the cell membranes which causes the cell to die

2 by breaking the strands of DNA molecules in the cell nucleus, which may cause cell mutation.

★ **Alpha radiation** is easily absorbed, highly ionising and therefore very harmful.

★ **Beta radiation** is less easily absorbed and less ionising. However, it can penetrate deep into the body from outside so it too is very harmful.

★ **Gamma radiation** easily penetrates soft tissue and is absorbed by bones, where its ionising effect can produce immense damage.

There is no lower limit below which ionising radiation is harmless. Therefore, extreme care is essential when radioactive substances are used and legal regulations for using radioactive substances must be observed. In a school laboratory, students under the age of 16 are not allowed to carry out experiments with radioactive materials.

> **Question**
>
> a) Why is a storage box for radioactive substances made of lead?
> b) Why is it essential for handling tongs to have long handles?

> **Answers**
> a) Lead is the best absorber of radioactivity.
> b) The tongs keep the source as far away from the user as possible.

3

round-up

How much have you improved?
Work out your improvement index on pages 308–9.

1 Natural uranium consists of about 99% $^{238}_{92}$U and about 1% $^{235}_{92}$U.
   a) How many protons and how many neutrons are present in each type of atom? [4]
   b) What is the name for different types of atoms of the same element? [1]
   c) $^{238}_{92}$U has a *half-life* of about 4500 million years. Explain what is meant by *half-life*. [1]

2 One type of smoke detector uses an alpha particle source, as shown.

alpha particle sensor is on whenever
smoke prevents the particles reaching it

   a) Why is an alpha source used rather than a beta or a gamma source? [2]
   b) Why is it important for the alpha source to have a half-life of more than 5 years? [1]

3 a) $^{220}_{82}$Rn emits alpha particles to form an isotope of the element polonium (Po). Write down the equation for this process. [2]
   b) Radon-220 has a half-life of 52 s. A pure sample of this isotope had an initial activity of 400 disintegrations per second. What was its activity after **(i)** 104 s **(ii)** 208 s? [2]

4 The thickness of hot rolled steel plate produced in a factory was monitored using a gamma source and detector, as shown below.

hot plate in   pressure rollers   Geiger counter   plate out
source of —
gamma radiation

   a) Why was gamma radiation used instead of alpha or beta radiation? [3]
   b) The counter reading increased every second as shown in the table below.

Time / s	0	1	2	3	4	5	6	7	8	9	10
Counter reading	0	204	395	602	792	1004	1180	1340	1505	1660	1825

   (i) What was the average count rate over the first 5 seconds? [1]
   (ii) What was the average count rate over the last 2 seconds? [1]
   (iii) What happened to the thickness of the plate? [1]

5 a) Background radioactivity accounts for 87% of the exposure to ionising radiations of the average person in Britain. Explain what is meant by
   (i) background radioactivity [1]
   (ii) ionising radiation. [1]
   b) State two further sources of ionising radiation. [2]
   c) Explain how you would use a Geiger counter and a stopwatch to measure background radioactivity. [2]

6 In a test to identify the type of radioactivity produced by a radioactive source, the following results were obtained with different sheets of materials placed between the source and the Geiger tube.

material	count rate / counts per second
none	450
tin foil	235
1 mm aluminium	230
10 mm aluminium	228
10 mm lead	160

Use these results to decide what types of radiation are emitted by the source. Explain your answer. [4]

7 a) Why is it essential to use long-handled tongs to move a radioactive source? [1]
   b) Cobalt-60 is a radioactive isotope that emits gamma radiation. It is used in hospitals to treat cancer.
   (i) What is gamma radiation and why is it necessary to use gamma radiation for this purpose? [2]
   (ii) With the aid of a diagram, explain how the gamma radiation is concentrated on the tumour. [3]

Waves

preview

At the end of this topic you will be able to:

- **describe different types of waves**
- **explain what is meant by a transverse wave and a longitudinal wave**
- **explain what is meant by the amplitude, wavelength and frequency of a wave**
- **relate the speed of a wave to its wavelength and its frequency**
- **describe reflection, refraction and diffraction as wave properties.**

MIND MAP
Page 215.

How much do you already know?
Work out your score on page 309.

Test yourself

1 State four different types of waves. [4]

2 a) What is the difference between a longitudinal wave and a transverse wave? [2]
   b) Is the primary component of a seismic wave longitudinal or transverse? [1]

3 State one type of wave that can travel through a vacuum, and one type that cannot. [2]

4 The diagram shows a snapshot of a wave travelling from left to right.

P

Use a millimetre rule to measure its wavelength and its amplitude. [2]

5 If the wave in **4** is travelling at 20 mm/s, what is
   a) its frequency [1]
   b) the number of complete cycles each point goes through in 1 minute? [1]

6 In the diagram in **4**, what is the displacement of point P
   a) exactly 1.0 s after the snapshot shown
   b) exactly 4.0 s after the snapshot shown? [2]

7 Why are waves on the sea shore not reflected when they run up the beach? [2]

8 What is meant by refraction of waves? [2]

9 When waves pass through a gap they spread out. Is the spreading increased or decreased when
   a) the gap is made narrower
   b) the wavelength is decreased? [2]

10 a) Calculate the frequency of sound waves in air which have a wavelength of 0.40 m, given that the speed of sound in air is 340 m/s. [1]
   b) Calculate the wavelength of ultrasonic waves of frequency 1.5 MHz in water, given that the speed of the waves is 1500 m/s. [1]

What is a wave?

Waves can carry energy without carrying matter. Drop a stone in a pond and observe the ripples as they spread out. A small object floating on the water would bob up and down as the ripples pass it. The ripples are waves on the water surface carrying energy across the pond. A water wave is an example of a disturbance in a substance which travels through the substance. Electromagnetic waves do not need a substance to travel through; all other types of waves do.

4.1 Transverse and longitudinal waves

Different types of waves

Some types of waves are listed below. You need to know how they are produced, what they have in common and how they differ from each other.

*   water waves
*   waves on a string or a rope
*   seismic waves
*   sound waves
*   electromagnetic waves (radio waves, microwaves, infrared radiation, visible light, ultraviolet light, X-rays, gamma rays)

Making waves

All waves except electromagnetic waves need a substance to travel through. Waves are sent through the medium when one part of the substance is made to vibrate. For example, waves can be sent along a long stretched coil by making one end vibrate. The vibrations can be in any direction, but there are two particular ways of sending waves down the coil:

FACTS

★ **Longitudinal waves** can be created by making one end vibrate to and fro along the coil. At any point, the vibrations are parallel to the direction in which the waves travel. The coil windings are squeezed and stretched as the waves pass down the coil.

★ **Transverse waves** can be created by making one end vibrate at right angles to the coil. At any point along the coil, the vibrations are at 90° to the direction in which the waves travel.

More about transverse waves

'Transverse' means 'across', so transverse waves vibrate in a direction that is across (perpendicular to) the

direction in which the wave travels. Examples of transverse waves include

*   waves on a rope or a string
*   electromagnetic waves
*   secondary (S) seismic waves.

Transverse waves are **polarised** if their vibrations are in one plane only. However, if the plane of vibration continually changes, the waves on the rope are **unpolarised**.

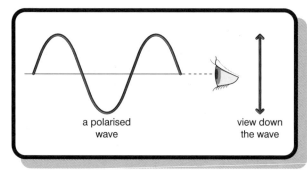

a polarised wave   view down the wave

Polarisation

More about longitudinal waves

'Longitudinal' means 'along', so longitudinal waves vibrate along (parallel to) the direction in which the wave travels. They squeeze and stretch the medium. Examples of longitudinal waves include

*   sound waves
*   primary (P) seismic waves.

making transverse waves

making longitudinal waves

Transverse and longitudinal waves

4.2 Measuring waves

Look at the snapshot of a transverse wave in the diagram below. The wave is travelling from left to right, but you can't tell this from the snapshot. Each point on the wave vibrates at 90° to the wave direction.

★ **One complete cycle** of vibration of any point returns the point to the same position and direction it had at the start of the cycle. In this time, a wave crest at the point is replaced by the next wave crest.

★ **The amplitude of a wave** is the height of the wave crest above the centre. This is the same as the depth of a wave trough below the centre.

★ **The wavelength of a wave** (symbol λ, pronounced 'lambda') is the distance from one crest to the next crest. This is the same as the distance from a trough to the next trough.

★ **The frequency of a wave** (symbol f) is the number of crests passing a given position each second. This is the same as the number of complete cycles of vibration per second of any point. The unit of frequency is the hertz (symbol Hz), equal to 1 cycle per second.

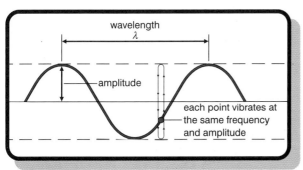

Question

1 What are the wavelength and the amplitude of the wave shown above?

Answers

1 Amplitude = 10 mm, wavelength = 40 mm
2 136 Hz, 340 m/s, 0.160 m, 0.040 m, 6 × 10¹⁴ Hz
3 2.4 Hz

Speed

★ The speed v of a wave is the distance travelled by a crest in one second. The unit of speed is the metre per second (m/s).

★ The speed of a wave can be calculated from its frequency and wavelength using the following equation:

speed = frequency × wavelength
(in m/s)   (in Hz)   (in m)

Maths workshop

• The equation for speed can be written in symbols as $v = f\lambda$, where v is the speed, f is the frequency and λ is the wavelength.

• To find the frequency f from $v = f\lambda$, the equation needs to be rearranged to make f its subject.

Start with $f\lambda = v$

then divide both sides by λ to give

$$\frac{f\lambda}{\lambda} = \frac{v}{\lambda}$$

then cancel λ top and bottom on the left-hand side of the equation to give

$$f = \frac{v}{\lambda}$$

• To find the wavelength λ from $v = f\lambda$, transfer f from the top on one side to the bottom on the other side to give

$$\lambda = \frac{v}{f}$$

Questions

2 Complete the table below by calculating the missing value of speed, frequency or wavelength.

wavelength/m	2.5	0.1			5 × 10⁻⁷
frequency/Hz		3400	500	3750	
speed/m/s	340		80	1500	3 × 10⁸

3 Suppose the wave in the diagram is travelling at a speed of 60 mm/s to the left. Calculate its frequency using the wavelength measurement from question **1**.

4.3 Wave properties

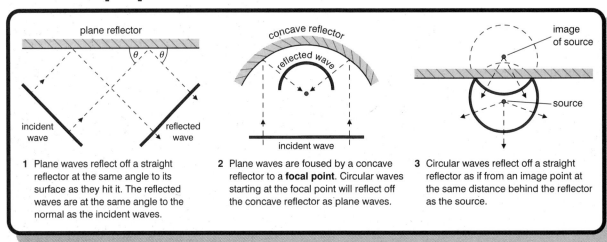

1 Plane waves reflect off a straight reflector at the same angle to its surface as they hit it. The reflected waves are at the same angle to the normal as the incident waves.

2 Plane waves are foused by a concave reflector to a **focal point**. Circular waves starting at the focal point will reflect off the concave reflector as plane waves.

3 Circular waves reflect off a straight reflector as if from an image point at the same distance behind the reflector as the source.

Reflections on reflection

Reflection

The shape and the direction of a reflected wave depend on the shape of the incident wave and on the shape of the reflecting surface.

Note
*Straight waves are sometimes called **plane waves**. A line perpendicular to a wall or boundary is called a **normal**.*

Refraction

When a plane wave passes across a straight boundary,

1 its wavelength changes if the wave speed changes at the boundary. The frequency does not change.

2 its direction of motion changes if its direction is not perpendicular to the boundary.

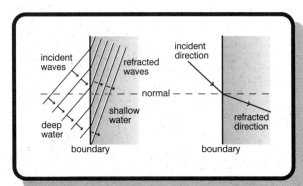

Refraction

Diffraction

Waves spread out when they pass through a gap or behind an obstacle. The longer the wavelength, the greater the spreading. The waves spread out more through a narrower gap.

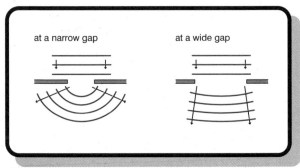

Diffraction

> **Question**

A satellite TV dish needs to be pointed in the correct direction to obtain a picture.
a) Using a diagram, explain how a satellite dish works.
b) Why are larger dishes needed in northern Europe than in southern Europe?

> **Answers**
> a) The dish is a concave reflector which focuses radio waves from the satellite onto an aerial at the focal point.
> b) The satellite is over the equator so the radio waves travel further through the atmosphere to reach northern Europe, so they become weaker. Hence a larger dish is needed to collect more radio waves.

round-up

How much have you improved?
Work out your improvement index on page 309.

1 a) Which of the following can be classified as **(i)** longitudinal waves **(ii)** transverse waves? water waves, radio waves, sound waves, waves on a rope [3]

b) State three differences between sound waves and light waves. [3]

2 Copy and complete each of these sketches, showing the wave after reflection. [4]

3 A stone is thrown into a pond at a point which is 2.0 m from the bank, which is a straight wall. The waves take 2.0 s to reach the wall. Copy the sketch below and show the position of the wave 3.0 s after the stone hit the water. [2]

stone hits water here

4 a) When light passes from air into glass, it slows down. What happens to its wavelength and its frequency? [2]

b) The diagram shows plane waves about to cross a boundary between shallow and deep water. Copy and complete the diagram by showing the waves in the deep water as well as the shallow water. [2]

shallow water

deep water

boundary

5 a) Sound travels at a speed of 1500 m/s in water. Calculate the wavelength in water of sound waves of frequency 3000 Hz. [1]

b) Plane water waves of wavelength 0.20 m travel past five ducks spaced 0.3 m apart in a straight line. Each crest takes 3.0 s to pass from the mother duck at one end to the last duck at the other end. Calculate **(i)** the speed **(ii)** the frequency of the waves. [2]

wave direction

Sitting ducks

6 a) When waves pass through a gap, they spread out. What is the name for this process? [1]

b) If the gap is made wider, what happens to the amount of spreading? [1]

7 a) A local radio station broadcasts at a frequency of 100 MHz. Calculate the wavelength of these radio waves, given that radio waves travel through air at a speed of 300 000 km/s. [1]

b) The aerial of a portable radio is turned through 90°, causing the reception to become weaker. Explain why this happens. [3]

c) A radio telescope consists of a large concave dish made from wire mesh with an aerial at its focal point. What is the purpose of the wire mesh? [1]

8 A boat travelling at constant speed produces bow waves as shown.

a) Explain how these waves are produced. [2]

b) How would the bow waves differ if the boat travelled faster? [1]

Bow waves

Sound waves and seismic waves

preview

At the end of this topic you will be able to:

- **describe how sound is produced and transmitted**
- **explain how pitch and loudness are related to frequency and amplitude**
- **describe reflection, refraction, diffraction and absorption of sound**
- **explain what ultrasound is and describe some uses of ultrasound**
- **explain how seismic waves are produced, measured and used.**

Work out your score on page 310.
Mind Map on page 215.

Test yourself

1 **a)** Are sound waves longitudinal or transverse? [1]
b) Are seismic waves longitudinal or transverse? [2]

2 What is special about the sound produced by a vibrating tuning fork? [1]

3 **a)** The pitch of a note produced by plucking a guitar string can be altered by changing the tension or changing the length of the vibrating section of the string. How does the pitch of the note change when the string is **(i)** tightened **(ii)** lengthened? [2]
b) Two guitar strings of the same material have equal lengths but different thicknesses. They are tuned to produce notes of the same pitch when plucked. Which string is under the greater tension? [2]

4 What is an echo? [1]

5 How does the amplitude and the wavelength of the sound waves from a loudspeaker change if the sound is made **a)** louder at the same pitch **b)** quieter at higher pitch? [4]

6 A teacher is talking in a classroom with the door to the corridor open. The teacher's voice can be heard down the corridor even though the teacher cannot be seen from there. What property of sound is responsible for this? [1]

7 **a)** Which frequency **A** to **D** is nearest to the highest sound frequency that can be heard by the human ear? [1]
A 200 Hz **B** 2000 Hz **C** 20 000 Hz **D** 200 000 Hz
b) Which frequency **A** to **D** is nearest to the frequency at which the human ear is most sensitive? [1]
c) A telephone circuit does not transmit frequencies above 4000 Hz. Explain how this affects voice signals. [1]

8 **a)** Outline how an ultrasonic depth gauge on a ship works. [5]
b) State two other uses of ultrasonics. [2]

9 **a)** Ultrasonic waves of frequency 2 MHz in air travel at a speed of 340 m/s. Calculate the wavelength of these waves. [1]
b) These waves travel faster in water than in air. On entering water from air, what change occurs in **(i)** the frequency **(ii)** the wavelength of the waves? [2]

10 **a)** What causes earthquakes? [2]
b) Why are secondary (S) waves from an earthquake unable to travel through the Earth's centre to the opposite side of the Earth? [3]

Measuring the speed of sound

Two people stand a measured distance apart, at least 500 m. The starter makes a loud short sound, for example with a large gong, in view of the other person (the timer). The timer times the interval between observing the sound being created and hearing it. The speed of sound is calculated from the distance divided by the time taken.

starter   person with stop watch

To account for wind speed, the two people change roles and the experiment is repeated to give an average value.

5.1 Properties of sound

Sound waves are longitudinal. They are created by an object vibrating in a medium. The object pushes and pulls on the medium. The particles of the medium vibrate to and fro along the direction in which the sound travels.

Sound waves can be displayed using a microphone and an oscilloscope, as shown.

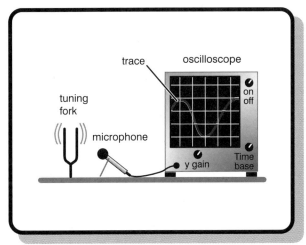

Displaying sound

The oscilloscope trace shows how the amplitude of the sound wave varies with time. The trace is usually referred to as the **waveform**. The trace on the screen is a transverse wave; the sound wave that creates the trace is a longitudinal wave.

★ If the sound is made louder, the trace becomes taller. The amplitude of a sound wave represents the volume.

★ If the sound is lowered in pitch, the trace is stretched out on the screen. The frequency of a sound wave represents the pitch.

★ Most sounds have more complicated waveforms than the pure waveform shown in the diagram.

Echoes

Sound is reflected by a hard surface such as a brick wall. **Echoes** are caused by sound reflections. First the original sound is heard, then an echo may be heard a little later due to reflection off the wall. The echo is delayed because the echo sound waves travel further than the direct sound waves.

Absorption of sound

Soft surfaces such as curtains absorb sound instead of reflecting it or transmitting it. This is why a curtained room sounds different to a bare room.

Refraction of sound

Like all waves, sound waves can be refracted. The speed of sound in air will change if the air temperature changes with height. Sound created on the ground may then be refracted, and may be heard a long way away from where it was produced.

Diffraction of sound

Sound waves spread through gaps and round obstacles. The sound from a car engine may be heard on the other side of a large building because of diffraction. The sound waves from the car engine pass round the edge of the building and spread round it on the other side.

Sound cannot travel through a vacuum

This fact is demonstrated by removing the air surrounding a ringing bell in a bell jar. The ringing bell can be heard before the air is pumped out. The sound of the bell fades away as the air is removed. If the air is allowed back into the bell jar, the sound returns.

A soundless bell

5.2 Ultrasound

Hearing

The human ear is a remarkable organ. The loudest sounds your ears can withstand without damage are about one million million times more powerful than the faintest sound you can hear. Loudness levels are expressed in **decibels** (dB) where 0 dB is at the lower threshold of hearing and every 10 dB extra corresponds to ten times more power. The graph shows how the lower threshold of hearing varies with frequency.

★ The human ear is most sensitive at a frequency of about 3000 Hz.

★ The upper frequency limit for the human ear is about 20 000 Hz.

★ Hearing usually deteriorates with age – your upper frequency limit will decrease as you become older.

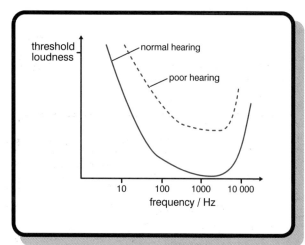

Hearing response

Ultrasound

Ultrasound is defined as sound at frequencies above the upper limit of the human ear. In other words, any sound waves of frequency above 20 kHz will be ultrasound.

Ultrasonic cleaning: dirt particles are removed from street lamps by immersing the lamp in an ultrasonic cleaning tank operating at 40 kHz. The ultrasonic waves in the water agitate the dirt particles which are then dispersed by the water.

Depth finding: the depth of the sea bed can be determined by sending ultrasonic pulses from a ship towards the sea bed, and timing how long the reflected pulses take to return to the ship. If the speed of sound c in water is known, the depth of the sea bed can be calculated from $\frac{1}{2}ct$, where t is the time taken for each pulse to travel to the sea bed and back.

Metal fatigue tests: cracks inside a metal weaken the metal, but cannot be seen from the outside. Such cracks can be detected using an ultrasonic probe. This sends ultrasonic waves into the metal and picks up reflections from internal boundaries within the metal.

Ultrasonic medical scanner: this is used to obtain images of organs within the body. It is also widely used to form images of unborn babies to monitor the health of the baby and the mother. An ultrasonic probe moved across the body surface directs ultrasonic waves into the human body. Internal boundaries partially reflect the ultrasonic waves, and the reflected waves are detected by the same probe, which is connected to a computer. The probe builds up an image of the reflecting boundaries inside the body. Unlike X-rays, ultrasonic waves do not cause ionisation, and are therefore thought to be harmless at low power.

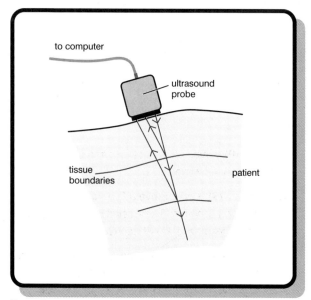

Ultrasonic scanner

5.3 Seismic waves

Inside the Earth

The Earth is thought to have formed about 5000 million years ago, originally in a molten state which gradually cooled and solidified. More dense materials such as iron sank to the centre when it was molten. The least dense material formed the Earth's crust.

Earthquakes

★ Earthquake belts occur where two plates press against each other or slide past each other. Stress builds up which is suddenly released when one plate gives way to the other. The crust shakes violently and seismic waves spread out through the Earth.

★ The point where the seismic waves originate from is called the **focus** of the earthquake. The nearest point on the surface directly above the focus is called the **epicentre**.

★ The energy released by an earthquake is measured on the **Richter scale** which is a 'times ten' scale. An earthquake that registers at a certain point on the Richter scale releases ten times as much energy as an earthquake that registers on the next point below.

Analysing seismic waves

An instrument called a **seismometer** is used to detect seismic waves.

Seismic waves

★ **Primary (P)** waves cause the first tremors. These are longitudinal waves.

★ **Secondary (S)** waves arrive a few minutes later, causing more tremors. They travel more slowly than P waves. These are transverse waves.

★ **Long (L)** waves arrive last to cause the main shock. These travel along the crust only, making the surface move violently up and down as well as to and fro.

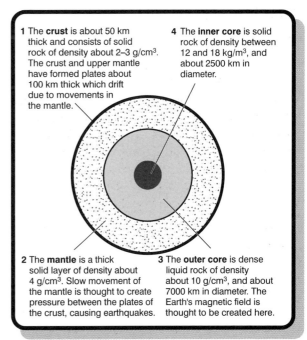

1 The **crust** is about 50 km thick and consists of solid rock of density about 2–3 g/cm³. The crust and upper mantle have formed plates about 100 km thick which drift due to movements in the mantle.

2 The **mantle** is a thick solid layer of density about 4 g/cm³. Slow movement of the mantle is thought to create pressure between the plates of the crust, causing earthquakes.

3 The **outer core** is dense liquid rock of density about 10 g/cm³, and about 7000 km in diameter. The Earth's magnetic field is thought to be created here.

4 The **inner core** is solid rock of density between 12 and 18 kg/m³, and about 2500 km in diameter.

The structure of the Earth

Handy hint

Hints & Tips

P waves **P**ush and **P**ull.
S waves **S**hake **S**ide to **S**ide.
L waves go the **L**ong way round.

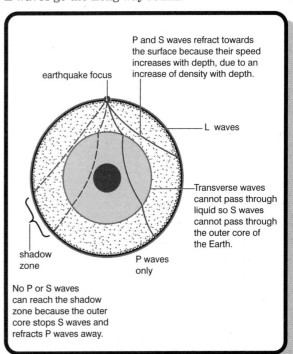

P and S waves refract towards the surface because their speed increases with depth, due to an increase of density with depth.

earthquake focus

L waves

Transverse waves cannot pass through liquid so S waves cannot pass through the outer core of the Earth.

shadow zone

P waves only

No P or S waves can reach the shadow zone because the outer core stops S waves and refracts P waves away.

Seismic waves inside the Earth

5

round-up

How much have you improved?
Work out your improvement index on page 310.

1 The diagram shows a ship at sea near a cliff.

An echo from the ship's siren is heard 5.0 s after the siren is sounded.
a) Calculate the distance from the ship to the cliff. The speed of sound in air is 340 m/s. [1]
b) If the ship was fog-bound, explain how the ship's captain could find out if the ship was moving towards or away from the cliffs. [2]

2 A loudspeaker connected to a signal generator is used to produce a continuous sound of constant pitch and loudness.
a) Explain how the vibrating surface of the loudspeaker creates sound waves. [2]
b) Why is a small loudspeaker likely to be able to produce sound waves of high frequency better than a large loudspeaker? [2]

3 The waveform of a note from a musical instrument is shown in the diagram below. Copy and draw on the diagram the waveform you would expect if the same instrument is
a) played more quietly [2]
b) played at a lower pitch. [1]

4 The speed of sound in air is 340 m/s.
a) Calculate the frequency of sound waves of wavelength 0.10 m in air. [1]
b) Calculate the wavelength of sound waves of frequency 5000 Hz in air. [1]

5 When indoors, noise from outside may be reduced by closing any open windows. How does this reduce the noise from outside? [2]

6 a) An ultrasonic cleaning tank operates at a frequency of 40 kHz. Calculate the wavelength of ultrasonic waves in water. The speed of sound waves in water is 1500 m/s. [1]
b) When using an ultrasonic hospital scanner, a paste is applied to the body surface where the probe is used.
(i) Explain why this is necessary. [2]
(ii) Give two reasons why each reflected pulse is weaker than the pulse emitted by the probe. [2]

7 a) The diagram shows a cross-section of the Earth. The inner core is labelled A.

(i) What are the parts labelled B, C and D? [3]
(ii) State which of the parts A to D are molten and which are solid. [4]
b) Why are earthquakes more common in certain parts of the world than in other parts? [1]

8 a) Are primary seismic waves longitudinal or transverse? [1]
b) (i) Sketch and describe a typical seismic wave trace, labelling the P waves, the S waves and the L waves. [3]
(ii) Why are S waves unable to travel through the Earth's core? [2]
(iii) Why do P waves and S waves in the mantle curve towards the surface? [2]
(iv) Copy the diagram above and use it to explain why shock waves from an earthquake can arrive without being preceded by tremors. [3]

Well done if you've improved. Don't worry if you haven't. Take a break and try again.

Light

preview

At the end of this topic you will be able to:

- **state the law of reflection and explain what is meant by refraction of light**
- **describe image formation by a plane mirror and a lens**
- **describe some uses of a plane mirror and of lenses**
- **explain how total internal reflection can occur**
- **describe some applications of fibre optics**
- **explain how diffraction affects image detail.**

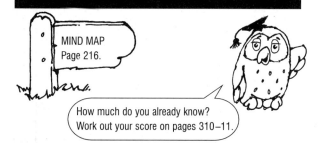

MIND MAP
Page 216.

How much do you already know?
Work out your score on pages 310–11.

Test yourself

1 a) State the law of reflection at a plane mirror. [1]

   b) A person stands 0.6 m in front of a plane mirror and observes his own image. How far away is the image from the person? [1]

2 a) When a light ray passes from air into glass at a non-zero angle to the normal, does it bend towards or away from the normal? [1]

   b) A light ray passes from a pool of water into air, emerging at an angle of 30° to the vertical, as in the following diagram. Is the angle between the light ray in the water and the vertical more than, less than or equal to 30°? [1]

   c) In **(b)**, the angle between the light ray in the water and the vertical is increased until the refracted ray emerges along the water surface.
What happens if this angle is made larger? [1]

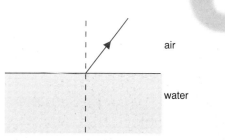

air

water

3 A convex lens is used to form an image of a distant object on a screen. State if the image is
a) real or virtual   **b)** upright or inverted
c) magnified or diminished. [3]

4 Why does a swimming pool appear shallower than it really is? [3]

5 A person with short sight can see near objects clearly but distant objects are out of focus. This sight defect is corrected using a suitable concave lens. What does a concave lens do to light from a distant point object? [2]

6 A distant object is focused on a screen using a convex lens. To focus a nearby object on the screen with the same lens, should the lens be moved towards or away from the screen? Explain your answer. [2]

7 a) A beam of white light is split into a spectrum by passing it through a glass prism. Which colour of the spectrum is refracted least? [1]

   b) A surface that appears blue in white light will appear black in red light. Why? [3]

8 Complete the path of the light rays in each diagram. [4]

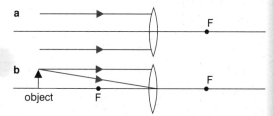

a

F

b

object   F

F

9 State two uses of fibre optics. [2]

10 a) Is the wavelength of red light less or more than the wavelength of blue light? [1]

   b) Why can you see more detail using a microscope with blue light instead of white light? [3]

Rays and waves

A light ray shows the direction in which light travels. Light rays are usually drawn as straight lines, since diffraction is only significant where fine detail is needed. Ray diagrams describe how light is affected by mirrors and lenses.

6.1 Reflection

The **law of reflection** states that the angle between the reflected ray and the normal is equal to the angle between the incident ray and the normal.

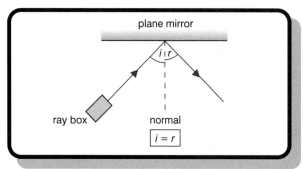

The law of reflection

The diagram shows how this can be tested using a ray box and a plane mirror. Note that the normal is the line which is perpendicular to the mirror at the point where the light ray meets the mirror.

Mirror images

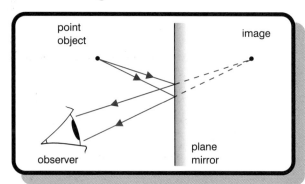

Image formation

The diagram shows how a plane mirror forms an image. Note that the image of an object viewed by reflection using a plane mirror is

- the same distance behind the mirror as the object is in front
- upright and the same size as the object
- virtual, which means it is formed where the reflected rays *appear* to come from
- laterally inverted, which means the image of a left-handed person is right-handed and vice versa. Try it if you don't believe it!

Uses of a plane mirror

1   **A wall mirror** needs to be at least half the height of the tallest person who uses it. It also needs to be mounted with its top edge level with the top of the head.

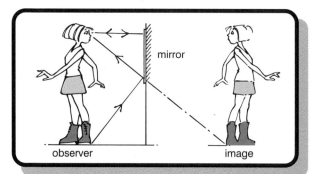

Using a wall mirror

2   **A periscope** is useful for seeing over a crowd. It is also used in submarines to see above the surface when the submarine is under water.

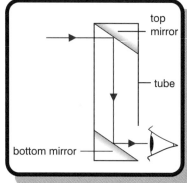

Using a periscope

3   **Parallax errors** caused by incorrectly reading the position of a pointer on a scale can be eliminated using a plane mirror. The image of the pointer must be directly under the pointer when reading the scale.

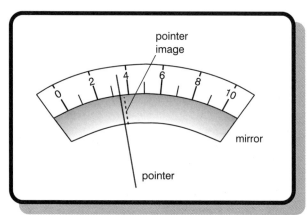

Parallax errors

Curved mirrors

A **concave mirror** may be used

- to focus sunlight for a solar energy collector. When the mirror faces the sun directly, the sunlight is concentrated at the **focal point** of the concave mirror.
- to produce a parallel beam of light by placing a point source of light at its focal point
- as a face mirror. The mirror must be held close to the face to produce a magnified upright virtual image.

A **convex mirror** may be used as a wide-angle mirror, such as a driving mirror.

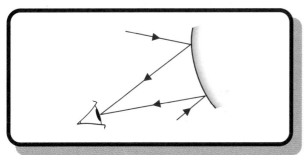

A wide-angle mirror

6.2 Refraction

Investigating refraction

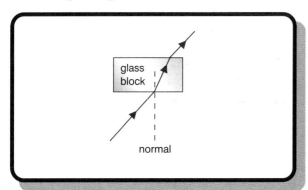

Refraction in a glass block

★ If a light ray is directed at a glass block as shown, the light ray changes its direction when it enters the glass. It is closer to the normal in glass than in air. This is an example of the **refraction** of light. It occurs because light waves travel more slowly in glass than in air.

★ When a light ray passes from glass into air at a non-zero angle to the normal, it bends away from the normal. This happens because the light waves speed up when they pass from glass into air.

★ Refraction happens when light passes from one transparent medium into another. The light ray is always closer to the normal in the 'slower' medium.

In deep water

A swimming pool appears shallower than it really is because light from the bottom of the pool is refracted away from the normal when it passes into air at the surface. Someone looking into the water from above sees an image of the bottom of the pool nearer the surface.

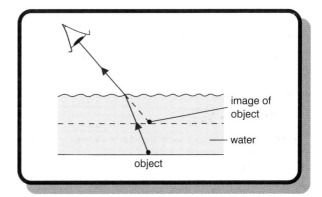

Fact file
The speed of light through air is 300 000 km/s. Light travels more slowly in a transparent medium than in air. For example, its speed in glass is 200 000 km/s. The ratio of its speed in air to its speed in glass is therefore 1.5. This ratio is called the **refractive index** of the medium.

Lenses

Light changes direction on passing through a lens, unless it passes through the exact centre. The effect of a lens on light depends on the shape of the lens.

1 The position of the image formed by a lens depends on the object position.

2 The image of a point object is **real** if it can be formed on a screen. An image seen in a mirror or a magnifying glass cannot be formed on a screen. It is said to be **virtual**.

The convex lens

★ The **focal point** of a convex lens is the point where light rays parallel to the lens axis are brought to a focus.

★ A light ray directed at the lens through the focal point always emerges parallel to the lens axis.

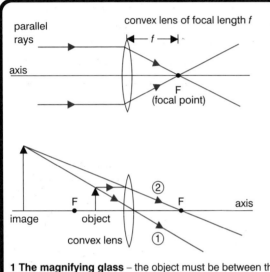

1 The magnifying glass – the object must be between the lens and the focal point F to give an enlarged, upright and virtual image on the same side as the object.

2 The projector lens – the slide transparency must be between F and 2F to give an enlarged real image beyond 2F on the other side of the lens. Note that the image is inverted.

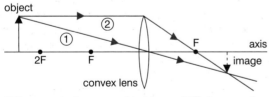

3 The camera lens – an object beyond 2F gives a real, inverted image on the other side of the lens between F and 2F.

Ray ① passes straight through the centre.

Ray ② passes through F.

Some uses of the convex lens

The concave lens

This makes a parallel beam of light spread out. The focal point is the point where light appears to diverge from. A concave lens can be used to widen a laser beam. It is also used to correct short sight.

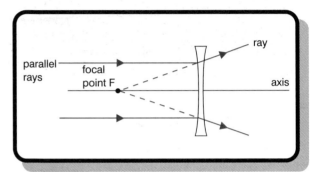

The concave lens

Question

1 A convex lens is used to project an image of a slide on a screen. If the lens is moved closer to the slide, describe how the position and the size of the image changes.

Sight correction

1 **Long sight** is corrected using a **convex** lens. This enables near objects to be seen in focus.

2 **Short sight** is corrected using a **concave** lens. This enables distant objects to be seen in focus.

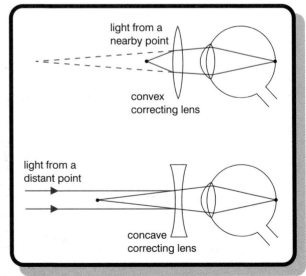

Sight correction

2 A short-sighted person under water can see distant objects clearly without the aid of spectacles. Why?

Answers

1 The image moves further away and becomes larger.

2 Less refraction occurs when light enters the eye under water. The image of a distant object is therefore formed on the retina instead of in front of it when the eye is under water.

6.3 Fibre optics

Total internal reflection

This occurs when light in a transparent medium strikes the boundary at an angle of incidence greater than a **critical angle**. The light ray reflects internally just as if the boundary is a mirror.

normal

i_1

$i_1 < c$

1 If the angle of incidence is less than the critical angle, the light ray bends away from the normal on leaving the glass.

normal

c

c = critical angle

2 If the angle of incidence is equal to the critical angle, the light refracts along the boundary.

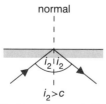

normal

i_2 i_2

$i_2 > c$

3 If the angle of incidence exceeds the critical angle, the light ray is totally internally reflected.

Total internal reflection

Optical fibres

An optical fibre is a thin fibre of transparent flexible material. A light ray that enters the fibre at one end emerges at the other end, even if the fibre is curved round. This happens because the light ray is totally internally reflected at the fibre surface wherever it hits the boundary. Each light ray in the fibre travels along a straight line through the fibre between successive reflections. Provided the bends in the fibre are not too tight, light rays in the fibre do not emerge from its sides.

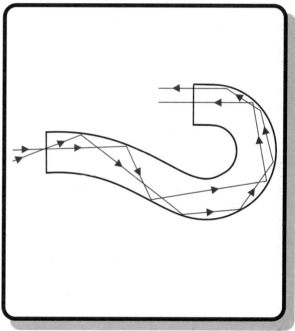

An optical fibre

White light consists of all the colours of the spectrum. In glass, the speed of light decreases from red to blue. A ray of white light is directed into an optical fibre at one end. If the fibre is curved more and more, blue light is seen emerging from its sides where it bends.
a) Why does this happen?
b) What colour emerges at the other end? Explain your answer.

Answers

a) The critical angle is bigger for red light than for blue light. Therefore blue light emerges first when the fibre is bent.

b) Yellow (white light minus blue light).

Using optical fibres

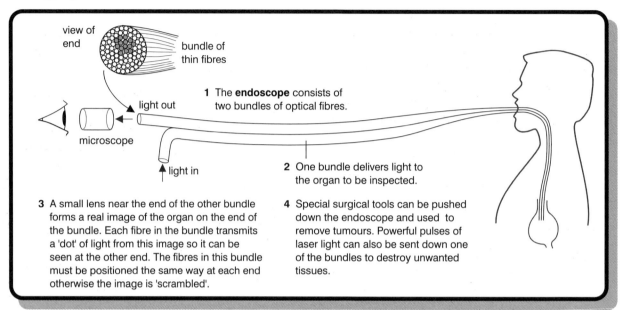

view of end

bundle of thin fibres

1 The **endoscope** consists of two bundles of optical fibres.

light out

microscope

↑ light in

2 One bundle delivers light to the organ to be inspected.

3 A small lens near the end of the other bundle forms a real image of the organ on the end of the bundle. Each fibre in the bundle transmits a 'dot' of light from this image so it can be seen at the other end. The fibres in this bundle must be positioned the same way at each end otherwise the image is 'scrambled'.

4 Special surgical tools can be pushed down the endoscope and used to remove tumours. Powerful pulses of laser light can also be sent down one of the bundles to destroy unwanted tissues.

In communications, optical fibres are used to guide pulses of infrared light. Because the frequency of light is much higher than that of radio waves or microwaves, an infrared light beam can carry many more pulses per second than radio waves or microwaves. This means much more information can be carried using optical fibres than by other means.

In medicine, optical fibres are used in an **endoscope** to see inside the body, and to treat internal tumours. Use of an endoscope avoids the need to cut open the body and therefore shortens the post-operation recovery period.

Reflectors for road safety

The back surface of a cycle reflector consists of lots of triangles. Light rays falling directly on the reflector are totally internally reflected twice at this surface, so they are reflected back.

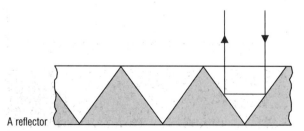

A reflector

6.4 Light and colour

The visible spectrum

This is produced by passing a beam of white light through a prism. Because the speed of light in glass decreases from red to blue, blue light is bent more than red light.

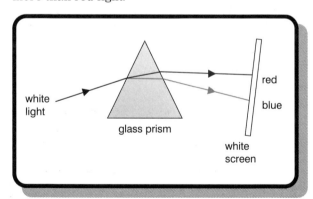

white light

glass prism

red

blue

white screen

Handy hints

Hints & Tips

★ Remember that **Blue Bends Better than red!**

★ Also remember the colours of the spectrum (**R**ed **O**range **Y**ellow **G**reen **B**lue **I**ndigo **V**iolet) from a mnemonic, such as Richard Of York Gave Battle In Vain, or remember Roy G Biv.

Colour and wavelength

- Light is diffracted when it passes through a gap, because it consists of waves. The narrower the gap or the longer the wavelength, the greater the amount of diffraction (spreading).
- For a gap of constant width, the spreading depends on the colour of the light. The closer the light is to the red part of the spectrum, the more it spreads.
- It therefore follows that the wavelength of light increases across the spectrum from blue to red. The amount of spreading can be used to work out the wavelength of the light.

colour

| red | orange | yellow | green | blue | indigo | violet |
| 700 nm | | | 550 nm | | | 400 nm |

wavelength

$(1 \, nm = 10^{-9} \, m)$

Colour and wavelength

Diffraction at work

A **telescope** is used to magnify distant objects. It does not necessarily produce a detailed image.

★ Light from a point object entering the telescope is diffracted at the entrance and so an image 'spot' is formed.

★ If two point objects are too close, their image spots will merge and be seen as one spot.

★ The wider the objective lens of a telescope, the less diffraction it produces, so the greater the image detail that can be seen.

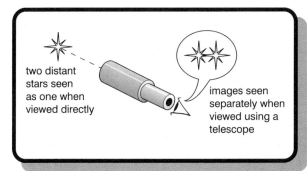

two distant stars seen as one when viewed directly

images seen separately when viewed using a telescope

Using a telescope

A **microscope** is used to observe details of small objects.

★ Light from each point of an object under view spreads when it enters the microscope and forms an image spot.

★ The spreading is less for blue light than for any other colour. This is because blue light has a shorter wavelength than other colours of light.

★ Therefore points on the object can be seen closer together in blue light than in any other colour. This is why more detail can be seen in an image if blue light is used instead of white light.

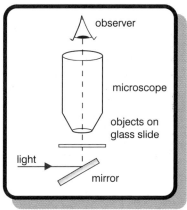

observer

microscope

objects on glass slide

light

mirror

Using a microscope

Question

Cheap cameras often produce images which are tinged in colours. The sketch below shows two rays of white light entering a convex lens at opposite edges. Each ray is split into coloured rays by the lens. The sketch shows the blue rays forming a point image on a colour film.
a) Describe what you would expect to see when the film is developed.
b) Which direction would you move the object to form a point image in red light?

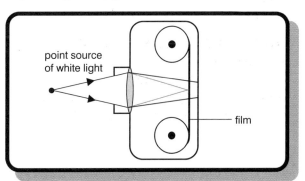

point source of white light

film

Answers

a) A point blue image surrounded by a reddish white disc.
b) Away from the lens.

round-up

How much have you improved?
Work out your improvement index on pages 311–12.

1 a) Complete the ray diagram to show where the image of point object O_1 is formed. [2]

b) Without drawing further rays on your diagram, mark the position where the image of point object O_2 is formed. [1]

c) Hence explain why the image of the arrow between O_1 and O_2 is the same length as the object. [2]

plane
mirror

2 a) A student stands 1.0 m in front of a wall-mounted plane mirror. What is the distance from the student to her image? [1]

b) The student is 1.80 m tall. With the aid of a diagram, explain why the mirror needs to be at least 0.9 m in length if she is to be able to see a full-length image. [4]

c) State two further uses of a plane mirror. [2]

3 a) Explain with the aid of a diagram what is meant by total internal reflection of light. [2]

b) The diagram shows a light ray entering an optical fibre. Complete the diagram showing the path of the light ray after it enters the optical fibre. [2]

c) Why does an optical fibre lose light if it is bent too tightly? [1]

d) State two applications of fibre optics. [2]

4 a) The diagram shows an optical system being used to make a parallel beam of light wider. Sketch a ray diagram showing how this could be achieved using a convex lens and a concave lens with a shorter focal length. [2]

b) With the aid of a ray diagram, explain how a convex lens and a concave lens may be used to make a wide parallel beam into a narrower parallel beam. [2]

5 a) A convex lens is used to project the image of a slide transparency onto a screen.
  (i) Describe how the image changes as a result of moving the screen away from the lens without moving the lens. [2]
  (ii) With the aid of a diagram, describe how the image could be made larger and kept in focus. [2]

b) Given three convex lenses of different focal lengths, which one would make the best magnifying glass? Explain your answer. [2]

6 a) A student sitting at the back of a class can read his book without the aid of spectacles but is unable to read writing on the board 5.0 m away. What is the name for this sight defect? [1]

b) With the aid of a diagram, explain the cause of this defect and describe how it can be corrected with a suitable lens. [3]

7 With the aid of a diagram, explain how a simple camera works. [3]

8 A military satellite is used to observe hostile troop movements. Explain why the satellite's camera must be fitted with a wide lens. [2]

Well done if you've improved. Don't worry if you haven't. Take a break and try again.

The electromagnetic spectrum

preview

At the end of this topic you will be able to:

- **state the six main bands of the electromagnetic spectrum in order of increasing wavelength**
- **outline the similarities and the main differences between the different bands**
- **describe some uses of electromagnetic waves in the home, in medicine and in communications**
- **relate uses of electromagnetic waves to their properties.**

MIND MAP
Page 216.

How much do you already know?
Work out your score on page 312.

Test yourself

1 Name the six main bands of the electromagnetic spectrum in order of increasing frequency. [6]

2 State one use for each of the main bands of the electromagnetic spectrum. [6]

3 Which two bands of the electromagnetic spectrum are not absorbed by the atmosphere? [2]

4 a) Which type(s) of electromagnetic radiation can cause ionisation? [2]
b) Which type of electromagnetic radiation are you emitting at this very moment? [1]
c) Which type of electromagnetic radiation causes sunburn? [1]

5 Name one type of electromagnetic radiation that can pass through a metal plate and one type that cannot. [2]

6 Which type of electromagnetic radiation is emitted when
a) high-speed electrons are suddenly stopped [1]
b) a sunbed is used? [1]

7 a) A satellite broadcasts at a frequency of 10 GHz. What type of electromagnetic radiation is at this frequency? [1]
b) Why is a satellite dish **(i)** concave **(ii)** made from metal? [2]

8 How does an invisible marker pen work? [3]

9 a) What type of electromagnetic radiation is detected by **(i)** a blackened thermometer **(ii)** a Geiger counter? [2]
b) Which type(s) of electromagnetic radiation cannot be detected using photographic film? [1]

10 a) A fibre optic link uses electromagnetic radiation of wavelength 1000 nm. What part of the electromagnetic spectrum is this? [1]
b) Which two types of electromagnetic radiation are emitted by a filament lamp? [1]

All electromagnetic waves

FACTS

1 do not need to be carried by a medium

2 travel at the same speed of 300 000 km/s in a vacuum

3 can be diffracted, refracted and reflected (although X-rays and gamma rays need special techniques)

4 make charged particles vibrate

5 are transverse waves and can be polarised.

7.1 Using electromagnetic waves

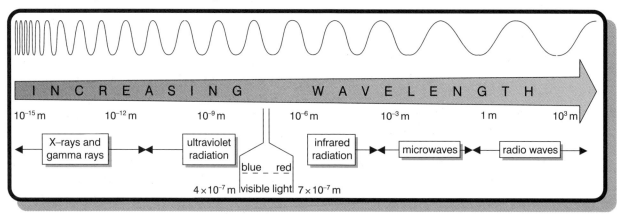

	production	detection	absorption or reflection	uses
radio waves	transmitter aerial, Sun	receiver aerial	reflected by metal	communications
microwaves	microwave transmitter	microwave detector	reflected by metal	communications, heating
infrared light	any object	blackened thermometer	reflected by shiny silvered surfaces, absorbed best by matt black surfaces	communications, heating
visible light	glowing objects	eye, photographic film	reflected by metal, absorbed by pigments	sight, communications
ultraviolet light	UV lamps, Sun	photocell, photographic film	absorbed by skin	security coding, sunbeds
X-rays and gamma rays	X-ray tube, radioactive isotopes	Geiger tube, photographic film	penetrates matter	medical

Electromagnetic waves at home

Microwave cookers: microwaves penetrate food and agitate water molecules within the food. This happens if the frequency is 2.5 GHz, so microwave cookers operate at this frequency. The oven case is metal, which reflects microwaves, so the oven does not heat up. All the electrical power supplied is used to heat the food.

Microwaves are also used for industrial heating, for example to dry wet fabrics after dyeing.

Infrared sensors: these are used for security purposes. **Passive** sensors detect infrared radiation emitted by intruders. **Active** sensors emit infrared rays and detect reflections from intruders. Infrared sensors fitted to TV cameras allow surveillance in the dark.

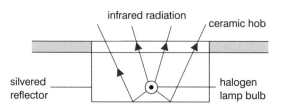

A halogen hob

Halogen hobs: cookers fitted with transparent ceramic cooker rings use halogen lamp bulbs that emit mostly infrared radiation. Little energy is used to heat the ceramic plate, and when the cooker ring is switched off it cools much more rapidly than an ordinary cooker ring.

UV-sensitive inks: these inks can only be seen using ultraviolet light. They are used for security marking.

7.2 Electromagnetic waves in medicine

A health warning

X-rays and gamma rays penetrate living tissues and so can be used in medicine to diagnose disorders and for treatment. These electromagnetic radiations are ionising, so excessive amounts will damage living cells. Great care is taken to ensure radiation doses given to patients are as low as possible and to ensure personnel are not exposed.

X-rays

These are produced in an **X-ray tube**. The X-ray beam consists of a continuous spread of wavelengths. The longer wavelengths are easily absorbed by tissues, unlike the shorter wavelengths which easily pass through tissues. A metal plate is placed in the path of the beam before the patient to remove longer wavelengths. This reduces absorption of X-rays by the patient.

X-ray photographs of internal organs are made with the aid of a suitable contrast medium. For example, a patient about to undergo a stomach X-ray may be given a barium meal in advance. Barium absorbs X-rays so the X-ray photograph shows a light image of the stomach on a darker background.

Personnel in a hospital X-ray department wear **film badges** to monitor their exposure to ionising radiations. If a film badge is over-exposed when it is developed, the wearer has been over-exposed too!

Gamma radiation

This is produced by radioactive isotopes. Gamma radiation is used at high doses to destroy unwanted tissue inside the body, and at low doses to 'image' internal organs.

1 **Treatment** – the use of gamma radiation from the radioactive isotope cobalt-60 is described on page 241. Re-read this section.

2 **Diagnosis** – the **gamma camera** is used with a suitable radioactive tracer to form an image of an internal organ. The tracer must emit gamma radiation and its half-life must be a suitable length. The tracer is given to the patient in advance, either by mouth or by injection.

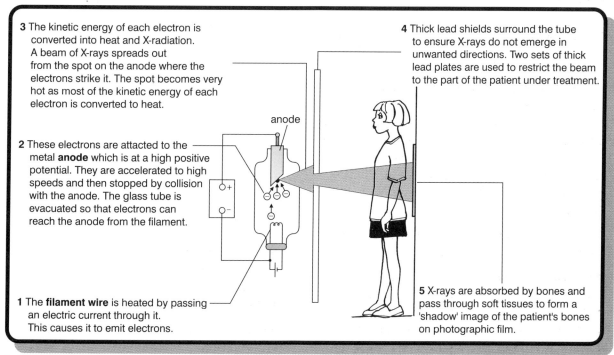

3 The kinetic energy of each electron is converted into heat and X-radiation. A beam of X-rays spreads out from the spot on the anode where the electrons strike it. The spot becomes very hot as most of the kinetic energy of each electron is converted to heat.

2 These electrons are attacted to the metal **anode** which is at a high positive potential. They are accelerated to high speeds and then stopped by collision with the anode. The glass tube is evacuated so that electrons can reach the anode from the filament.

1 The **filament wire** is heated by passing an electric current through it. This causes it to emit electrons.

anode

4 Thick lead shields surround the tube to ensure X-rays do not emerge in unwanted directions. Two sets of thick lead plates are used to restrict the beam to the part of the patient under treatment.

5 X-rays are absorbed by bones and pass through soft tissues to form a 'shadow' image of the patient's bones on photographic film.

An X-ray tube in use

7.3 Communications

Radio waves, microwaves, infrared light and visible light are all used to carry information. The higher the frequency of the **carrier waves**, the more information can be carried. The information is carried by **modulating** the carrier wave:

1   in **analogue form**, by modulating the amplitude (AM) or the frequency (FM) of the carrier wave

2   in **digital form** as a stream of pulses.

The spread of frequencies in the signal determines the **bandwidth** of the carrier wave. Each carrier wave is allocated a frequency channel wide enough to transmit the bandwidth of the signal. For example, a channel width of 4000 Hz in telephone channels covers most of the audio range. A TV channel needs to be 8 MHz wide to carry all the information for TV pictures.

Electrical **noise** is created in amplifiers used to boost weak signals, causing loss of information. Digital pulses can be 'cleaned up' to eliminate noise.

Optical fibre communications

Optical fibres can carry pulses of infrared light hundreds of kilometres without interruption. The frequency of light is about 1 million times higher than the frequency of microwave radiation, so an optical fibre can carry much more information than a microwave beam or an electrical cable.

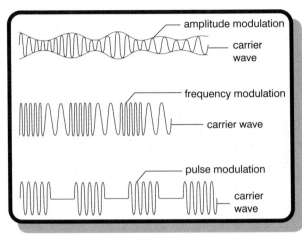

Amplitude modulation, frequency modulation and pulse modulation

Frequency bands

	frequency range	uses
long wave (LW)	up to 300 kHz	international AM radio
medium wave (MW)	300 kHz–3 MHz	AM radio
high frequency (HF)	3–30 MHz	AM radio
very high frequency (VHF)	30–300 MHz	FM radio
ultra high frequency (UHF)	300–3000 MHz	TV broadcasting, mobile phones
microwave	above 3000 MHz	satellite TV, global phone links
light	500 THz approx	fibre optic communication links

Note: 1 MHz = 1 000 000 Hz. 1 THz = 1 million MHz.

Mobile phone links are only possible if the receiver is near a transmitter. A mobile phone signal is allocated a channel of bandwidth 25 kHz in the UHF band at a frequency of about 900 MHz. The transmitter is linked to the international phone network which uses undersea cable links, local microwave links and satellite links.

Radio broadcasts at frequencies below 30 MHz travel long distances due to reflection from a layer of ionised gases in the upper atmosphere. Long wave broadcasts spread round the Earth because long wavelength radio waves follow the Earth's curvature.

SELL NOW!

Satellite TV signals are carried by microwaves from a geostationary satellite. This orbits the Earth once every 24 hours round the equator, so stays in the same place above the Earth. A reflecting dish pointed towards the satellite focuses the microwaves on an aerial, which detects the signal and passes it onto a decoder.

Terrestrial TV signals are carried by radio waves in the UHF band range. Receiving aerials need to be in the line of sight of the transmitter. TV pictures from the other side of the world reach us via satellite links and ground stations.

round-up

How much have you improved?
Work out your improvement index on page 312.

1 a) List the six main bands of the electromagnetic spectrum in order of increasing wavelength. [6]
b) (i) State two common properties of all electromagnetic waves. [2]
(ii) List the types of electromagnetic waves that blacken photographic film. [3]
(iii) List the types of electromagnetic waves that are used in communications. [4]

2 a) Microwave cookers operate at 2500 MHz and microwave satellites operate at about 10 000 MHz. Calculate the wavelength in air in each case. The speed of light in air is 300 000 km/s. [2]
b) Food can be heated using a microwave oven or an ordinary oven. What are the advantages of using a microwave oven? [1]

3 a) Why is it possible to detect radio broadcasts from distant countries? [2]
b) (i) What is meant by the carrier frequency of a radio or TV broadcast? [1]
(ii) Why is necessary for TV transmitter stations in adjacent regions to broadcast at different carrier frequencies? [1]
c) Why is it necessary to use a concave metal dish to detect electromagnetic waves from a satellite but not from a TV transmitter mast? [2]

4 a) A soap powder manufacturer decides to mix a substance into the powder which absorbs ultraviolet light and emits visible light as a result. Why would this make clothes washed in this powder seem very white in bright sunlight? [2]
b) (i) Why is ultraviolet light harmful? [2]
(ii) Why is it important to use protective skin cream if you are outdoors for a long time in summer? [2]

5 a) Why can an infrared TV camera see people and animals in darkness? [1]
b) (i) What main type of electromagnetic radiation is emitted by a halogen lamp in a ceramic cooker hob? [1]
(ii) Why does a ceramic hob heat food up more quickly than a conventional cooker ring does? [2]

6 a) In an X-ray tube, why is it essential to
(i) make the anode positive relative to the filament
(ii) focus the electron beam onto a small spot of the anode? [3]
b) (i) A photograph of a broken limb can be obtained using X-rays. What properties of X-rays are made use of in this process? [2]
(ii) Before a stomach X-ray is taken, the patient is given a barium meal. Why? [2]

7 a) The diagram shows the waveform of two carrier waves with different frequencies. Identify the high frequency carrier wave and explain why it can carry more pulses than the low frequency carrier wave. [3]

b) Mobile phones operate at a frequency of about 900 MHz, each channel occupying a bandwidth of 25 kHz.
(i) How many mobile phone channels can be carried in the frequency band from 900 to 925 MHz? [1]
(ii) Terrestrial TV programmes are carried at lower frequencies and satellite TV is carried at higher frequencies. Why are no TV channels allocated to the frequency band from 900 to 925 MHz? [1]

8 A communications satellite must be in a geostationary orbit.
a) What is meant by a geostationary orbit? [2]
b) Why is it necessary for a communications satellite to be in such an orbit? [1]

Well done if you've improved. Don't worry if you haven't. Take a break and try again.

Force and motion

preview

At the end of this topic you will be able to:

- **define speed, velocity, acceleration, force, weight and work and state the unit of each quantity**
- **carry out calculations relating the above quantities to each other and to measurements of distance and time**
- **carry out calculations using the formulae for kinetic energy and potential energy**
- **sketch and interpret graphs of distance against time and speed against time**
- **describe the motion of a falling object with and without drag forces, including its energy changes.**

MIND MAP
Page 216.

How much do you already know?
Work out your score on pages 312–13.

Test yourself

1 A walker travelled a distance of 10 km in 2 hours. Calculate the walker's average speed in
   a) km/h **b)** m/s. [2]

2 **a)** What feature of a graph of speed against time gives the distance travelled? [1]
   b) What does the gradient of a distance against time graph represent? [1]

3 A 1000 kg car accelerates from rest to a speed of 10 m/s in 20 s. Calculate the acceleration of the car and the force needed to produce this acceleration. [2]

4 A car is travelling at a speed of 15 m/s when the driver sees a tree lying across the road ahead and is forced to brake. The graph shows how its speed changed with time.

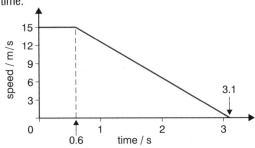

a) If the driver's reaction time is 0.6 s, how far does the car travel before the driver applies the brakes? [1]

b) The car takes 2.5 s to stop after the brakes are first applied. Calculate its deceleration. [1]

c) (i) Use the graph to calculate the braking distance. [1]

   (ii) Hence calculate the total stopping distance. [1]

5 A lift of total mass 400 kg descends at a constant speed of 2 m/s.
   a) Calculate **(i)** its weight and its kinetic energy
   (ii) its loss of potential energy per second. [3]
   b) What happens to the potential energy lost by the lift? [3]

6 Explain why the shape of a vehicle affects its top speed. [3]

7 Why does a parachutist fall at constant speed? [3]

An aeroplane of total mass 8000 kg is in level flight at a constant speed of 60 m/s.

direction
of
motion

8 Calculate its weight and the lift force acting on the aeroplane. [2]

9 The output power of its engines is 200 kW. Calculate
   a) the distance it moves in 100 s
   b) the energy output from the engine in this time. [2]

10 What happens to the energy supplied by the engine when the aeroplane is moving at constant speed in level flight? [1]

8.1 Speed and distance

Fact file

★ **Speed** is defined as distance travelled per unit time.

★ The **unit** of speed is the metre per second (m/s).

★ Average speed (in m/s) = $\dfrac{\text{distance travelled (in m)}}{\text{time taken (in s)}}$

★ **Velocity** is speed in a given direction.

Distance–time graphs for a moving object

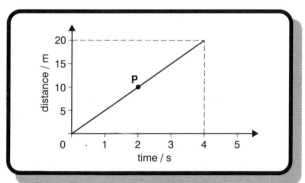

Constant speed

At **constant speed**, the distance travelled increases steadily with time as shown on the graph above.

1   The graph is a straight line with a constant gradient.

2   The steeper the line, the greater the speed.

3   The gradient of the graph is equal to the speed of the object.

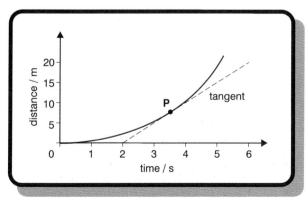

Distance–time graph for an object that accelerates from rest

At **changing speed**, the gradient of the line changes, as in the distance–time graph for an object that accelerates from rest.

1   The gradient changes with time.

2   The speed at any point is equal to the gradient of the tangent to the curve.

3   The speed is zero where the gradient is zero. This is at the origin 0 on the graph.

Question

a) Determine the speed at point P on each graph.
b) On the second graph, how can you tell if the object is moving faster or slower after point P?

Speed and velocity

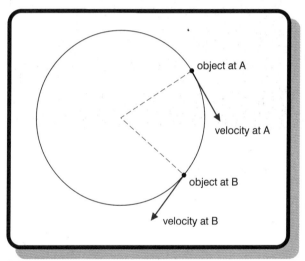

Going round in circles

Velocity is defined as speed in a given direction. An object moving round a circular path at a steady rate has a constant speed. However, it is continuously changing its direction so its velocity continually changes. Velocity is an example of a **vector** quantity, which is any quantity that has magnitude *and* direction. Other examples of vectors include acceleration, force and weight. Non-directional quantities such as speed, mass and energy are called **scalar** quantities.

Answers
a) 5 m/s, 5 m/s b) The gradient becomes steeper so the speed is increasing.

8.2 Acceleration

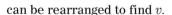

Fact file

★ **Acceleration** is defined as change of velocity per unit time.

★ The **unit** of acceleration is the metre per second per second (m/s²).

★ Acceleration is a vector quantity.

Constant acceleration

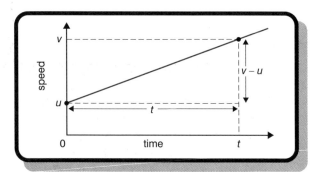

The graph shows how the speed changes with time for an object moving along a straight line at constant acceleration.

1   The gradient of the line is equal to the acceleration of the object.

2   The acceleration can be calculated using the equation

$$\text{acceleration} = \frac{\text{change of velocity}}{\text{time taken}}$$

If u represents the initial velocity and v represents the velocity at time t, the equation can be written as

$$\text{acceleration } a = \frac{(v - u)}{t}$$

3   The distance moved s in time t can be calculated using the equation

distance moved = average speed × time

Since the average speed $= \dfrac{(u + v)}{2}$, this

equation can written as $s = \dfrac{(u + v)t}{2}$

4   The area under the line gives the distance travelled.

Maths workshop

The equation

$$a = \frac{(v - u)}{t}$$

can be rearranged to find v.

Step 1: multiply both sides of the equation by t to give $at = (v - u)$.

Step 2: Take u across to the other side to give $u + at = v$ or $v = u + at$.

> **Question**

The graph below shows how the speed of a train changed as it travelled between two stations.

a) Determine the acceleration and the distance moved in each of the three parts of the journey.

b) Hence calculate the average speed of the train.

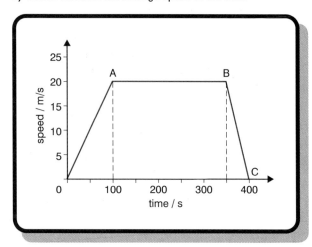

Acceleration due to gravity, *g*

The acceleration of an object falling freely is constant, equal to 10 m/s². This means that an object falling freely increases its speed by 10 m/s every second – it accelerates at a constant rate.

Non-uniform acceleration

The acceleration can be determined at any point by drawing the tangent to the curve at that point and measuring the gradient of this line.

Answers

b) 16 m/s
Distance = 1000 m; 5000 m; 500 m
a) Acceleration = 0.2 m/s²; 0; –0.4 m/s²

8.3 On the road

Stopping distances

The chart shows the shortest stopping distances of a car in good condition on a dry road for different speeds.

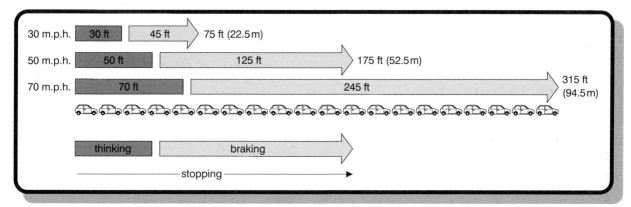

* ★ **The thinking distance** is the distance travelled by the car in the time it takes the driver to react.

* ★ **The braking distance** is the distance travelled by the car from the point where the brakes are applied to where it comes to rest.

* ★ **The stopping distance** is the thinking distance added to the braking distance.

The graphs show how each of these distances (in m) increases with speed (in m/s).

Distance–speed graphs for a braking car

1 **The thinking distance is proportional to the speed.** This is because the vehicle travels at constant speed during the reaction period before the brakes are applied. For constant speed, distance moved = speed × time. Prove for yourself from the graph that the reaction time for the data is 0.7 s. This is the average reaction time for a driver in an alert state of mind.

2 **The braking distance is proportional to the square of the speed.** This assumes the vehicle's deceleration is constant during braking.

> **Question**
>
> Determine the thinking distance and the stopping distance at a speed of 27 m/s (= 60 m.p.h.).

What affects the stopping distance?

1 **Reaction time**: the driver's reaction time depends on alertness.

2 **Road conditions**: when the brakes are applied, friction between the brakes and the wheels reduces the vehicle's speed, provided the tyres don't skid on the road. Skidding occurs if the braking force exceeds the grip (the maximum amount of friction possible) between the tyres and the road. Grip depends on the road conditions as well as the tyre conditions.

> **Answer**
>
> Thinking distance = 18 m, stopping distance = 55 m.

8.4 Force and acceleration

Balanced forces

★ A **force** is anything that can change the velocity of an object.

★ If there is no force acting on an object, the object moves at constant velocity (constant speed without changing direction) or remains stationary.

★ If an object is acted on by two or more forces which balance each other out, the object either remains at rest or continues to move at constant velocity.

Changing velocity

The velocity of an object changes if the object is acted on by a force or by several forces which do not balance out. The combined effect of different forces acting on an object is called the **resultant force** on the object.

If an object is at rest or moving at constant velocity, the resultant force on it must be zero. This is known as **Newton's first law of motion**.

If an object's velocity is changing, the resultant force on it is not zero. Experiments show that the acceleration of an object is proportional to the resultant force on the object. This is known as **Newton's second law of motion** and it can be written as an equation.

$$\underset{\text{(in newtons, N)}}{\text{force}} = \underset{\text{(in kg)}}{\text{mass}} \times \underset{\text{(in m/s}^2\text{)}}{\text{acceleration}}$$

The unit of force is the **newton** (abbreviated N), equal to the force needed to give a 1 kg mass an acceleration of 1 m/s^2.

The newton

Weight

The **weight** of an object is the force of gravity on it. An object falling freely is acted on by gravity only. Since the acceleration due to gravity g is constant, then the force of gravity on an object (its weight) must be equal to its mass × g.

$$\underset{\text{(in N)}}{\text{weight}} = \underset{\text{(in kg)}}{\text{mass}} \times \underset{\text{(in m/s}^2\text{)}}{g}$$

Note that the unit of g may be written as N/kg or m/s^2 since 1 N = 1 kg m/s^2.

Terminal speed

Terminal speed

When an object moves through a liquid or a gas, it experiences friction due to the liquid or gas, which opposes its motion. This resistance to its motion is called **drag**. The drag force increases with speed, and depends on the shape of the object and the substance the object is moving through.

★ An object released in air accelerates gradually until its speed is such that the drag force is equal and opposite to its weight. This speed is called the **terminal speed**.

★ A vehicle reaches its top speed when the drag force is equal and opposite to the engine force. The top speed can be increased by reshaping a vehicle to reduce the drag force on it.

A car of total mass 800 kg can accelerate from rest to a speed of 20 m/s in 20 s. Calculate

a) the acceleration of the car

b) the force producing this acceleration, assuming the drag force is negligible

c) the ratio of this force to the total weight of the car. Assume $g = 10$ m/s^2.

Answers a) 1 m/s^2 b) 800 N c) 0.1

8.5 Work and energy

Fact file

At work

* A force does **work** on an object when it moves the object in the direction of the force.

* **Work done** = force × distance moved in the direction of the force.

* **Energy** is the capacity to do work.

* The unit of work and of energy is the **joule** (J), equal to the work done when a force of 1 N moves its point of application through a distance of 1 m.

* **Power** is defined as rate of transfer of energy. The unit of power is the **watt** (W), equal to 1 J/s.

Gravitational potential energy

Gaining height

If a mass m is moved through a height h,

its change of gravitational potential energy = mgh,

where g is the acceleration due to gravity. This is because the force of gravity on the object (its weight) is mg.

1   Any object at rest is acted on by a support force which is equal and opposite to its weight.

2   If the object is raised, the work done by the support force is mgh (equal to force × distance). This is therefore the gain of potential energy of the object.

3   If the object is lowered, the work done by gravity is mgh (equal to force × distance). This is therefore the decrease of potential energy of the object.

Kinetic energy

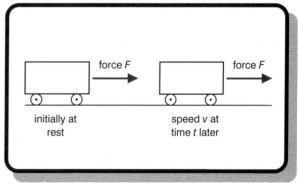

Kinetic energy

For a mass m moving at speed v, its kinetic energy = $\frac{1}{2}mv^2$.

This can be proved by considering a constant force F acting on an object of mass m, initially at rest, for time t. From page 270 and above,

1   its distance moved $s = \dfrac{vt}{2}$ where v is its speed at time t

2   its acceleration $a = \dfrac{v}{t}$ hence $F = ma = \dfrac{mv}{t}$

3   Hence the work done $= Fs = \dfrac{mv}{t} \times \dfrac{vt}{2} = \frac{1}{2}mv^2$,

which is therefore the kinetic energy of the object.

273

Practice questions

Set out your answers clearly. In an examination, if you slip up on a calculation, you will only lose one mark if you have shown clearly that you understand the principles involved. Where necessary, assume $g = 10\,\text{m/s}^2$.

falling   rising

1 A tennis ball of mass 0.20 kg is released from rest at a height of 2.0 m above a concrete floor. It rebounds to a height of 1.5 m. Calculate
  a) its kinetic energy and speed just before impact
  b) its kinetic energy and speed just after impact
  c) its loss of energy between release and its maximum height after rebounding.

2

A fairground train of total mass 600 kg descended a total height of 50 m into a dip after it went over the highest point on the track. Calculate

a) its loss of potential energy in this descent
b) its kinetic energy and speed at the bottom of the dip, assuming air resistance was negligible and its kinetic energy at the highest point was zero.

3 An aeroplane of mass 600 kg takes off from rest in 50 s over a distance of 1500 m.
  a) Calculate **(i)** its speed when it lifts off
    (ii) its acceleration during take-off
    (iii) the force needed to produce this acceleration.
  b) Why is the engine force greater than the force calculated in **a) (iii)**?

4 A hot air balloon and its occupants have a total weight of 5000 N. It is descending at a constant speed of 0.5 m/s.

Constant speed

  a) What is the total upward force on it during this descent?
  b) Calculate its kinetic energy.
  c) Calculate its loss of height and loss of potential energy in 1 minute.
  d) Explain why it does not gain kinetic energy.

Answers

1 a) 4 J, 6.3 m/s **b)** 3 J, 5.5 m/s **c)** 1 J
2 a) 300 kJ **b)** 300 kJ, 32 m/s
3 a) (i) 60 m/s **(ii)** 1.2 m/s² **(iii)** 720 N
  b) Because of air resistance.
4 a) 5000 N **b)** 62.5 J **c)** 30 m, 150 kJ **d)** All the potential energy is transferred to the air by the upward force.

round-up

How much have you improved?
Work out your improvement index on page 313.

The acceleration of a freely falling object $g = 10\,\text{m/s}^2$.

1 a) A walker leaves a car park and walks at a steady speed of 1.2 m/s for 1 hour. How far did the walker travel in this time in
    (i) metres **(ii)** kilometres?   [2]
  b) A runner leaves the same car park 40 minutes after the walker and catches up with the walker at a distance of 4 km from the car park. What was the runner's speed?   [1]

2 The graph shows the progress of two cyclists in a 10 km road race.

  a) One cyclist X maintained a constant speed throughout. What can you deduce from the graph about the speed of the other cyclist Y?   [4]
  b) (i) From the graph, calculate the speed of X.   [1]
    (ii) From the graph, calculate the speed of Y when Y overtook X.   [1]

round-up

3 a) Explain the difference between speed and velocity. [2]

b) A police car joins a motorway and travels north at a constant speed of 30 m/s for 5 minutes. It then leaves the motorway at a motorway junction, rejoins it immediately and travels south in the opposite direction for 20 minutes at a steady speed of 20 m/s to the scene of an accident.

(i) How far did the police car travel in each direction? [2]
(ii) How far from the point where the police car first joined the motorway was the scene of the accident? [1]

4 A vehicle of mass 700 kg accelerates steadily from rest to a speed of 8 m/s in a time of 5 s. The graph shows how the speed of the vehicle increased with time.

a) Calculate the acceleration of the vehicle and the distance travelled in this time. [2]
b) What force acting on the vehicle is necessary to produce this acceleration? [1]

5 a) A ball of mass 0.2 kg is thrown directly upwards with an initial speed of 25 m/s. Calculate how long it took to reach its highest point, assuming $g = 10$ m/s^2. [1]

b) The graph shows how its vertical position changed after it left the thrower's hand.

(i) What was its initial kinetic energy? [1]
(ii) Calculate its maximum gain of potential energy. [1]
(iii) Calculate its maximum gain of height. [1]

6 a) An athlete runs a distance of 100 m in a time of 10.5 s. Calculate the athlete's average speed over this distance. [1]
b) The athlete's mass is 60 kg. Calculate the athlete's kinetic energy at the speed calculated in **a)**. [1]
c) If all the kinetic energy calculated in **b)** could be converted into potential energy by the athlete, what height gain would be possible? [1]
d) A pole vaulter is capable of jumping considerably higher. Discuss how this is achieved. [1]

7 A train of total mass 30 000 kg is travelling at a constant speed of 10 m/s when its brakes are applied, bringing it to rest with a constant deceleration in 50 s.
a) Sketch a graph to show how the speed of the train changed with time. [2]
b) Calculate **(i)** the distance moved by the train in this time **(ii)** its acceleration. [2]
c) Hence calculate the force of the brakes on the train. [1]
d) Calculate the ratio of the braking force to the train's weight. [1]

8 a) Explain why a moving car skids if the brakes are applied too hard. [1]
b) Explain why the stopping distance of a car travelling at a certain speed is greater if the road surface is wet. [4]

c) The graph shows how the speed of a car of mass 1200 kg on a dry road decreases with time when it stops safely in the shortest possible distance. The car is initially moving at a speed of 15 m/s. Calculate **(i)** the braking distance **(ii)** the deceleration of the car and the braking force. [3]
d) On a wet road, the braking force is reduced by half. Calculate the time it would take to brake safely from a speed of 15 m/s on a wet road and determine the braking distance in this condition. [2]

Forces in balance

preview

At the end of this topic you will be able to:

- identify the forces acting on a body in equilibrium
- explain what is meant by centre of gravity
- describe the use of levers as force multipliers
- state and use Hooke's law and describe elastic and plastic behaviour
- carry out simple pressure and density calculations
- describe pressure applications, including hydrostatic pressure and hydraulics
- explain gas pressure and relate it to volume
- describe atmospheric pressure effects and the operation of a barometer.

Work out your score on page 313.
Mind Map on page 216.

Test yourself

1 What forces are acting on your body at the moment? [2]

2 State whether each of the following is in stable, unstable or neutral equilibrium
a) a ball at rest on the floor b) a child sitting on a fence
c) a coat hanger hanging from a rail. [3]

3 The diagram shows a person pushing a wheelbarrow containing sand. The total weight of the wheelbarrow and its contents is 800 N.

a) Estimate how far the centre of gravity of the wheelbarrow is from the handle. [1]
b) Explain why the force needed to lift the wheelbarrow as shown is much less than 800 N. [2]
c) The wheelbarrow contains 0.020 m³ of sand. The density of the sand is 2500 kg/m³. Calculate the mass of sand in the wheelbarrow. [1]

4 a) (i) Explain why a sharp knife cuts more easily than a blunt knife. [1]
   (ii) Explain why a suction cap pushed onto a smooth vertical tile doesn't fall off. [2]
b) A spade has a rectangular blade which measures 25 cm × 20 cm. It is used to flatten a mound of earth. Each impact of the blade's flat surface on the mound creates a force of 300 N. Calculate the pressure due to this force. [2]

5 a) What is meant by elastic behaviour? [1]
b) What is meant by plastic behaviour? [1]

6 A steel spring stretches by 4 cm when it is stretched by a force of 1 N applied at either end.
a) What is the extension of the spring when it is stretched by a force of 5 N? [1]
b) How much force is needed to extend the spring by 10 cm? [1]

7 A spanner is used to unscrew a wheel nut on a bicycle. Why is it easier to do this using a long spanner rather than a short spanner? [2]

8 A metre rule is pivoted on a knife edge at its centre with a 1.0 N weight on a thread suspended from the 10 cm mark of the rule. The rule is then balanced by suspending an object of unknown weight W at its 65 cm mark. The arrangement is shown in the diagram below. Calculate
a) the moment of the 1.0 N weight about the pivot [1]
b) the weight W of the unknown object. [2]

```
0   10              50   65              100 cm
├─────────────────────┬──────────────────────┤
       │            pivot │
       □              ▲    □
      1.0 N                W
```

9 Why does the pressure of a gas increase when it is heated? [4]

10 In a chemistry experiment, 20 cm³ of a gas are collected at a pressure of 100 kPa in a syringe. The volume of this gas in the syringe is then reduced to 10 cm³. Calculate the pressure of the gas in the syringe. [1]

9.1 Equilibrium

Fact file

★ Different types of force include **weight** (the force of gravity), **tension** (forces that stretch), **compression** (forces that squeeze), **twisting forces**, **electrical forces** and **magnetic forces**.

★ The unit of force is the **newton** (N). Note that 10 N is the weight of a mass of 1 kg at the Earth's surface.

★ The **centre of gravity** of an object is the point where its weight may be considered to act.

★ The **moment** of a force about a point is equal to the force × the perpendicular distance from the line of action of the force to the pivot.

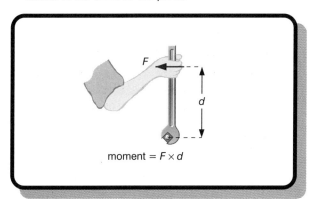

$$\text{moment} = F \times d$$

Turning a nut

Stability

If an object at equilibrium is displaced slightly then released, it is said to be

1 **in stable equilibrium** if it returns to equilibrium

2 **in neutral equilibrium** if it stays at its new position

3 **in unstable equilibrium** if it moves away from the point where it was in equilibrium.

stable

neutral

unstable

At rest

An object in equilibrium is **at rest** because

• **the forces acting on it balance each other out**. Some examples of objects in equilibrium are shown in the diagram at the top of the page.

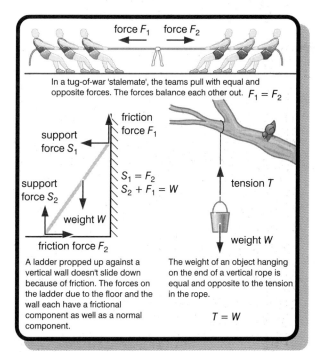

In a tug-of-war 'stalemate', the teams pull with equal and opposite forces. The forces balance each other out. $F_1 = F_2$

$S_1 = F_2$
$S_2 + F_1 = W$

A ladder propped up against a vertical wall doesn't slide down because of friction. The forces on the ladder due to the floor and the wall each have a frictional component as well as a normal component.

The weight of an object hanging on the end of a vertical rope is equal and opposite to the tension in the rope.

$T = W$

Equal and opposite forces

• the **moments of the forces about any point balance each other out**. This is known as the **principle of moments**. Two examples are shown in the diagram below.

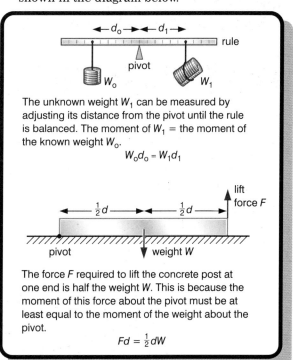

The unknown weight W_1 can be measured by adjusting its distance from the pivot until the rule is balanced. The moment of W_1 = the moment of the known weight W_0.

$$W_0 d_0 = W_1 d_1$$

The force F required to lift the concrete post at one end is half the weight W. This is because the moment of this force about the pivot must be at least equal to the moment of the weight about the pivot.

$$Fd = \tfrac{1}{2} dW$$

Equal and opposite moments

9

Tilting and toppling

The diagram shows a tall cupboard tilted on one side. It will topple if released because the perpendicular from its centre of gravity to the ground falls outside its base. This means its weight tries to turn it anticlockwise about the edge which acts as the pivot. A force *F* as shown is necessary to provide an equal and opposite moment. Toppling

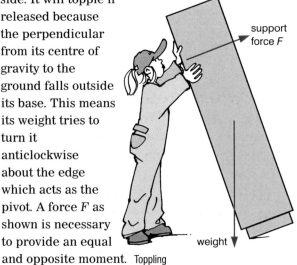

support force *F*

weight

Action and reaction

Whenever two objects interact, they exert equal and opposite forces on each other. For example, if you lean on a wall with a certain force, you experience an equal and opposite force from the wall. The same rule applies when two objects collide; they push on each other with an equal and opposite force.

Question

A plank of weight 200 N rests horizontally on two bricks, one at either end as shown.
a) What force does the plank exert on each brick?
b) What force is necessary to lift the plank at one end?

centre of gravity

plank

200 N

Answer   a) 100 N b) 100 N

9.2 Strength of solids

Solids under test

The particles in a solid are locked together by strong chemical bonds. This is why a solid has its own shape and cannot flow. The diagram shows a solid acted upon by external forces. These forces can alter the shape of the solid, depending on whether or not the forces between the particles are strong enough to withstand the external forces.

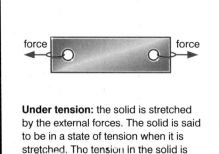

force   force

Under tension: the solid is stretched by the external forces. The solid is said to be in a state of tension when it is stretched. The tension in the solid is equal and opposite to the external force.

beam

pillar

In compression: the solid is compressed by the external forces. Most solids are very difficult to compress and huge forces are needed, such as using a vice.

bolt

metal plates

Shear: the external forces are trying to shear the bolt because they are not acting along the same line.

Twist: the external forces are twisting the solid.

Solids under test

Solids and strength

★ **Stiffness** is the ability to withstand being stretched or bent.

★ **Toughness** is the ability to withstand fracture.

★ **Strength** is a measure of how much force is needed to break an object.

★ **Brittleness** is a measure of how easily an object snaps.

Question

Describe the ideal mechanical properties of
a) a running shoe **b)** a biscuit.

Answers
a) Tough and strong, not too stiff and not brittle.
b) Stiff and brittle, but not too tough or strong.

Hooke's law

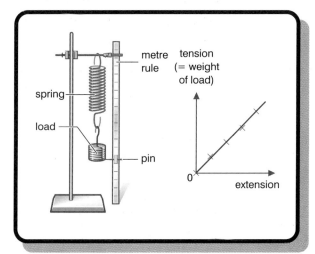

Hooke's law

This law states that **the extension of a spiral spring is proportional to the force used to stretch it**. The diagram shows how Hooke's law may be tested, and a graph of some typical results for a steel spring. Note that the extension is the change of length from its unstretched length.

Hooke's law may be written in the form $T = ke$ where T is the tension in the spring, e is the extension of the spring and k is a constant. This is the equation for the line in the graph. The line is

straight and it passes through the origin because the tension is proportional to the extension. Its gradient is equal to the spring constant k. Note that the equation $T = ke$ may be rearranged to give

$$e = \frac{T}{k} \text{ or } k = \frac{T}{e}$$

Elastic and plastic behaviour

★ **Elastic behaviour** is the ability of a solid to regain its shape when the external forces are removed. The atoms return to their original positions when the external forces are removed.

★ **The elastic limit** of a solid is the limit of its ability to regain its shape. Beyond its elastic limit, it deforms permanently.

★ **Plastic behaviour** occurs when the shape of a solid is permanently changed by external forces. The atoms are pulled out of position permanently.

The graphs below show how the extension of different objects under tension increases with the external force.

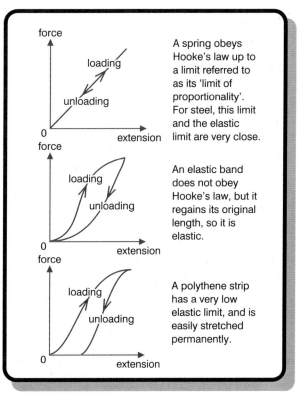

A spring obeys Hooke's law up to a limit referred to as its 'limit of proportionality'. For steel, this limit and the elastic limit are very close.

An elastic band does not obey Hooke's law, but it regains its original length, so it is elastic.

A polythene strip has a very low elastic limit, and is easily stretched permanently.

Stretching materials

9.3 Pressure and its measurement

Fact file

★ **Pressure** is defined as force per unit area acting normally on a surface.

★ The unit of pressure is the **pascal** (Pa), equal to 1 N/m^2.

★ Density = $\dfrac{\text{mass}}{\text{volume}}$

★ The unit of density is the **kilogram per cubic metre** (kg/m^3).

★ The pressure p due to a force F acting normally on an area A may be calculated from the equation

$$p = \frac{F}{A}$$

★ Note that an area of 1 m^2 is equal to $10\,000 \text{ cm}^2$ ($= 100 \text{ cm} \times 100 \text{ cm}$).

Therefore a force of 1 N acting on an area of 1 cm^2 gives a pressure of 10 kPa ($= 10\,000 \text{ Pa}$).

Pressure points

The larger the area of surface over which a force acts, the smaller the pressure. The smaller the area, the greater the pressure.

> **Question**
>
> Calculate the pressure in N/m^2 exerted by a 60 kg person standing on the floor if the total area of contact between the person's feet and the floor is 100 cm^2. Assume $g = 10 \text{ N/kg}$.

> **Answer**
> 60 kPa

Pressure in a liquid

The pressure in a liquid

• acts equally in all directions
• increases with depth
• is the same at all points at the same depth
• depends on the density of the liquid.

Floating and sinking

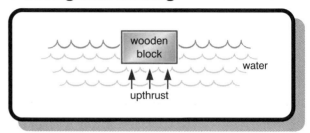

A floating object

An **upthrust** acts on any object in a fluid. This is because the pressure of the fluid is greater on the bottom of the object than on the top. If an object is slowly lowered into a liquid, the upthrust on it increases gradually. The object will

• **float** if the upthrust becomes large enough to support its weight
• **sink** if the upthrust at maximum depth is not enough to support its weight.

The U-tube manometer

This device is used to measure gas pressure.

The U-tube manometer

• The pressure at X is due to the gas supply.
• The pressure at Y is caused by atmospheric pressure at Z + the pressure of the liquid column YZ.
• The pressure at Y = the pressure at X since they are on the same level.
• Therefore the gas supply pressure = the pressure due to YZ + atmospheric pressure.
• Hence the height of column YZ is a measure of how much the gas supply pressure exceeds atmospheric pressure (the 'excess' gas pressure).

9.4 Hydraulics

Vehicle brakes

A brake system exerts a large braking force on the wheels as a result of a much smaller force being applied to the foot pedal.

The force on the foot pedal creates pressure on the brake fluid in the master cylinder.

The pressure is transmitted through the fluid to the slave cylinders at each wheel.

The slave cylinder pistons push the brake pads onto the wheels, creating friction which acts against the motion of the wheels.

Disc brakes

Using the pressure equation

1 The pressure exerted on the fluid is given by the equation $p = \frac{F_1}{A_1}$ where F_1 is the force on the master cylinder and A_1 is the area of the master cylinder.

2 This pressure is transmitted to the slave cylinders without loss. This assumes no air in the brake system.

3 The force exerted by each slave cylinder $F_2 = pA_2$, where A_2 is the area of each slave cylinder.

4 Hence $F_2 = \frac{F_1 A_2}{A_1}$.
   Since A_2 is much larger than A_1, then it follows that F_2 is much larger than F_1.

Question

A brake system has a master cylinder of area 5 cm² and each slave cylinder has an area of 100 cm². A force of 20 N is applied to the master cylinder.
a) Calculate **(i)** the pressure in the system in pascals **(ii)** the force exerted by each slave piston.
b) Why is it important not to allow any air into the brake system?

More hydraulic machines

A hydraulic car jack is used to raise a car wheel off the ground. The car jack handle is a lever which multiplies the effort applied to it. The lever force is then magnified further by the hydraulic cylinders which contain oil. The force of the slave cylinder on the vehicle is enough to raise the vehicle at that point.

A hydraulic car jack

A hydraulic press is capable of exerting enough force to stamp metals into shape. The effort is applied to a lever which acts on the master piston. The pressure in the oil is then transmitted to the much wider slave cylinders which then exert a much greater force on the object to be stamped.

A hydraulic press

Answers
a) (i) 40 000 Pa **(ii)** 400 N
b) Unlike a liquid, air can be compressed. Therefore the pressure would not be transmitted to the slave cylinders.

9.5 Gases

Fact file

★ A gas does not have its own surface, unlike a liquid or a solid. It fills any container it is released into. **Its volume is therefore the volume of the space it fills**.

★ **A gas can easily be compressed**. This means its density can easily be changed, unlike a solid or a liquid.

★ **A gas exerts pressure on any surface it is in contact with**.

★ **The pressure of a gas** can be increased by increasing its temperature or by reducing its volume.

Gases and vapours

When a liquid is heated, it vaporises. If the vapour comes into contact with a cold surface, it condenses. Another way to turn a vapour into liquid is to increase the pressure on it. Latent heat is given out by a vapour when it condenses. This is why the grid of narrow piping at the back of a refrigerator feels warm; vapour inside the pipes condenses under pressure.

Above a certain temperature, a gas cannot be liquefied no matter how much pressure is applied to it. This temperature is called the **critical temperature** of the gas. The term **vapour** is used for a gas below its critical temperature.

Gas pressure

Gas pressure

A gas consists of molecules which move about very fast in random motion, colliding repeatedly with each other and with solid surfaces present. Each impact on a surface exerts a force on the surface. These impacts are what causes the pressure exerted by the gas on the surface. The pressure is constant because there is an enormous number of impacts per second, so the surface is under continuous bombardment. Heating a gas makes the molecules move faster, causing harder and more frequent impacts – hence the pressure goes up.

Measurement of gas pressure

The bourdon gauge

1   **The bourdon gauge** measures the absolute pressure of a gas. The flexible copper tube uncoils slightly when the gas pressure is applied to it. This moves a pointer across the scale.

2   **The U-tube manometer** measures the excess pressure of a gas (see page 280). This is its absolute pressure less atmospheric pressure.

Absolute zero

Heating a gas makes its pressure rise; cooling it makes its pressure fall. The temperature at which the pressure of a gas would become zero is called **absolute zero**. Measurements give absolute zero as $-273\,°C$. Absolute zero is the zero point of the absolute scale of temperature (see page 230).

Boyle's law

Testing Boyle's law

For a fixed mass of gas at constant temperature,
its pressure × its volume is constant. The diagram
above shows how this law can be tested. The table
below shows some typical results, which are also
plotted on the graph of pressure against volume
above.

pressure / kPa	100	150	200	250	300
volume / cm³	30	20	15	12	10
pressure × volume	3000	3000	3000	3000	3000

Maths workshop

Boyle's law may be written as $pV = $ **constant**:

1. To calculate the pressure at a certain volume,
   use $p = \dfrac{\text{constant}}{V}$

2. To calculate the volume at a known pressure,
   use $V = \dfrac{\text{constant}}{p}$

For the gas at the same temperature which gave the results
in the table, calculate
a) the pressure necessary to reduce the volume to 5 cm³
b) the volume at which the pressure would be 50 kPa.

Answer   **a)** 600 kPa **b)** 60 cm³

Atmospheric pressure

Some applications of atmospheric pressure are
shown below. Each application works because of
the force due to atmospheric pressure.

Using atmospheric pressure

Atmospheric pressure
decreases with height,
and changes slightly with
the weather. At sea level,
its mean value is 100 kPa.
It can be measured using
a barometer. The
diagram shows one type
of barometer.

An aneroid barometer

round-up

How much have you improved?
Work out your improvement index on pages 313–14.

1 a) Why do the rear wheels of a tractor need to be
much larger than the wheels of a van of equal
weight? [2]
b) With the aid of a diagram, explain why the shape
of a bowling alley pin makes it easy to knock over. [2]

2 a) Calculate the pressure exerted by a person of
weight 600 N when she is
(i) standing on both feet, with an area of contact
between each foot and the floor of 0.0015 m² [1]
(ii) sitting on a chair, with a total area of contact
on the chair of 0.10 m². [1]
b) Calculate the total area of contact between the
tyres of a bicycle and the ground if the air
pressure in each tyre is 150 kPa and the total
weight of the bicycle and cyclist is 600 N. [1]

round-up

3 A student proposes to replace a steel spring in a spring balance with an elastic band. She tests the stiffness of the elastic band and the spring in separate experiments. The graphs show her results.

a) Use these results to compare the stiffness of the elastic band and the steel spring. [2]

b) Would the elastic band be satisfactory in place of the steel spring? Give a reason for your answer. [2]

4 a) In an experiment to compare the densities of salt water and pure water, the following measurements were made.

(1) mass of an empty measuring cylinder = 120 g

(2) mass of this measuring cylinder containing 100 cm³ of pure water = 220 g

(3) mass of this measuring cylinder containing 100 cm³ of salt water = 228 g

Use these measurements to calculate the density of pure water and of salt water in

(i) g/cm³

(ii) kg/m³. [4]

b) Why do objects float more easily in salt water than in pure water? [3]

5 The diagram shows a metre rule in equilibrium in a horizontal position. The rule is pivoted at its midpoint and it supports two weights W_1 and W_2 at distances d_1 and d_2 from the pivot. The following table shows four incomplete sets of measurements taken with different weights. Calculate each missing measurement. [4]

	W_1 / N	W_2 / N	d_1 / m	d_2 / m
set 1	3.2	1.6	0.2	?
set 2	?	1.5	0.4	0.3
set 3	2.5	?	0.4	0.1
set 4	4.5	3.2	?	0.27

6 A steel spring of length 300 mm was used to measure the weight of an object. With the spring hanging vertically from a fixed point, its length was measured when it supported different known weights. Then its length was measured when it supported the unknown weight W. The measurements are given below.

weight / N	0	1	2	3	4
spring length / mm	300	340	382	419	461

Spring length for the unknown weight = 376 mm

a) Plot a graph of weight (vertical axis) against the extension of the spring. [4]

b) Use your graph to determine the unknown weight W. [1]

7 a) Explain in terms of molecules why a gas exerts pressure on any surface it is in contact with. [3]

b) A gas and some powder are sealed in a hollow cylinder of internal volume 50 cm³ at a pressure of 100 kPa. The volume is reduced to 20 cm³ at constant temperature, causing the pressure to rise to 400 kPa. Use these results to calculate the volume of the powder. [2]

Well done if you've improved. Don't worry if you haven't. Take a break and try again.

Electric charge

preview

At the end of this topic you will be able to:

- explain how objects become charged
- describe the law of force between charged objects
- describe some of the uses and some of the dangers associated with charged objects
- explain how earthing works and why it is necessary
- recall that an electric current is a flow of charge, and recall the units of current and charge
- describe examples of electrolysis
- explain how electricity is conducted by a metal and by an electrolyte.

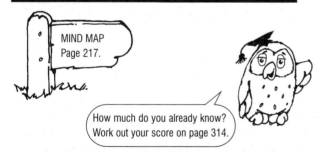

MIND MAP
Page 217.

How much do you already know?
Work out your score on page 314.

Test yourself

1 Two charged objects X and Y repel each other. Which of the following statements could be true?
   A X is positive and Y is negative.
   B X is positive and Y is positive.
   C X is negative and Y is negative. [2]

2 a) When a polythene rod is charged by rubbing it with a dry cloth, it becomes negatively charged. This happens because
   A electrons transfer from the rod to the cloth
   B protons transfer from the rod to the cloth
   C electrons transfer from the cloth to the rod
   D protons transfer from the cloth to the rod. [1]

b) A negatively charged rod is touched on a metal sphere which is insulated. As a result, electrons transfer
   A to earth **B** to the sphere
   C to the rod **D** from the sphere. [1]

3 a) Why does a metal conduct electric charge? [2]
   b) Why is an electrical insulator unable to conduct electric charge? [2]

metal cap
insulator
earthed metal case
leaf
charged rod

The gold leaf electroscope

4 The diagram shows a gold leaf electroscope. When a charged rod is held above the cap of the electroscope, the electroscope leaf rises. Explain why this happens. [4]

5 An electroscope is charged negatively so the leaf is at an angle of 45° to the stem. Explain what will happen to the leaf if a positively charged object is brought near to the cap of the electroscope. [2]

6 A road tanker is used to deliver heating oil from a refinery to homes and offices. When oil is being pumped from the road tanker, the outlet pipe must be earthed. Why is this necessary? [2]

7 State two applications of static electricity. [2]

8 In a copper-plating experiment, a current of 0.20 A is passed through the electrolytic cell for 30 minutes exactly. How much charge passes through the cell in this time? [2]

9 When current is passed through an electrolytic cell, chlorine gas bubbles off at the anode and hydrogen gas at the cathode. Explain why this happens. [3]

10 State two applications of electrolysis. [2]

10.1 Electrostatics

Atomic structure

★ The atom consists of a nucleus surrounded by electrons. The nucleus is made up of neutrons and protons. Most of the mass of an atom is carried by the nucleus. A proton and an electron carry equal and opposite charge. A neutron is uncharged.

★ An uncharged atom has equal numbers of electrons and protons. Removing one or more electrons from an uncharged atom makes the atom into a positive ion. Adding one or more electrons to an uncharged atom makes the atom into a negative ion.

The law of force between charged objects

Any two charged objects exert a force on each other. This type of force is called an **electrostatic force**. The greater the distance between two charged objects, the weaker the electrostatic force between them.

• **Like charges repel; unlike charges attract.**

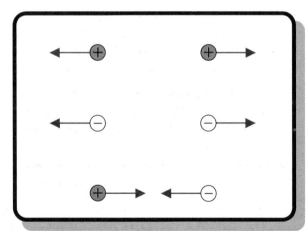

The law of force

Conductors and insulators

1 **In an insulator**, all the electrons are firmly attached to atoms.

2 **In a conductor**, such as a metal, some electrons have broken away from the atoms. These electrons move about freely inside the conductor.

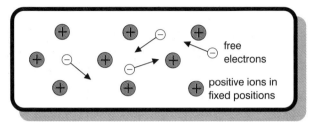

Inside a metal

Charging by friction

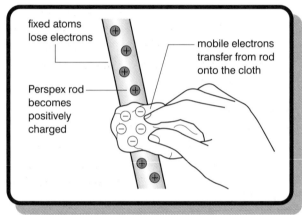

fixed atoms lose electrons

mobile electrons transfer from rod onto the cloth

Perspex rod becomes positively charged

Charging by friction

★ Certain insulators can be charged by rubbing with a dry cloth.

★ This happens as a result of the transfer of electrons to or from the surface atoms of the insulator.

★ Insulators that lose electrons to the cloth become positively charged (e.g. **P**ers**P**ex; **P** for positive!).

★ Insulators that gain electrons from the cloth become negatively charged (e.g. polythe**N**e; **N** for negative!).

Charging an insulated metal object by direct contact

An uncharged insulated metal object can be charged by direct contact with a charged insulator.

1 **To make the metal object positive**, a positively charged rod is touched on the object. Free electrons in the metal transfer onto the positive rod, where they become trapped by the surface atoms. As a result, the metal object becomes positively charged and the rod becomes less positive.

Charging a metal object positively

2   **To make the metal object negative**, a
    negatively charged rod is touched on the
    object. Electrons from the surface atoms of the
    rod transfer to the metal. As a result, the metal
    object becomes negatively charged and the rod
    becomes less negative.

Earthing

A charged metal object can be discharged by
connecting it to the earth with a wire. Electrons
transfer between the object and the earth so the
object loses its charge. This process is referred to
as **earthing**.

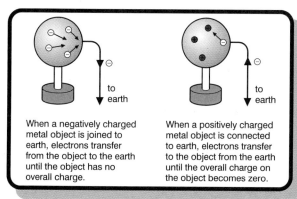

When a negatively charged
metal object is joined to
earth, electrons transfer
from the object to the earth
until the object has no
overall charge.

When a positively charged
metal object is connected
to earth, electrons transfer
to the object from the earth
until the overall charge on
the object becomes zero.

Earthing

> **Question**
>
> Comb your hair with a polythene comb and see if the comb
> can then pick up bits of paper. Explain in terms of electrons
> why a negatively charged object can pick up uncharged bits
> of paper.
>
> **Answer**
>
> The comb repels electrons in the paper to
> the far side of the paper, leaving the near side
> positive. The force of attraction on the near side is greater
> than the force of repulsion on the far side, so the paper is
> attracted to the comb.

A paper puzzle

Rub a Perspex
ruler with a dry cloth
and you will find the ruler
can pick up uncharged bits
of paper. This happens
because paper is not a
perfect insulator. The
positively charged
Perspex rod attracts
electrons to the nearest
side of the paper, leaving the far side of the paper
positive. The force of attraction on the near side
is greater than the force of repulsion on the far
side of the paper. The bit of paper is therefore
held on the rod.

positive rod

attraction

bit of paper

Picking up paper

The gold leaf electroscope

This device is used to detect charge, and to
determine whether the charge is positive or
negative. If a charged object is touched on the cap
of the electroscope, electron transfer makes the
electroscope charged.

1   **If the charge on the object is negative**, the
    electroscope gains electrons. The leaf and the
    stem of the electroscope both become negative
    so the leaf rises as it is repelled from the stem.

2   **If the charge on the object is positive**, the
    electroscope loses electrons. The leaf and the
    stem of the electroscope both become positive
    so the leaf rises as it is repelled from the stem.

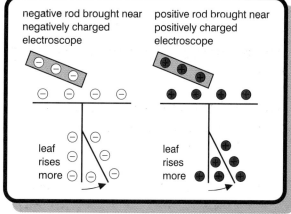

Detecting negative charge   Detecting positive charge

10.2 Electrostatics at work

Electrostatics is used in a wide range of devices. In addition, safety measures are necessary to eliminate static electricity as a hazard in a wide range of situations.

The electrostatic paint spray

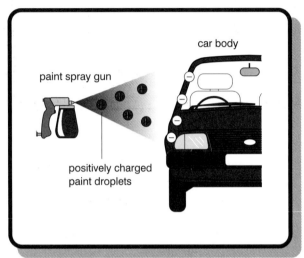

Electrostatic paint spray

A fixed potential difference is maintained between the paint spray nozzle and the metal panel to be painted. The paint droplets in the spray become charged when they are forced out of the spray gun. They are then attracted onto the metal panel to form an even layer of paint on the panel.

The electrostatic precipitator

The ash and dust from coal burned at a power station is prevented from entering the atmosphere by an electrostatic precipitator in the chimney. The dust particles touch the charged wire grid of the precipitator and become charged. The particles are then attracted on to the earthed metal tube surrounding the grid.

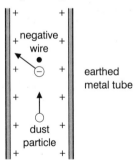

Attracting dust particles

Electrostatic hazards

In an operating theatre, a tiny spark could make an anaesthetic gas leak explode. Such a spark could be generated if charge builds up on an insulated metal object. All metal objects, and the theatre floor itself, must therefore be earthed.

Pipe flow: powders and non-conducting fluids being pumped out of a metal pipe charge the pipe up, unless it is earthed. This occurs because of friction between the metal and the powder or fluid. If the pipe is not earthed, charge builds up on it until a spark jumps from the pipe to earth. If the powder or the fluid is flammable, a disaster could follow! Earthing the pipe prevents the pipe becoming charged.

Computer damage: expensive computer chips need to be handled with care since they are damaged by static electricity. Anyone handling a computer chip should not touch the pins of the chip, otherwise the pins will become charged if a charged object is nearby. This process, known as **charging by induction**, is explained in the diagram below.

Charging without direct contact

Charging by induction

10.3 Current and charge

Fact file

★ An **electric current** is a flow of electric charge.

★ The unit of electric current is the **ampere** (A); the unit of electric charge is the **coulomb** (C).

★ **Electrons** are responsible for the flow of charge through a **metal** when it conducts electricity.

★ **Positive and negative ions** are responsible for the flow of charge through an **electrolyte** when it conducts electricity.

Steady currents

A steady current

The diagram shows a simple electric circuit in which a cell is connected in series with an ammeter and a torch bulb.

1   **The current in this circuit is constant**. This means that charge passes through each component at a steady rate. Electrons pass through each component at a steady rate.

2   **The current through each component is the same**. Equal amounts of charge pass through each component in a set period of time. The number of electrons per second passing through each component is the same.

Equation for charge flow

★ **One coulomb of charge** is defined as the amount of charge passing a point in a circuit in one second when the current is one ampere.

★ **The charge passing a point in a circuit** that is carrying a steady current is calculated as follows:

$$\text{charge passed} = \text{current} \times \text{time taken}$$
$$\text{(in C)} \qquad \text{(in A)} \qquad \text{(in s)}$$

At a junction

current from cell = current through B_1 + current through B_2

At a junction

In this circuit, two torch bulbs B_1 and B_2 are in parallel with each other. Each electron from the cell passes through one torch bulb then returns to the positive terminal of the cell. The flow of electrons from the cell divides at junction X and recombines at junction Y.

The charge flow per second from the cell = charge flow per second through B_1 + charge flow per second through B_2. Since charge flow per second is current, it follows that cell current = current through B_1 + current through B_2.

In other words, at a junction in a circuit,

The total current entering the junction is equal to the total current leaving the junction.

Question

a) Calculate the charge that flows through a torch bulb carrying a steady current of 0.25 A in
   (i) 1 minute
   (ii) 5 minutes.
b) Calculate how long it takes for a charge of 100 C to pass through a torch bulb that is carrying a steady current of 0.2 A.

Answers
a) (i) 15 C (ii) 75 C
b) 500 s

10.4 Electrolysis

Electrolytic conduction

This occurs when a substance is decomposed by an electric current passing through it. Decomposition does not happen when an electric current passes through a wire – the chemical composition of the wire is unaffected by the electric current. In comparison, the passage of an electric current through sodium chloride solution causes a gas to bubble off at each electrode. In an electrolytic cell,

- the **electrolyte** is the conducting liquid
- the **anode** is the positive electrode
- the **cathode** is the negative electrode.

ELECTROLYSIS
Pages 128–32.

Electrolysis

In an electrolyte

An electrolyte is a liquid which contains positive and negative ions. For example, in sodium chloride solution, the positive ions are hydrogen ions (H^+) and sodium ions (Na^+). The negative ions are chloride ions (Cl^-) and hydroxide ions (OH^-).

The positive ions are attracted to the cathode because they carry the opposite charge. Where there is more than one type of positive ion, the ion that attracts an electron most easily off the cathode is discharged. In sodium chloride solution, hydrogen gas bubbles off the cathode because the hydrogen ions are more easily discharged than the sodium ions.

The negative ions are attracted to the anode. The ion that gives up an electron most easily is discharged at the anode. In sodium chloride solution, chlorine gas bubbles off at the anode.

Copper-plating

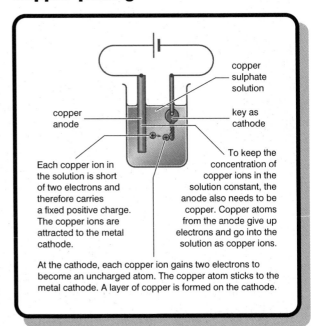

Each copper ion in the solution is short of two electrons and therefore carries a fixed positive charge. The copper ions are attracted to the metal cathode.

To keep the concentration of copper ions in the solution constant, the anode also needs to be copper. Copper atoms from the anode give up electrons and go into the solution as copper ions.

At the cathode, each copper ion gains two electrons to become an uncharged atom. The copper atom sticks to the metal cathode. A layer of copper is formed on the cathode.

Copper-plating a key

A metal object can be copper-plated by making the object the cathode in an electrolytic cell containing copper sulphate solution.

Each copper atom deposited on the cathode adds the same mass and gains the same amount of charge (2 electrons). The mass of copper deposited is therefore proportional to the charge flow through the cell. Hence the mass deposited is proportional to the **current** and the **time taken**.

Question

In a copper-plating experiment, a metal key was used as the cathode. Its initial mass was 25.25 g. After being used for 30 minutes as the cathode with a steady current of 0.25 A, its mass had increased to 25.40 g. Calculate
a) the amount of charge needed to deposit 1 g of copper
b) the mass of copper that would be deposited by a current of 0.1 A for exactly 3 hours.

Answers   a) 3000 C b) 0.36 g

round-up

How much have you improved?
Work out your improvement index on page 314.

1 An insulated metal object M can become charged without making direct contact with a charged object O. The diagram shows how one stage in this process could happen. The complete sequence of actions including the stage shown in the diagram are listed below in the wrong order.

charged object

metal object

insulation

 (i) The earth connection to the metal object M is removed.
 (ii) The charged body O is brought near the metal object M.
 (iii) The charged body O is removed.
 (iv) The metal object M is earthed.
a) Rewrite the list in the correct order. [4]
b) What type of charge is left on the metal object M if the charged body O carries a negative charge? [1]
c) Does the total charge on the charged object O alter as a result of M being charged in this way? [1]

2 A gold leaf electroscope is charged by direct contact with a positively charged rod, as shown.

positive rod

a) Explain in terms of electrons why the leaf rises when the electroscope is charged in this way. [3]
b) Explain why the leaf remains in the position shown when the charged rod is removed. [1]
c) Explain how the electroscope could be charged negatively using a positively charged rod. [4]
d) Describe how the electroscope could be used to determine the type of charge on a charged object. [3]

3 a) In dry weather, the metal body of a car becomes charged when the car is in motion on a dry road. If the car is not fitted with a trailing conductor,
 (i) explain why someone who touches the car when it stops would receive a shock [2]
 (ii) explain why the car driver would receive a shock on getting out of the car after it stops. [2]
b) Why does the metal body of a car not become charged
 (i) if a trailing conductor is fitted to the car [1]
 (ii) in wet weather? [2]

4 In an electroplating experiment, a layer of copper was being deposited on a metal plate. The initial mass of the plate was measured at 64.50 g. The current was maintained at 0.1 A for 30 minutes, then the plate was carefully dried and reweighed at 64.56 g. It was then reconnected and the current was increased to 0.30 A for a further 60 minutes.
a) Calculate the charge passed through the cell in each of the two parts of the experiment. [2]
b) Calculate the increase in mass of the plate in the first part of the experiment. [1]
c) Hence calculate the increase in mass in the second part of the experiment. [1]
d) What steady current would have given the same total increase in mass in a total time of 1 hour? [1]

5 a) A plastic ruler will pick up small uncharged bits of paper if it is rubbed first with a dry cloth. Explain why this happens, regardless of whether the charged ruler is positive or negative. [4]
b) Explain why dust particles are attracted to a TV screen when the TV is switched on. [2]

6 a) Describe the principle of operation of an electrostatic precipitator used to remove ash and dust particles from the flue gases of a power station.

negative wire

dust particles [3]

b) An electronic chip may be damaged if its metal pins become charged. With the aid of a diagram, explain how it is possible to charge an insulated metal pin simply by touching the pin in the presence of a nearby charged object. [2]

Electric circuits

preview

At the end of this topic you will be able to:

- explain what is meant by potential difference
- describe series and parallel circuits in terms of current and voltage
- describe how to use an ammeter to measure current and a voltmeter to measure voltage
- recognise the circuit symbols for common electrical components and know their characteristics
- define resistance and carry out calculations involving current, voltage, resistance and power
- describe how mains electricity is supplied and costed
- identify dangers of mains electricity and explain safety features and devices to minimise dangers.

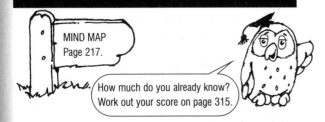

MIND MAP Page 217.

How much do you already know? Work out your score on page 315.

Test yourself

1 Two identical torch bulbs, a switch, an ammeter and a 1.5 V cell are connected in series with each other.
   a) Draw the circuit diagram. [2]
   b) The ammeter reading was 0.20 A when the switch was closed. How much energy was delivered to each torch bulb in one minute? [2]

2 A 1.5 V cell was connected in series with an ammeter, a switch and a torch bulb X. A second torch bulb Y was connected in parallel with X. The switch was then closed to light both torch bulbs.

   a) Draw the circuit diagram. [2]
   b) The ammeter reading was 0.30 A. Calculate the energy supplied by the cell in
   (i) one second **(ii)** one minute. [2]

3 In the circuit shown, ammeter A_1 reads 0.5 A and ammeter A_2 reads 0.3 A.

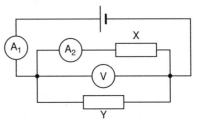

   a) Calculate the current through resistor Y. [1]
   b) The voltmeter in parallel with resistor Y reads 1.0 V when ammeter A_1 reads 0.5 A. Calculate the resistance of resistor Y. [2]

4 A current of 2.5 A is passed through a 6.0 Ω resistor. Calculate **a)** the p.d. across the resistor
   b) the power supplied to the resistor. [2]

5 a) Draw a circuit diagram to show a diode connected in series with a 1.5 V cell and a torch bulb lit up. [2]
   b) If the 1.5 V cell is connected in the circuit in the reverse direction, the torch bulb would not light. Why? [2]

6 Give the symbol and state the main characteristic of each of the following components:
   a) a light-dependent resistor
   b) a thermistor. [4]

7 An electric heater is rated at 240 V, 1000 W. Calculate
   a) the electrical energy delivered to the heater in 300 s
   b) the current through the heater when it operates at its rated power. [3]

8 a) State the purpose of a fuse in an electric circuit.
   b) Explain how a fuse achieves its purpose. [3]

9 A set of Christmas tree lights contains 20 light bulbs rated at 6 W. The light bulbs are connected in series to be operated from 240 V mains. When in normal use, calculate **a)** the current through each bulb
   b) the voltage across each bulb. [4]

10 A microwave oven rated at 800 W is used for 15 minutes to heat some food. Calculate
   a) the number of units of electricity used
   b) the cost of the electricity used, if each unit of electricity is priced at 6.0p. [3]

11.1 Current and potential difference

Fact file

★ An **electric current** is a **flow of charge**. The unit of electric current is the **ampere** (A).

★ The **potential difference** (p.d.) between any two points in a circuit is the **work done per unit charge** when charge moves from one point to the other point. Voltage is an alternative word for potential difference.

★ The unit of charge is the **coulomb** (C). One coulomb is equal to the charge passing a point in a circuit in one second when the current is one ampere.

★ The unit of potential difference is the **volt** (V), equal to one joule per coulomb.

Four rules about current

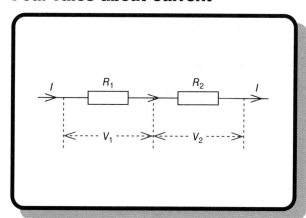

Series resistors

1   The current entering a component is the same as the current leaving it. A component does not use up current; it uses the electrical energy supplied to it by the charge that passes through it.

2   At a junction, the total current leaving the junction is equal to the total current entering the junction.

3   Components in series pass the same current.

4   An ammeter is a meter designed to measure current. It is always connected in series with a component. An ideal ammeter has zero resistance.

Four rules about voltage

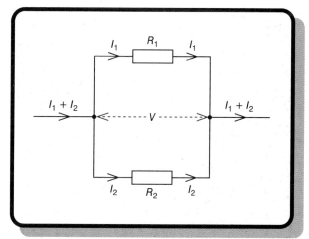

Parallel resistors

1   The voltage across a component is the number of joules delivered to the component by each coulomb of charge that passes through it.

2   Components in parallel have the same voltage across them.

3   For two or more components in series, the total voltage is equal to the sum of the individual voltages.

4   A voltmeter is a meter designed to measure voltage (potential difference). It is always connected in parallel with a component. An ideal voltmeter has infinite resistance.

Four rules about power

Consider a component in a circuit which has voltage V across its terminals and which passes a steady current I.

1   In a time interval t, charge Q flows through the component where $Q = It$.

2   The electrical energy E delivered by charge Q is QV, since V is defined as the electrical energy delivered per unit charge.

3   Hence the electrical energy E delivered in time t is ItV.

4   The electrical power =

$$\frac{\text{electrical energy delivered}}{\text{time taken}} = IV.$$

11.2 Resistance

Fact file

★ The **resistance** R of an electrical component

in a circuit $= \dfrac{\text{the voltage across the component}}{\text{the current through the component}}$

★ The unit of resistance is the **ohm** (Ω), defined as one volt per ampere.

★ **To calculate resistance**, use the equation

$$\text{resistance} = \dfrac{\text{voltage}}{\text{current}}$$

★ **Ohm's law** states that for a wire under constant physical conditions, the current is proportional to the voltage. This is equivalent to stating that its resistance is constant.

★ A **resistor** is a component designed to have a particular value of resistance. This resistance is caused by opposition to the motion of electrons round the circuit.

Note

The following prefixes are used for large or small values of current, voltage or resistance:

mega (M)	*kilo (k)*	*milli (m)*	*micro (μ)*
1 000 000	*1000*	*0.001*	*0.000 001*
10^6	10^3	10^{-3}	10^{-6}

What does current depend on?

1 the voltage of the cell, battery or power supply unit

2 the resistance of the components in the circuit.

Resistors can be used to control the current in a circuit.

Measuring resistance

Measuring resistance   Voltage against current

The diagram shows how the resistance of a resistor may be determined using an ammeter and a voltmeter. Note that the voltmeter is in parallel with the resistor, and the ammeter is in series.

1 With the switch closed, the variable resistor is adjusted to change the current in steps. At each step, the current and voltage are measured from the ammeter and the voltmeter respectively.

2 The measurements are plotted as a graph of voltage (on the vertical axis) against current, as shown. The plotted points define a straight line passing through the origin.

3 The gradient of the line is measured. This is equal to the resistance of the resistor.

Question

a) Determine the resistance of the resistor that gave the results plotted on the graph.

b) Calculate the current through this resistor when the voltage across it is **(i)** 5.0 V **(ii)** 0.1 V.

Answers   a) 4.0 Ω b) (i) 1.25 A (ii) 25 mA

Resistance heating

All the electrical energy supplied to a resistor is transformed to thermal energy, heating the surroundings as a result.

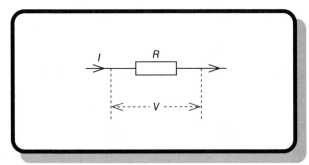

Heating effect

1 The voltage V across the resistor $= IR$, where I is the current through the component.

2 The power supplied to the resistor $P = IV = I^2R$. This is the rate of heat produced in the resistor.

11.3 Components

The circuit shown on the opposite page (bottom left) for measuring resistance may be used to investigate the variation of current with voltage for any device. The graphs show the results of such investigations for different components, plotted with current on the y-axis and voltage on the x-axis.

1   For a wire-wound resistor at constant temperature, the graph is a straight line – the resistance is constant.

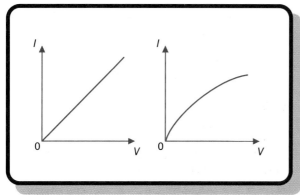

Fixed resistor   Filament bulb

2   For a filament bulb such as a torch bulb, the graph is a curve – the resistance increases as the filament becomes hotter.

3   For a diode in its forward direction, the graph shows that the resistance decreases as the current increases. In the reverse direction, the graph shows that the diode has an extremely high resistance.

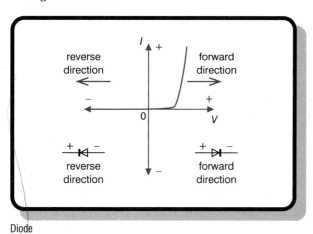

Diode

4   For a light-dependent resistor (LDR), its resistance depends on the intensity of light falling on it. Increasing the intensity makes the resistance lower; conversely, decreasing the intensity makes the resistance higher. More electrons are freed from the atoms if the light intensity is increased, causing the resistance to fall.

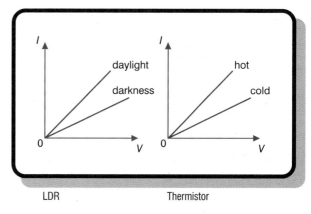

LDR   Thermistor

5   For a thermistor, the resistance decreases with increasing temperature and vice versa. More electrons are freed from the atoms if the temperature is increased, causing the resistance to fall.

Question

A 1000 Ω resistor was connected in series with a thermistor, a milliammeter and a 2.0 V cell. The reading on the milliammeter was 1.0 mA. Calculate
a) the voltage across the 1000 Ω resistor when its current was 1.0 mA
b) the voltage across the thermistor when its current was 1.0 mA.

Answers   a) 1.0 V b) 1.0 V

11.4 Mains electricity

Alternating current

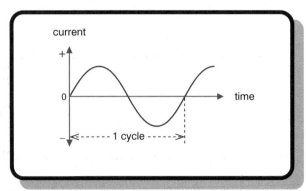

Alternating current

1   The electric current through a mains appliance alternates in direction. The current reverses direction then reverses back each cycle.

2   The **frequency** of an alternating current is the number of cycles per second. In the UK, the mains frequency is 50 Hz.

The three-pin plug

A mains plug

Electricity costs

★ One kilowatt hour (kWh) is the electrical energy supplied to a one kilowatt appliance in exactly one hour.

★ The kilowatt hour is the unit of electricity for costing purposes.

★ A domestic electricity meter records the total number of units used.

Mains circuits

Each circuit from the fuse board is protected with its own fuse. If the fuse 'blows', the live wire is therefore cut off from appliances supplied by that circuit.

The mains cable from the substation to a building is connected via the electricity meter to the circuits in the building at the distribution fuse board. The live wire from the substation is connected via a main fuse to the electricity meter.

The two wires used to supply an electric current to an appliance are referred to as the **live** and the **neutral** wires. The neutral wire is earthed at the nearest mains substation.

Mains wires need to have as low a resistance as possible, otherwise heat is produced in them by the current. This is why mains wires are made from copper. All mains wires and fittings are insulated.

The fuse in a lighting circuit is in the fuse box. Each light bulb is turned on or off by its own switch. When the switch is in the off position, the appliance is not connected to the live wire of the mains supply.

A **ring main** is used to supply electricity to appliances via wall sockets. A ring main circuit consists of a live wire, a neutral wire and the **earth wire** which is earthed at the fuse board. The wires of a ring main are thicker than the wires of a lighting circuit because appliances connected to a ring main require more current than light bulbs do.

Each appliance is connected to the ring main by means of a three-pin plug which carries a fuse. An appliance with a metal chassis is earthed via the three-pin plug and the earth wire. This prevents the metal chassis from becoming live if a fault develops in the appliance. Appliances connected to the ring main can be switched on or off independently since they are in parallel with each other.

Mains circuits

11.5 Electrical safety

Faults and fuses

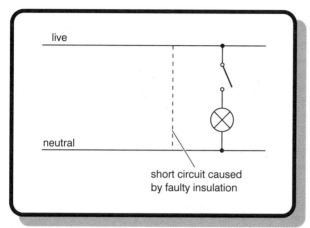

A short circuit

A **short circuit** occurs where a fault creates a low resistance path between two points at different voltages. The current through the short circuit is much greater than the current along the correct path between the two points, enough to create a fire through overheating.

Fuses are intended to prevent excessive currents flowing. A fuse is a thin piece of resistance wire which overheats and melts if too much current passes through it. The fuse wire breaks when it melts, thus cutting the current off and protecting the appliance or the wires leading to it from overheating due to excessive current.

Faults in mains circuits can arise due to

- **poor maintenance** e.g. frayed cables or damaged plugs or fittings such as sockets and switches
- **carelessness** e.g. cables that are too long, coiling a cable (which prevents heat from escaping from it)
- **overloading a circuit** e.g. too many appliances connected to the same circuit or connecting a powerful appliance to a low current circuit.

Earthing

Any appliance with a metal case must be earthed through the ring main to protect the user. If such an appliance is not earthed and a fault develops in which a live wire touches the case, anyone who subsequently touches the case will be electrocuted. The victim effectively provides a short circuit path to earth from the live case.

Circuit breakers

Both switches are pulled open by an electromagnetic switch if the live current and the neutral current differ.

A residual current circuit breaker

A lethal electric shock is possible with currents as small as 50 mA passing through the body. The **residual current circuit breaker** is designed to cut an appliance off from the mains if the current in the live wire differs from the current in the neutral wire by more than 30 mA. This difference would arise if current leaks to earth from a poorly insulated live wire.

A **simple circuit breaker** is a switch operated by an electromagnet in series with the switch. When the switch is closed, if the current reaches a certain value, the electromagnet pulls the switch open and cuts the current off. The circuit breaker switch then needs to be reset once the fault causing the current rise has been remedied. A circuit breaker does not need to be replaced like a fuse each time it cuts the current off.

Double insulation

This is a safety feature of mains appliances like hand-held hair dryers and electric shavers which have insulated cases.

Double insulation symbol

Question

State the purpose of **a)** a fuse **b)** a residual current circuit breaker.

Answers **a)** To protect the appliance or the wiring from overheating due to excessive current. **b)** To protect the user from shocks.

round-up

How much have you improved?
Work out your improvement index on pages 315–16.

1 In this circuit, the ammeter reading was 0.25 A and the voltmeter reading was 3.0 V.

a) Calculate the resistance of resistor R. [1]
b) If a second resistor identical to R was connected in parallel with R how would the ammeter and voltmeter readings alter? [2]

2 a) A 1500 W, 240 V electric heater is connected to the ring main in a house and then switched on.
  (i) Calculate the current through the heater. [1]
  (ii) How many units of electricity would be used by this heater in 2 hours? [1]
 b) (i) What is the function of the earth wire in a ring main circuit? [2]
  (ii) Given mains fuses rated at 3 A, 5 A and 13 A, which one would you choose for a microwave oven rated at 650 W, 240 V? [1]
  (iii) In **(ii)**, if the wrong fuse is chosen, what problems might occur? [2]

3 The circuit diagram shows two 5 Ω resistors P and Q in series with each other, an ammeter and a 3.0 V cell.

a) **(i)** What is the voltage across each resistor? [1]
   (ii) What is the current through each resistor? [1]
b) Hence calculate the power supplied to each resistor. [1]
c) A third 5 Ω resistor R is then connected in parallel with resistor P. How does this affect the current passing through each of the other two resistors? [2]

4 A 24 W heating element for a 12 V heater is to be made using a suitable length of resistance wire.
a) Calculate the expected current and the required resistance. [2]
b) The resistance wire has a resistance of 5 Ω per metre. Calculate the length of wire required to make this heating element. [2]
c) With the aid of a circuit diagram, describe how you could check the resistance per metre of a reel of this resistance wire. [5]

5 The following mains appliances were used in a household over a period of 24 hours:
  (i) two 100 W light bulbs, each for 6 hours
  (ii) a 5000 W electric oven for 2 hours
  (iii) a 3000 W electric kettle used four times for five minutes each time.
a) Calculate the number of units of electricity used in each case. [3]
b) Calculate the total cost of the electricity used if the unit price of electricity was 5p. [1]
c) How long would it take a 5000 W electric oven to use the same number of electricity units as a 100 W electric light bulb would use in 24 hours? [2]

6 a) Why is it dangerous to touch a mains appliance when you have wet hands? [3]
b) A mains electric mower should never be connected to the mains unless a residual current circuit breaker is used. Why? [3]
c) Why is it dangerous to use a mains electric mower with its mains cable coiled up? [2]

Well done if you've improved. Don't worry if you haven't. Take a break and try again.

Electromagnetism

preview

At the end of this topic you will be able to:

- draw and explain the magnetic field of a bar magnet, a long straight current-carrying wire and a solenoid
- describe how magnets affect each other
- describe the operation of devices that contain an electromagnet
- explain the principle and operation of a moving-coil loudspeaker and an electric motor
- explain the principle and operation of an alternating current generator and a transformer
- explain how electric power is transmitted via the grid system.

MIND MAP
Page 217.

How much do you already know?
Work out your score on page 316.

Test yourself

1 State a suitable material from which to make **a)** the core of an electromagnet **b)** a permanent magnet. [2]

2 a) One end of a bar magnet is held near a plotting compass, as shown. What is the polarity of this end of the bar magnet? [1]

b) The north pole of a bar magnet repels pole P of another bar magnet. What is the polarity of P? [1]

3 Sketch the lines of the magnetic field produced by
a) a long straight wire carrying a direct current [2]
b) a solenoid carrying a direct current. [2]

4 State whether each of the following devices contains a permanent magnet or an electromagnet:
a) a loudspeaker **b)** a relay **c)** an electric motor. [3]

5 a) The diagram shows a vertical wire between the poles of a U-shaped magnet, arranged so the magnetic field of the magnet is horizontal. When a current passes up the wire, the wire is forced outwards. If the magnetic field is reversed and the current is reversed, in which direction would the force on the wire then be? [1]

b) Explain why a direct current electric motor cannot work on alternating current. [2]

6 a) State two ways in which the voltage from an alternating current generator would change if its rate of rotation was reduced. [2]
b) Why is alternating current used to transmit electric power through the grid system? [3]

7 An aluminium plate placed between the poles of an electromagnet supplied with alternating current, as shown, becomes warm. Explain how this happens. [2]

aluminium plate

a.c. supply

electromagnet

8 A transformer has 60 turns in its primary coil and 1200 turns in its secondary coil. A 240 V, 100 W lamp is connected to the terminals of its secondary coil. The primary coil is connected to an alternating voltage supply.
a) Calculate the voltage of this supply if the lamp lights normally. [1]
b) Calculate the maximum possible current through the primary coil when the 100 W lamp is on. [1]

Magnetic field patterns

The lines of force of a magnetic field are defined by the direction of a plotting compass in the magnetic field. A bar magnet suspended on a thread aligns itself with the Earth's magnetic field. The end that points north is the north-seeking pole; the other end is the south-seeking pole.

12.1 Magnetism

Fact file

★ Two magnets act on each other at a distance. The force of interaction decreases with increased distance.

★ The law of force for magnetic poles is that **like poles repel and unlike poles attract**.

★ Iron and its steel alloys can be magnetised and demagnetised.

★ Permanent magnets are made from steel because it is hard to demagnetise once magnetised.

★ Electromagnets are made from soft iron because it is easy to magnetise and demagnetise.

Permanent magnets

A bar magnet produces lines of force which loop round from one end to the other end. The lines emerge from the north-seeking pole and end at the south-seeking pole.

Magnetic fields

The magnetic effect of a steady electric current

Near a long straight wire, the magnetic field lines are concentric circles centred on the wire in a plane perpendicular to it.

Near a long solenoid, the magnetic field lines are concentrated at the ends, similar to the field of a bar magnet.

Electromagnets

An electromagnet consists of a solenoid with an iron core. When a current is passed through the coil of wire, the iron bar is magnetised. The magnetic field is much stronger than the field created by the empty coil. It can be switched off by switching the current off, and its strength can be altered by changing the current.

Using electromagnets

To lift scrap iron: a powerful electromagnet suspended from a crane cable is used to lift scrap iron in a scrapyard. Switching the electromagnet off causes the scrap iron to fall off the electromagnet.

The relay: when current is passed through the coil of a relay, the electromagnet attracts a soft iron armature. The movement of this armature opens or closes a switch which is part of a different circuit.

A normally open relay

When the current is switched off, the armature springs back to its normal position and the switch reverts to its original state.

The electric bell: the electromagnet coil is part of a 'make-and-break' switch. When current passes through the coil, the electromagnet attracts the soft iron armature which makes the hammer hit the bell. The movement of the armature opens the 'make-and-break' switch which switches the electromagnet off, allowing the armature to spring back to its initial position and close the switch. Current then passes through the electromagnet again, causing the sequence to be repeated.

An electric bell

12.2 The electric motor

The motor effect

A force is exerted on a current-carrying wire placed at right angles to the lines of force of a magnetic field. The diagram shows a current-carrying wire between the poles of a U-shaped magnet. The force is perpendicular to the wire and to the lines of force of the magnet.

The motor effect

The force occurs because the magnetic field created by the wire interacts with the applied magnetic field (the magnetic field in which the wire is placed). The combined field is very weak on one side where the two fields are in opposite directions to each other. The force acts towards the side where the combined field is very weak.

Combined fields

The left-hand rule is a convenient way to remember the force direction if you know the current direction and the direction of the applied magnetic field.

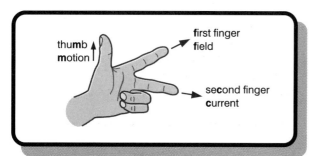

The left-hand rule

The electric motor

A model electric motor is shown in the next diagram. The rectangular coil is on a spindle between the poles of a U-shaped magnet. Current enters and leaves the coil via a split-ring commutator.

Current passes along each side of the coil in opposite directions. Each side is therefore acted on by a force due to the magnetic field. The force on one side is in the opposite direction to the force on the other side.

When the coil is parallel to the field, the forces on the sides rotate the coil. As the coil turns through the position at 90° to the field, the split-ring commutator reverses its connections to the battery, reversing the current direction round the coil.

Rotation by more than 90° has swapped the positions of the two sides and reversed the current direction in the coil. Therefore, the forces acting on each side continue to turn the coil in the same direction as before, so the coil rotates continuously in one direction.

The electric motor

Question

For the electric motor above, what would be the effect of
a) reversing the current direction **b)** reversing the current direction *and* reversing the direction of the magnetic field?

Practical electric motors

- A mains electric motor works with alternating current because it has an electromagnet, not a permanent magnet. Each time the current reverses, the magnetic field does too, so the rotation direction is unchanged.
- The armature may comprise 20 different coils, each at a fixed angle to the next. Each coil has its own pair of segments of a split-ring commutator. This produces a much steadier speed of rotation than a single coil.
- The power supply is connected to the split-ring commutator using two spring-loaded graphite brushes which press on the commutator. Graphite conducts electricity and allows the commutator to turn with very little friction.

Answers The rotation direction would **a)** reverse **b)** be unchanged

The loudspeaker

This contains a coil of insulated wire on a plastic tube in a magnetic field, as shown. The coil is at the centre of a diaphragm. When current is passed through the coil, it is forced to move by the magnetic field. With alternating current,

A loudspeaker

the coil is forced to move to and fro. This vibrating motion makes the diaphragm vibrate, creating sound waves in the surrounding air.

12.3 Electromagnetic induction

Fact file

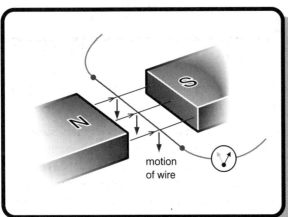

Electromagnetic induction

★ When a wire cuts across the lines of force of a magnetic field, a voltage is induced in the wire.

★ If the wire is part of a complete circuit in which there is no other voltage source, the induced voltage drives a current round the circuit.

★ The faster the wire moves across the field lines, the greater the induced voltage.

★ The stronger the magnetic field, the greater the induced voltage.

Laws of electromagnetic induction

Lenz's law

Lenz's law: the induced current in a circuit is always in such a direction as to oppose the change which causes it. This can be tested by inserting a bar magnet into a coil connected to a centre-reading milliammeter. The direction of the induced current is given by the deflection of the pointer of the meter. Inserting the magnet generates a current which creates a magnetic pole to oppose the incoming pole.

Faraday's law of electromagnetic induction: the induced voltage is proportional to the speed at which the wire cuts the magnetic field lines. The induced current is small if the magnet is inserted slowly. If the magnet is inserted rapidly, the induced current is much larger.

The alternating current generator

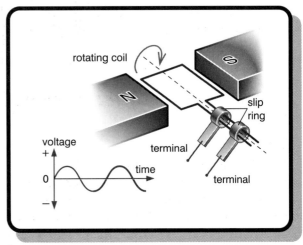

An a.c. generator

The a.c. generator consists of a rectangular coil of insulated wire which is made to rotate at steady speed in a uniform magnetic field. Work done to turn the coil is converted into electrical energy. The alternating voltage induced across the terminals of the coil can be displayed on an oscilloscope.

★ The frequency of the alternating voltage is equal to the frequency of rotation of the coil.

★ The peak voltage is proportional to the speed of rotation of the coil (Faraday's law).

★ The peak voltage occurs when the sides of the coil cut across the field lines at 90°. The voltage is zero when the coil sides move parallel to the field lines.

★ A direct voltage can be generated if the two slip rings are replaced by a split-ring commutator, as shown. This makes the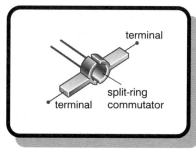

Producing direct current

connections to the coil change each half-cycle so the voltage polarity does not change. However, the voltage is not steady.

The dynamo

In a dynamo, the magnet rotates and the coil remains stationary. The magnet and coil move relative to each other such that the coil windings cut across the magnetic field lines. Hence a voltage is induced.

A dynamo

The microphone

Sound waves make the microphone diaphragm vibrate. A coil attached to the diaphragm moves in and out of the magnetic field of a permanent magnet, generating an alternating voltage across the coil terminals. The voltage from a microphone is usually referred to as an audio signal.

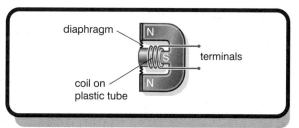

A microphone

Question

A bicycle is fitted with a dynamo lamp. Explain why the cyclist must pedal harder after switching the lamp on.

The tape recorder

A tape recording

The tape is coated on one side with a thin film of magnetic material.

Recording: the tape is made to run at a steady speed past a recording head. This is a small electromagnet to which the audio signal is supplied. The changes of magnetism due to the audio signal are recorded by the magnetic film on the tape.

Playback: the tape is made to run at a steady speed past the same recording head. This time, the recording head is connected to an amplifier and a loudspeaker. The changes in magnetism on the tape induce an alternating voltage in the coil of the electromagnet. This is the audio signal recreated.

Answer Electrical energy for the lamp is provided from work done by the cyclist. Hence the cyclist must do more work by exerting more force to keep the speed the same.

12.4 Transformers

How a transformer works

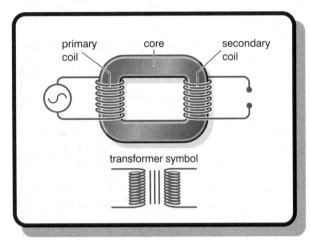

A model transformer

A transformer steps an alternating voltage up or down. It consists of two coils wound on an iron core.

1 The voltage to be transformed is applied to the **primary coil** of the transformer.

2 The alternating current through the windings of the primary coil creates an alternating magnetic field in the transformer's iron core.

3 The continuously changing magnetic field through the core induces an alternating voltage in the **secondary coil**.

The transformer rule

$$\frac{\text{voltage induced in the secondary coil } V_s}{\text{voltage applied to the primary coil } V_p} = \frac{\text{number of turns on the secondary coil } N_s}{\text{number of turns on the primary coil } N_p}$$

For a **step-up transformer**, the number of secondary turns is greater than the number of primary turns. Hence the secondary voltage is greater than the primary voltage.

For a **step-down transformer**, the number of secondary turns is less than the number of primary turns. Hence the secondary voltage is less than the primary voltage.

Transformer efficiency

A practical transformer

The percentage efficiency of a transformer is defined as $\dfrac{\text{output power}}{\text{input power}} \times 100\%$.

For a transformer that is 100% efficient, the output power equals the input power. In other words, primary current × primary voltage = secondary current × secondary voltage. Thus if the voltage is stepped up, the current is stepped down and vice versa.

Question

A transformer has a 100-turn primary coil and a 2000-turn secondary coil. A 240 V, 60 W lamp is connected to the secondary coil. Calculate **a)** the primary voltage needed to make the lamp light normally **b)** the primary current when the lamp lights normally, assuming the transformer is 100% efficient.

High-voltage transmission of electrical power

The grid system operates at high voltage because the higher the voltage, the less the current needed for the same power. Less power is therefore wasted due to resistance heating in the cables used to carry the current. Alternating voltages can easily be stepped up or down using transformers. Hence power is transmitted on the grid system using alternating voltage.

Answers   a) 12V b) 5A

round-up

How much have you improved?
Work out your improvement index on page 316.

1 a) With the aid of a diagram, explain the operation of a make-and-break switch in an electric bell or a buzzer. [8]

b) The diagram shows the construction of a different type of electric bell. When the switch is closed, the iron bar is pulled into the electromagnet, causing the wooden striker X to hit the metal plate with a 'ding'. When the switch is released, the iron bar springs back and the other wooden striker Y hits the other plate with a 'dong'.

(i) Why is it essential that the bar is made of iron? [1]

(ii) When the switch is open, why is it necessary for the iron bar to be partly in and partly out of the solenoid? [1]

(iii) Explain whether or not the device would work with an alternating current supply instead of a direct current supply. [2]

2 a) With the aid of a labelled diagram, explain the operation of a relay that is normally open. [6]

b) A metal-detector consists of an electromagnet connected to a low voltage alternating current supply. When a piece of metal is held near the electromagnet, the current through the coil increases. Explain why this increase of current occurs. [2]

3 a) With the aid of a labelled diagram, explain the operation of an alternating current generator. [6]

b) (i) Sketch the waveform produced by an alternating current generator. [2]

(ii) Show on the waveform you have drawn a point where the coil is parallel to the magnetic field. [1]

c) How does the voltage waveform of an alternating current generator change if the generator turns faster? [2]

4 a) The diagram shows the construction of a step-down transformer.

(i) Explain the operation of this transformer. [2]

(ii) Why are the windings of the secondary coil thicker than the windings of the primary coil? [1]

(iii) Why is the core constructed from laminated iron plates? [2]

b) A step-down transformer has a primary coil with 1200 turns and a secondary coil with 60 turns.

(i) If the primary coil is connected to 240 V a.c. mains, what will the secondary voltage be? [1]

(ii) The percentage efficiency of the transformer was measured and found to be 80%. If the primary current is not to exceed 0.1 A, what is the maximum current that can be delivered to a 12 V light bulb connected to the secondary coil? [2]

5 a) (i) Why is electrical power transmitted through the grid system at high voltage? [2]

(ii) Domestic consumers in the UK are supplied with mains electricity at 240 V. In the USA, the mains voltage is 110 V. Which system is safer and why? [2]

b) The cables used to distribute electricity through the grid system are often carried by pylons. Give one advantage and one disadvantage of using pylons rather than underground cables for this purpose. [2]

Well done if you've improved. Don't worry if you haven't. Take a break and try again.

Equations you should know

Read, learn and inwardly digest the formulas below. To test yourself, cover each equation with a blank card after the first word and see if you can write the rest of the equation on the card.

voltage = current × resistance

electrical power = voltage × current

charge = current × time

energy transferred = potential difference × charge

$$\text{energy transferred} = \text{power} \times \text{time}$$
$$\text{(kWh)} \qquad \text{(kW)} \quad \text{(h)}$$

$$\frac{\text{voltage across coil 1}}{\text{voltage across coil 2}} = \frac{\text{number of turns in coil 1}}{\text{number of turns in coil 2}}$$

$$\text{pressure} = \frac{\text{force}}{\text{area}}$$

$$\text{speed} = \frac{\text{distance}}{\text{time}}$$

$$\text{acceleration} = \frac{\text{change of velocity}}{\text{time taken}}$$

force = mass × acceleration

work done = force × distance moved in direction of force

energy transferred = work done

$$\text{efficiency} = \frac{\text{useful energy transferred by device}}{\text{total energy supplied to device}}$$

$$\text{power} = \frac{\text{work done}}{\text{time taken}}$$

weight = mass × gravitational field strength (g)

change of potential energy = weight × change in height

kinetic energy = $\frac{1}{2}$ × mass × (speed)^2

moment of a force = force × perpendicular distance to pivot

$$\text{sum of clockwise moments} = \text{sum of anticlockwise moments}$$

wave speed = frequency × wavelength

pressure × volume = constant

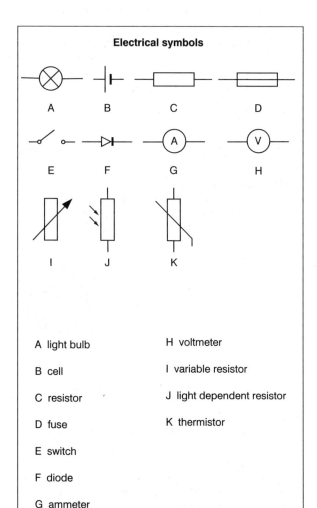

Electrical symbols

A   B   C   D

E   F   G   H

I   J   K

A light bulb   H voltmeter

B cell   I variable resistor

C resistor   J light dependent resistor

D fuse   K thermistor

E switch

F diode

G ammeter

Answers

1 Test yourself (page 218)

Beyond the Earth

1 VMJUN (✓ for each correct answer)

2 In northern summer, the Earth's North Pole is tilted towards the Sun and the South Pole is tilted away from the Sun (✓). This is when the northern hemisphere receives more sunlight each day than the southern hemisphere (✓).

3 The Moon moves through the Earth's shadow (✓). Sunlight cannot reach the Moon so it cannot be seen (✓).

4 The stars we see each night are in the opposite direction to the Sun (✓). As the Earth moves round the Sun, the stars we see at night change during the year (✓).

5 a) Mars (✓) b) Jupiter (✓)

6 a) Speeding up (✓). b) Moving towards the Sun (✓).

7 Nuclear fusion (✓).

8 A massive star exploding at the end of its life (✓) releasing an enormous amount of energy in a short time (✓).

9 The light spectrum from the star is shifted towards the red end of the spectrum (✓) due to the star receding (✓).

10 Distant galaxies are moving away from us (✓) at speeds in proportion to their distances away (✓).

Your score: ☐ out of 22

1 Round-up (page 225)

Beyond the Earth

1 a) The first sketch was drawn a few days after the new moon (✓). One week later, the Moon is almost opposite the Sun and will reach full moon a few days later (✓).

b)

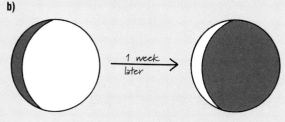

1 week later

(✓)

2 The Earth spins eastwards (✓), so the constellations appear to move across the sky westwards (✓).

3 a) Planets reflect sunlight (✓).
b) Sketch A is when Venus is in position 2, nearer Earth (✓). Its disc appears larger and crescent shaped (✓).

4 a) See page 220 (✓✓).
b) Totality covers only a small area of the Earth's surface (✓). As the Earth spins, only a small fraction of its surface passes through the area of totality (✓).

5 a) Jupiter shown in the opposite direction to the Sun (Sun Earth Jupiter) (✓).

b) (i) Mars is smaller, further from the Sun, is colder than Earth, and has no oxygen in its atmosphere (✓✓✓✓).
(ii) Jupiter is larger, not solid, further from the Sun than Earth, and spins faster (✓✓✓✓).
(iii) Saturn is larger, not solid, further from the Sun than Earth, and has a ring system (✓✓✓✓).

6 a) It is close to the Sun (✓) and can therefore only be seen just before sunrise (✓) or just after sunset (✓).
b) Neptune's orbit is circular (✓) whereas Pluto's orbit is elliptical and partly inside Neptune's orbit (✓).
c) Neptune (✓)
d) They become cold and dark when they move away from the Sun (✓), so cannot be seen (✓) until the Sun's gravity pulls them round back near the Sun (✓).

7 a) It is red (✓) and much larger than the Sun (✓).
b) The Sun will become a red giant (✓) and then collapse to become a white dwarf (✓) before radiating all its energy (✓) and becoming invisible (✓).
c) A massive star which explodes after the white dwarf stage (✓) because its internal pressure is too great (✓).

8 a) They must acquire sufficient speed to overcome gravity (✓) to gain orbital height (✓) then go into orbit (✓).
b) Its radius (✓) and density are smaller (✓).

9 See page 224 (✓✓✓✓).

10 a) See your textbook or an encyclopedia. Mind map a few brief notes before you write your account. Give a sketch if appropriate (✓✓✓✓).
b) Voyager 2 took several years to reach Jupiter, a distance which light takes about 30 minutes. The journey to Proxima Centauri would take tens of thousands of years using present rocket technology (✓✓✓✓).

Your score: ☐ out of 59

Your improvement index: $\dfrac{\boxed{}/59}{\boxed{}/22} \times 100\% = \boxed{}\%$

2 Test yourself (page 226)

Energy resources and energy transfer

1 B (✓)

2 Weight – the newton (✓), power – the watt (✓).

3 1200 J (✓)

4 a) KE = 6 J (✓), PE = 2 J (✓)
b) KE = 8 J (✓), PE = 0 (✓)

5 10 (✓) (= 4 + 6(✓))

6 PE loss = 2000 J (✓), KE gain = 250 J (✓), therefore required ratio = 8 (✓).

7 Metals contain electrons which move about freely inside the metal (✓). When the metal is heated, the electrons at the point of heating gain kinetic energy (✓) which they transfer to other parts of the metal (✓).

8 **a** and **b** (✓✓).

9 **c** only (✓).

10 **b)** Heat due to friction (✓). **c)** Electrical energy (✓). **d)** Sound (✓). **e)** Light (✓). **f)** Heat due to electrical resistance (✓).

Your score: ☐ out of 24

2 Round-up (page 235)

Energy resources and energy transfer

1 **a)** Chemical energy in the battery → electrical energy → sound energy (✓).
b) Gravitational potential energy → kinetic energy (✓) + work done against air resistance (✓).

2 **a)** **(i)** 800 J (✓) **(ii)** 40 J/s (✓) **b)** 0.2 (= 20%) (✓)

3 **a)** 2750 J (✓) **b)** 5.0 m (✓)

4 **a)** 160 MJ (✓) **b)** 3.2 MW (✓)

5 **a)** 6.75 kWh (✓) **b)** 40.5p (✓)

6 **a)** 22.5 kJ (✓) **b)** **(i)** 16.8 kJ (✓) **(ii)** 26 W (✓)

7 **a)** China is a better thermal insulator but shiny metal radiates less (✓). The china teapot is likely to be better unless it has very thin walls (✓).
b) There is a larger open surface in the wide-brimmed cup so there is more evaporation (✓) and thermal radiation (✓) from the wide-brimmed cup. Hence the tea in it loses thermal energy faster and it cools more quickly (✓).
c) A double-glazed unit traps a layer of still air between its two panes (✓). This is a good thermal insulator (✓).
d) **(i)** Condensation occurs where moist air meets a cold surface (✓). A classroom full of people will be full of moist air and in winter, the windows will be cold enough to cause condensation (✓).
(ii) The inner glass pane is warmer than the outer pane (✓) so the moist air does not come into contact with a cold surface (✓).

Your score: ☐ out of 26

Your improvement index:

3 Test yourself (page 236)

Radioactivity

1 **a)** Negative (✓) **b)** Positive (✓) **c)** Uncharged (✓) **d)** Positive (✓) **e)** Negative (✓)

2 **a)** 2p + 2n (✓✓) **b)** 92p + 143n (✓✓)

3 Positive (✓)

4 Alpha, beta and gamma radiation (✓✓✓), alpha radiation is most easily absorbed (✓).

5 Radioactivity from the surroundings or caused by cosmic radiation (✓).

6 The Geiger counter (✓).

7 Half-life – the time taken for half the atoms of a given radioactive isotope to disintegrate (✓). Isotope – atoms of an element with the same number of neutrons and protons (✓).

8 A nucleus of an atom splits (✓) into two approximately equal halves (✓).

9 The waste from the spent fuel rods contains radioactive isotopes with very long half-lives (✓). Radiation released by radioactive isotopes is harmful (✓).

10 See page 241 (✓✓).

Your score: ☐ out of 24

3 Round-up (page 244)

Radioactivity

1 **a)** U-238 = 92p + 146n (✓✓); U-235 = 92p + 143n (✓✓)
b) Isotopes (✓)
c) The time taken for half the initial number of atoms of a given isotope to decay (✓).

2 **a)** Smoke absorbs alpha radiation (✓) but not beta or gamma radiation (✓).
b) If the half-life was much shorter than 5 years, the decrease in activity of the source within a year would set the alarm off (✓).

3 **a)** $^{220}_{82}$Rn → $^{216}_{80}$Po + $^{4}_{2}\alpha$ (✓✓)
b) **(i)** 100/s (✓) **(ii)** 25/s (✓)

4 **a)** Steel plate stops alpha and beta radiation (✓✓) but not gamma radiation (✓).
b) **(i)** 200/s (✓) **(ii)** 160/s (✓) **(iii)** It became thicker (✓).

5 **a)** **(i)** See page 238 (✓). **(ii)** It produces ions (✓).
b) X-rays, radioactive waste (✓✓).
c) Start the Geiger counter and the stopwatch together. Stop the Geiger counter after exactly 600 seconds (✓). Measure the number of counts recorded by the counter. Divide this number by 600 to give the count rate (✓).

6 Alpha and gamma radiation (✓✓), the tin foil stops alpha radiation (✓) whereas even thick lead is unable to stop the gamma radiation completely (✓).

7 a) The radiation becomes weaker with distance (✓).
   b) (i) Electromagnetic radiation of very short wavelength (✓), it penetrates the body (✓).
   (ii) The source is enclosed in a thick-walled lead container with a small hole to let the gamma radiation out in a thin beam (✓). The beam is directed at the tumour from different directions (✓) so as not to damage the surrounding healthy tissue (✓).

Your score: ☐ out of 35

Your improvement index: $\dfrac{\boxed{}/35}{\boxed{}/24} \times 100\% = \boxed{}\,\%$

4 Test yourself (page 245)

Waves

1 Any four from: sound waves, water waves, waves on a string, electromagnetic waves (radio, microwaves, infrared, visible, ultraviolet, X-rays, gamma rays) (✓✓✓✓).

2 a) Longitudinal waves vibrate along the direction in which the wave travels (✓); transverse waves vibrate at 90° to the direction in which they travel (✓).
   b) Longitudinal (✓)

3 Any electromagnetic wave can pass through a vacuum (✓); any other type of wave needs a medium (✓).

4 Wavelength = 40 mm (✓); amplitude = 15 mm (✓).

5 a) Frequency = $\frac{\text{speed}}{\text{wavelength}} = \frac{20\,\text{mm/s}}{40\,\text{mm}} = 0.50\,\text{Hz}$ (✓)
   b) 30 (✓)

6 a) −15 mm (✓) **b)** +15 mm (✓)

7 There is no hard surface to reflect them (✓). The amplitude becomes less and less as they run up the shore (✓).

8 Refraction is the change of direction (✓) due to a change of speed when waves pass across a boundary (✓).

9 a) Increased (✓) **b)** Decreased (✓)

10 a) 850 Hz (✓) **b)** 1.0 mm (✓)

Your score: ☐ out of 23

4 Round-up (page 249)

Waves

1 a) (i) Sound waves (✓)
   (ii) Radio waves (✓), waves on a rope (✓).
   b) (1) Light is transverse; sound is longitudinal (✓).
   (2) Light can travel through a vacuum; sound cannot (or sound requires a medium; light does not) (✓).
   (3) Light travels faster than sound (✓).

2 (✓✓) (✓✓)

3 (✓✓)

4 a) Its wavelength becomes smaller (✓). Its frequency stays the same (✓).
   b)

boundary (✓✓)

5 a) 0.50 m (✓) **b) (i)** 0.40 m/s (✓) **(ii)** 2.0 Hz (✓)

6 a) Diffraction (✓)
   b) The spreading becomes less (✓).

7 a) 3.0 m (✓)
   b) The radio waves from the station are polarised (✓). As the aerial is turned, it moves more and more out of line with the plane of polarisation (✓) until it can no longer detect the signal (✓).
   c) The wire mesh reflects radio waves onto the aerial (✓).

8 a) The boat moves faster than the waves (✓) so the waves are left behind as they spread out (✓).
   b) The bow waves would form a sharper 'V' at the bow (✓).

Your score: ☐ out of 29

Your improvement index: $\dfrac{\boxed{}/29}{\boxed{}/23} \times 100\% = \boxed{}\,\%$

5 Test yourself   (page 250)

Sound waves and seismic waves

1 a) Longitudinal (✓)
  b) Primary waves are longitudinal (✓); secondary waves are transverse (✓).

2 It produces a note at a precise frequency (✓).

3 a) (i) Increases (✓)   **(ii)** Decreases (✓)
  b) The thicker string (✓) because it would produce sound at a lower pitch if it was at the same tension, and the pitch increases if the tension is increased (✓).

4 A reflected sound wave from a hard smooth surface (✓).

5 a) The amplitude increases (✓); the wavelength is unchanged (✓).
  b) The amplitude decreases (✓); the wavelength is shorter (✓).

6 Diffraction (✓)

7 a) C (✓) **b)** B (✓)
  c) Deeper (✓) (because the higher frequencies are cut out).

8 a) Ultrasonic pulses are directed towards the sea bed (✓). On hitting the sea bed the pulses are reflected back to the surface (✓). Each pulse is timed from when it is emitted to when it is detected after reflection (✓). The time taken t for each pulse to reach the sea bed $= 0.5 \times$ the time from when it is emitted to when it is detected (✓). The depth of the sea bed = speed of ultrasound in water $\times$ time t (✓).
  b) One of: medical imaging; crack detection; depth finding (✓✓).

9 a) 0.17 mm (✓)   **b) (i)** No change (✓)   **(ii)** Increases (✓)

10 a) The plates of the Earth's crust press against each other at certain parts (✓). An earthquake occurs when one of the plates gives way (✓).
  b) S waves are transverse (✓); transverse waves cannot pass through a liquid (✓); the outer core is liquid (✓).

Your score: [ ] out of 32

5 Round-up   (page 254)

Sound waves and seismic waves

1 a) 850 m (✓)
  b) Sound the siren briefly every 10 seconds and measure the time between each pulse being emitted and its return (✓). The timing becomes shorter if the ship is approaching the cliffs (✓).

2 a) The surface pushes and pulls the air near it back and forth (✓). The air near the speaker pushes and pulls on the air further away (✓).
  b) A small loudspeaker is lighter (✓) and so can vibrate faster (✓).

3 a) Amplitude less (✓), horizontal spacing the same (✓).
  b) Waves are stretched out horizontally (✓).

4 a) 3400 Hz (✓)   **b)** 68 mm (✓)

5 The glass panes reflect most of the sound (✓). Some sound penetrates the room because the glass panes vibrate when they reflect the sound waves (✓).

6 a) 37.5 mm (✓)
  b) (i) Without the paste, the ultrasound pulses from the probe would be almost completely reflected at the air–body boundary (✓). With the paste, the pulses from the probe travel directly into the body from the paste without passing into the air (✓).
    (ii) Reflection at each internal boundary is partial (✓); the pulses spread out as they move away from the probe (✓).

7 a) (i) B = outer core (✓), C = mantle (✓); D = crust (✓).
    (ii) B = molten (✓); A, C, D = solid (✓✓✓).
  b) They are more common where the plates of the Earth's crust meet (✓).

8 a) Longitudinal (✓)
  b) (i) See page 253 (✓✓✓).
    (ii) The outer core is liquid (✓); S waves are transverse waves and therefore cannot travel through liquid (✓).
    (iii) The speed of a seismic wave increases with depth (✓). The seismic waves not moving directly towards the centre are therefore refracted away from the centre (✓).
    (iv) See page 253. S waves cannot reach the other side of the Earth from the epicentre (✓). Also, P waves cannot reach part of this zone because they refract back to the surface (✓). L waves therefore arrive without being preceded by P or S waves (✓).

Your score: [ ] out of 38

Your improvement index: $\dfrac{[\ ]/38}{[\ ]/32} \times 100\% = [\ ]\%$

6 Test yourself   (page 255)

Light

1 a) The angle between the reflected ray and the normal = the angle between the incident ray and the normal (✓).
  b) 1.20 m (✓)

2 a) Towards (✓)   **b)** Less than 30° (✓).
  c) The light ray is totally internally reflected (✓).

3 a) Real (✓)   **b)** Inverted (✓)   **c)** Diminished (✓)

4 Non-vertical light rays from any point at the bottom of the pool are refracted at the surface (✓) away from the normal (✓) and therefore appear to come from an image of the bottom of the pool nearer the surface (✓).

5 It makes the light spread more (✓) as if it has come from nearby (✓).

6 Away from the screen (✓); if the object distance is reduced, the image distance must be increased (✓).

7 a) Red (✓)
  b) The surface absorbs all colours except blue (✓) which it reflects (✓). Therefore in red light, no light is reflected so it appears black (✓).

8

(✓✓)

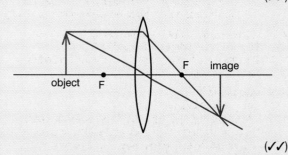

(✓✓)

9 Communications, to carry light pulses (✓); medicine, to see inside the body ✓).

10 a) More (✓)
b) The wavelength of blue light is less than that of any other colour (✓); blue light is diffracted less than any other colour when it enters the microscope (✓), therefore separate images seen in blue light can be closer together than seen in any other colour (✓).

Your score: ☐ out of 29

6 Round-up   (page 262)

Light
1

a) (✓✓)   **b)** (✓)

c) Image I_1 is directly opposite O_1 and image I_2 is directly opposite O_2 (✓). Hence distance I_1I_2 is the same as distance O_1O_2 (✓).

2 a) 2.0 m (✓)
b) The top of the mirror needs to be just above eye level (✓) to be able to see the head (✓). The bottom of the mirror needs to be opposite the midpoint between the floor and eye level (✓) to be able to see the feet (✓).
c) Two of: in a periscope; to make a corner cube reflector; to read a scale (✓✓).

3 a) See page 259 (✓✓).
b)

(✓✓)

c) The angle of incidence at the point of incidence becomes less than the critical angle (✓).
d) Communications, to carry light pulses (✓); medicine, to see inside the body (✓).

4 a)

(✓✓)

b)

(✓✓)

5 a) (i) The image becomes blurred (✓) and larger (✓).
    (ii) Move the screen away from the lens to make the image larger (✓), then the lens needs to be moved towards the object until the image is back in focus (✓).
b) The lens with the shortest focal length (✓); it can be held closest to the object without forming a blurred image (✓).

6 a) Short sight (✓)
b) A concave correcting lens is needed (✓); see page 258 (✓✓).

7

convex lens (✓)
point object O
film (✓)
convex lens focuses light from O onto film (✓)

311

8 The wider the lens, the less the diffraction of light (✓), giving more detail in the image (✓).

Your score: ☐ out of 38

Your improvement index: $\dfrac{\boxed{}/38}{\boxed{}/29} \times 100\% = \boxed{}\%$

7 Test yourself   (page 263)

The electromagnetic spectrum

1 Radio (✓), microwaves (✓), infrared (✓), visible (✓), ultraviolet (✓), X-rays and gamma rays (✓).

2 See page 264 (✓✓✓✓✓✓).

3 Visible light (✓) and radio (✓).

4 a) X-rays and gamma radiation (✓✓).
  b) Infrared radiation (✓)
  c) Ultraviolet light (✓)

5 X-rays or gamma radiation can (✓); radio waves cannot (✓).

6 a) X-rays (✓)
  b) Ultraviolet light (✓)

7 a) Microwave radiation (✓)
  b) (i) To focus microwave radiation from the satellite onto the dish aerial (✓).
    (ii) Metal reflects microwaves (✓).

8 The pigment in the ink does not absorb visible light (✓). It absorbs ultraviolet light and emits visible light (✓). Under a UV lamp, the ink is therefore visible (✓).

9 a) (i) Infrared radiation (✓)
    (ii) X-rays and gamma radiation (✓).
  b) Radio waves and microwaves (✓).

10 a) Infrared radiation (✓)
  b) Visible light and infrared radiation (✓).

Your score: ☐ out of 33

7 Round-up   (page 267)

The electromagnetic spectrum

1 a) X-rays and gamma rays (✓), ultraviolet (✓), visible (✓), infrared (✓), microwave (✓), radio (✓).

  b) (i) Any two of: travel at the same speed in a vacuum; transverse waves; do not need a substance/pass through a vacuum; can be reflected or refracted or diffracted; make charged particles vibrate (✓✓).
    (ii) Visible (✓), ultraviolet (✓), X-rays and gamma rays (✓).
    (iii) Radio (✓), microwaves (✓), infrared (✓), visible (✓).

2 a) Cooker 0.12 m (✓), satellite 0.03 m (✓).
  b) Faster, uses less energy, cooks the food throughout (✓).

3 a) Long wave radio waves follow the Earth's curvature (✓), medium wave radio waves reflect from the ionosphere (✓).

b) (i) The frequency of the electromagnetic waves that carry the audio or TV signals (✓).
  (ii) If they broadcast at the same frequency, the broadcasts would interfere with each other where they overlap (✓).
c) The satellite signals are much weaker (✓); a dish is used to focus them onto an aerial (✓).

4 a) Ultraviolet light in bright sunlight would be absorbed by the powder molecules in the clothing (✓). The molecules would emit visible light, making the clothes seem brighter (✓).
  b) (i) It damages the retinal cells of the eye (✓); it causes sunburn (✓).
    (ii) To absorb ultraviolet light from sunlight (✓), to prevent sunburn (✓).

5 a) Their bodies emit infrared light which can be detected by an infrared camera (✓).
  b) (i) Infrared light (✓)
    (ii) A conventional heating element consists of resistance wire surrounded by an electrical insulator in a metal tubing (✓); conduction of heat from the resistance wire to the metal tubing is very slow and so the hob takes much longer to heat up than a ceramic hob (✓).

6 a) (i) To attract electrons from the heated filament (✓).
    (ii) The X-rays need to originate from a small spot on the anode (✓) otherwise the image they produce will be blurred (✓).
  b) (i) X-rays pass through soft tissues and are absorbed by bone (✓). X-rays blacken photographic film (✓).
    (ii) The stomach consists of soft tissues only (✓). The barium meal in the stomach enables the lining of the stomach to be seen because barium absorbs X-rays (✓).

7 a) There are more cycles per second of the waveform at the higher frequency (✓). Each pulse needs the same number of cycles per second (✓), so more pulses per second are possible at higher frequencies (✓).
  b) (i) 1000 (✓)
    (ii) They would interfere with mobile phone communications (✓).

8 a) An orbit directly above the equator (✓) with an orbital time of exactly 24 hours (✓).
  b) The satellite is always in the same position over the equator (✓).

Your score: ☐ out of 49

Your improvement index: $\dfrac{\boxed{}/49}{\boxed{}/33} \times 100\% = \boxed{}\%$

8 Test yourself   (page 268)

Force and motion

1 a) 5 km/h (✓) **b)** 1.4 m/s (✓)

2 a) The area under the line (✓). **b)** Speed (✓)

3 $0.5 \, \text{m/s}^2$ (✓), 500 N (✓)

4 a) 9.0 m (✓) **b)** $-6.0 \, \text{m/s}^2$ (✓)
  c) (i) 19 m (✓) **(ii)** 28 m (✓)

5 a) (i) 4000 N (✓), 800 J (✓) **(ii)** 8000 J (✓)
 b) Potential energy is converted into thermal energy (or heat) (✓) by the braking force acting on the lift cable (✓). This force is necessary to prevent the lift from falling freely (✓).

6 The force of air resistance depends on the speed and the shape of the vehicle (✓). The speed increases until the force of air resistance is equal to the engine force (✓). Changing the shape to reduce the force of air resistance enables the car to reach a higher top speed (✓).

7 The force of air resistance increases with speed (✓). As the parachutist falls, his/her speed increases until the force of air resistance is equal and opposite to the weight of the parachutist (✓). The speed therefore becomes constant as the overall force becomes zero (✓).

8 80 000 N (✓), 80 000 N (✓)

9 a) 6000 m (✓), **b)** 20 MJ (✓)

10 It is carried away by the air as thermal energy (✓).

Your score: ☐ out of 27

8 Round-up (pages 274–5)

Force and motion

1 a) (i) 4320 m (✓) **(ii)** 4.32 km (✓) **b)** 4.3 m/s (✓)

2 a) It was steady (✓) and less than the speed of X for most of the journey (✓). Then the speed of Y was greater than that of X (✓) and Y overtook X (✓).
 b) (i) 10 m/s (✓) **(ii)** 15 m/s (✓)

3 a) Speed is distance travelled per second (✓); velocity is speed in a given direction (✓).
 b) (i) 9 km north (✓) then 24 km south (✓).
 (ii) 15 km south (✓).

4 a) 1.6 m/s^2 (✓), 20 m (✓) **b)** 1120 N (✓)

5 a) 2.5 s (✓)
 b) (i) 63 J (✓) **(ii)** 63 J (✓) **(iii)** 31 m (✓)

6 a) 9.5 m/s (✓) **b)** 2.7 kJ (✓) **c)** 4.5 m (✓)
 d) The pole vaulter uses his or her arm muscles to gain height (✓).

7 a) Graph to show a straight line with a negative gradient (✓) from 10 m/s to 0 in 50 s (✓).
 b) (i) 250 m (✓) **(ii)** −0.2 m/s^2 (✓)
 c) −6000 N (✓)
 d) 0.02 (✓)

8 a) The car skids if the force of the brakes on the wheels exceeds the frictional force of the road on the tyre (✓).
 b) The maximum frictional force of the road on the tyres is less on a wet road (✓). This force is equal and opposite to the force of the road on the car (✓). Hence the maximum braking force for no skidding must be less on a wet road (✓), so it takes longer to stop from a given speed (✓).
 c) (i) 22.5 m (✓) **(ii)** −5.0 m/s^2 (✓), 6000 N (✓)
 d) 6 s (✓), 45 m (✓)

Your score: ☐ out of 41

Your improvement index: $\dfrac{\boxed{}/41}{\boxed{}/27} \times 100\% = \boxed{}$%

9 Test yourself (page 276)

Forces in balance

1 Your weight (✓), the support force from your chair (✓).

2 a) Neutral (✓) **b)** Unstable (✓) **c)** Stable (✓)

3 a) 1.2 m (✓)
 b) The point at which the lift force is exerted is three times further from the pivot than the centre of gravity (✓). Hence the lift force is one-third of the weight (✓).
 c) 50 kg (✓)

4 a) (i) The force is applied to a much smaller contact area if the knife is sharp (✓).
 (ii) Atmospheric pressure acting on the outer surface is greater than the pressure of the air trapped between the cap and the tile (✓). The pressure difference creates sufficient force to hold the cap on the wall (✓).
 b) 6 kPa (✓✓)

5 a) The original shape is regained after the removal of applied forces (✓).
 b) The original shape is not regained after the removal of applied forces (✓).

6 a) 20 cm (✓) **b)** 2.5 N (✓)

7 The moment of the applied force is greater with a long spanner than with a short spanner (✓). Hence less force is needed to produce the necessary moment (✓).

8 a) 0.40 N m (✓) **b)** 2.7 N (✓✓)

9 The molecules move faster on average (✓), so they hit the sides harder (✓) and more often (✓), causing more forces of greater impact (✓).

10 200 kPa (✓)

Your score: ☐ out of 28

9 Round-up (pages 283–4)

Forces in balance

1 a) The tyres are wider to create less pressure on the soft ground (✓). Also, the tractor can tilt further with big wheels before it topples over (✓).
 b) Your diagram should show a small base and a high centre of gravity (✓). The pin needs to tilt only a little before it falls over because of its high centre of gravity in relation to its small base (✓).

2 a) (i) 200 kPa (✓) **(ii)** 6 kPa (✓) **b)** 0.004 m^2 (✓)

3 a) The stiffness of the steel spring is constant (✓); the stiffness of the elastic band changes as it is stretched (✓).
 b) No (✓), it does not give equal changes in length for equal increases in force (✓).

313

4 a) (i) Pure water 1.00 g/cm³ (✔); salt water 1.08 g/cm³ (✔).
(ii) Pure water 1000 kg/m³ (✔); salt water 1080 kg/m³ (✔).
b) Salt water has a greater density than pure water (✔). This means the pressure is greater at the same depth (✔); hence the upthrust on an object is greater in salt water than in pure water (✔).

5 0.4 m (✔), 1.1 N (✔), 10 N (✔), 0.19 m (✔)

6 a) Your graph should show axes labelled correctly and units shown (✔), points plotted correctly (✔), points covering at least half of each scale (✔), a straight line drawn through the points (✔).
b) 1.9 N (✔)

7 a) The molecules rebound repeatedly off the container surface (✔). Each impact exerts a force on the surface (✔). The pressure is caused by the average force of many impacts per second (✔).
b) 10 cm³ (✔✔)

Your score: ☐ out of 32

Your improvement index: $\dfrac{\boxed{}/32}{\boxed{}/28} \times 100\% = \boxed{}\%$

10 Test yourself (page 285)

Electric charge

1 B and C (✔✔)

2 a) C (✔) **b)** B (✔)

3 a) A metal contains electrons which move about freely inside the metal (✔). These electrons carry charge and hence transfer charge through the metal when a potential difference is set up across the metal (✔).
b) All the electrons are firmly attached to atoms (✔) and so cannot transfer charge through the material (✔).

4 If the charged rod is negative, it repels electrons from the cap onto the leaf (✔) and stem which then repel each other (✔). If the charged rod is positive, it attracts electrons onto the cap from the leaf and stem (✔). This makes the leaf and stem positive, so the leaf is repelled from the stem (✔).

5 The leaf falls (✔) as electrons are attracted from the leaf and the stem to the cap (✔).

6 The pipe would become charged due to fluid friction, and a spark might be created (✔). This would be dangerous since it might ignite oil vapour (✔).

7 Any two from: electrostatic paint spray; ink jet printer; electrostatic precipitator (✔✔).

8 360 C (✔✔)

9 The liquid in the cell contains hydrogen ions and chloride ions (✔). Hydrogen ions are positive and are discharged at the anode (✔); chloride ions are negative and are discharged at the anode (✔).

10 Any two from: chromium electroplating; tin plating; extraction of aluminium from its ore; purification of copper (✔✔).

Your score: ☐ out of 25

10 Round-up (page 291)

Electric charge

1 a) ii, iv, i then iii (✔✔✔✔). **b)** Positive charge (✔) **c)** No (✔)

2 a) Electrons transfer from the electroscope to the rod (✔) so the leaf and stem both become positive (✔). Hence the leaf is repelled by the stem (✔).
b) No charge can transfer to or from the electroscope once the rod has been removed (✔).
c) Hold the rod near the electroscope (✔). Earth the electroscope cap (✔). Remove the earth connection (✔). Remove the rod (✔). (See page 288.)
d) Charge the electroscope with a known charge. Bring the unknown charge near the cap (✔). If the leaf rises, the unknown charge is the same as the charge on the electroscope (✔). If the leaf falls, it is oppositely charged (✔).

3 a) (i) The charge on the metal car body discharges to earth (✔) through a person in contact with the ground who touches the car (✔).
(ii) The car driver would be charged from the car (✔) and would discharge to earth on setting foot out of the car (✔).
b) (i) The charge on the car leaks to earth through the trailing conductor (✔).
(ii) Rainwater conducts electricity (✔) so allows the charge on the car body to transfer to earth (✔).

4 a) 180 C (✔), 1080 C (✔) **b)** 0.06 g (✔) **c)** 0.36 g (✔)
d) 0.35 A (✔)

5 a) The charged ruler attracts unlike charge to the nearest part of each bit of paper (✔) and repels like charge to the furthest part (✔). The force of attraction on the unlike charge is greater than the force of repulsion on the like charge (✔) because the unlike charge is nearer the ruler (✔).
b) Static electricity on the TV screen (✔) attracts uncharged dust particles (✔).

6 a) Uncharged dust particles are attracted to the live wire grid (✔) where they become charged the same as the grid (✔) and are then attracted onto the earthed tube and stay there (✔).
b) In the presence of a nearby charged object, touching a pin allows opposite charge to transfer to it from earth (✔). Removing the earth connection leaves the pin charged (✔).

Your score: ☐ out of 40

Your improvement index: $\dfrac{\boxed{}/40}{\boxed{}/25} \times 100\% = \boxed{}\%$

11 Test yourself (page 292)

Electric circuits

1 a)

(✓✓)

b) $0.2 \times 1.5 \times \frac{60}{2}$ (✓) $= 9\,J$ each (✓).

2 a)

(✓✓)

b) (i) $0.45\,J$ (✓) **(ii)** $27\,J$ (✓)

3 a) $0.2\,A$ (✓) **b)** $\frac{1.0\,V}{0.2\,A}$ (✓) $= 5.0\,\Omega$ (✓)

4 a) $15.0\,V$ (✓) **b)** $37.5\,W$ (✓)

5 a)

(✓✓)

b) The diode is now reverse biased (✓) so it will not conduct (✓).

6

    a)   b)

(✓✓)

a) An LDR's resistance depends on the incident light intensity (✓).

b) A thermistor's resistance depends on temperature (✓).

7 a) $300\,kJ$ (✓) **b)** $\frac{1000\,W}{240\,V}$ (✓) $= 4.2\,A$ (✓)

8 a) A fuse is intended to protect an appliance or the connecting wires from excessive current (✓).

b) If the current rises above a certain value, the fuse wire overheats and melts (✓) causing a gap in the circuit (✓).

9 a) $\frac{20 \times 6\,W}{240\,V}$ (✓) $= 0.5\,A$ (✓) **b)** $\frac{240}{20}$ (✓) $= 12\,V$ (✓)

10 a) $0.8\,kW \times 0.25\,h$ (✓) $= 0.2$ (✓)
b) $1.2p$ (✓)

Your score: ☐ out of 34

11 Round-up (page 298)

Electric circuits

1 a) $12\,\Omega$ (✓)
b) The ammeter reading would double (✓); the voltmeter reading would be unchanged (✓).

2 a) (i) $6.3\,A$ (✓) **(ii)** 3 (✓)
b) (i) It is used to earth the metal frame of an appliance connected to the ring main (✓). It therefore prevents the frame from becoming live (✓).
(ii) $3\,A$ (✓)
(iii) If the fuse rating is too low, the fuse will blow when the appliance is switched on (✓). If the fuse rating is too large, the fuse will not blow if the current becomes excessive. This would create a risk of fire due to resistance heating (✓).

3 a) (i) $1.5\,V$ (✓) **(ii)** $0.3\,A$ (✓) **b)** $0.45\,W$ (✓)
c) The current in P becomes less (✓); the current in Q becomes greater (✓).

4 a) $2\,A$ (✓), $6\,\Omega$ (✓)
b) $\frac{6\,\Omega}{5\,\Omega/m}$ (✓) $= 1.2\,m$ (✓)
c)

wire under test

(✓)

Connect an exact length of $1.0\,m$ into the circuit (✓) and measure the current and p.d. using the ammeter and the voltmeter (✓✓). Calculate the resistance from p.d./current (✓).

5 a) (i) 1.2 (✓) **(ii)** 10 (✓) **(iii)** 1.0 (✓)
b) $61p$ (✓)
c) 29 minutes (✓✓)

6 a) Tap water conducts electricity (✓). Water might run into the appliance and provide a conducting path to earth via the user (✓). Also, the contact resistance between the appliance and the user is reduced by water (✓).
b) If the case became live (✓), current leakage to earth via the user might not be enough to blow the fuse (✓). An RCCB would cut the mains supply off if the leakage current exceeds $30\,mA$ (✓).
c) The cable would become warm due to its resistance (✓). If it overheated, the insulation might melt (✓).

Your score: [ ] out of 38

Your improvement index: $\dfrac{\boxed{}/38}{\boxed{}/34} \times 100\% = \boxed{}\%$

12 Test yourself　(page 299)

Electromagnetism

1 a) Soft iron (✓)　**b)** Steel (✓)

2 a) North (✓)　**b)** North (✓)

3 a) See page 300 (✓✓).　**b)** See page 300 (✓✓).

4 a) and **c)** Permanent magnet (✓✓)　**b)** Electromagnet (✓)

5 a) The same (✓)
 b) The turning effect on the coil would reverse each time the current reversed (✓), so the coil would be unable to spin (✓).

6 a) The peak voltage would decrease (✓) and the time for one cycle would increase (✓).
 b) Alternating current can be stepped up to high voltage on the grid system (✓). The same power can then be delivered with smaller currents than would be necessary if the voltage was low (✓). There is less resistance heating in the grid cables and therefore less power is wasted (✓).

7 The electromagnet creates a changing magnetic field through the aluminium plate, which induces alternating current in the plate (✓). Resistance heating therefore occurs in the plate (✓).

8 a) 12 V (✓) **b)** 8.4 A (✓)

 Your score: [ ] out of 23

12 Round-up　(page 305)

Electromagnetism

1 a) See page 300 for diagram (✓✓✓). The electromagnet attracts the iron armature when current passes through the electromagnet coil (✓). The make-or-break switch opens (✓), the current switches off and the electromagnet no longer attracts the armature (✓). The armature springs back and closes the switch gap (✓). Current passes again and the process is repeated (✓).
 b) **(i)** The iron bar is attracted into the solenoid when the switch is closed (✓).
 (ii) To ensure it is pulled into the coil when the switch is closed (✓).
 (iii) It would operate on a.c. (✓) since the bar is attracted into the coil whatever the direction of the current (✓).

2 a) See page 300 for diagram (✓✓✓). Current through the electromagnet coil causes magnetism in its core (✓). The armature is attracted to the core (✓). The switch is opened by the movement of the armature (✓).
 b) The alternating current in the coil of the electromagnet creates an alternating magnetic field (✓). This field induces an alternating current in any conductor it passes through (✓).

3 a) See page 302 for diagram (✓✓✓). The sides of the coil cut the magnetic field lines as the coil turns (✓) so a voltage is induced in the coil (✓). The voltage alternates because the angle between the direction of motion of the coil sides and field lines changes continuously (✓).
 b) **(i)** See page 302 (✓✓).
 (ii) Any maximum or minimum (✓).
 c) The peaks are higher (✓) and nearer to each other (✓).

4 a) **(i)** A changing primary current causes a changing magnetic field in the core (✓). A changing magnetic field through the secondary coil causes an induced voltage in the secondary coil (✓).
 (ii) The secondary current is greater since the voltage is stepped down (✓).
 (iii) The plates are made of iron to make the magnetic field as strong as possible (✓). The plates are laminated to reduce induced currents in the core (✓).
 b) **(i)** 12 V (✓)　**(ii)** 1.6 A (✓✓) (✓ for answer 2.0 A)

5 a) **(i)** There is less current for the same power (✓) so less heat is produced due to resistance in the cables (✓).
 (ii) UK – the higher voltage in the UK is more dangerous (✓) but smaller currents for the same power in the UK mean less risk of overheating (✓).
 b) Advantages: no underground trenches need to be dug, no waterproof insulating material needed round cable (✓). Disadvantages: liable to lightning strikes, unsightly (✓).

Your score: [ ] out of 45

Your improvement index: $\dfrac{\boxed{}/45}{\boxed{}/23} \times 100\% = \boxed{}\%$

Index